Middle School 3-1
기말고사 완벽대비

KB093625

적중 100

영어 기출 문제집

중 3

동아 | 윤정미

Best Collection

구성과 특징

교과서의 주요 학습 내용을 중심으로 학습 영역별 특성에 맞춰 단계별로 다양한 학습 기회를 제공하여
단원별 학습능력 평가는 물론 중간 및 기말고사 시험 등에 완벽하게 대비할 수 있도록 내용을 구성

Words & Expressions

Step1   Key Words 단원별 핵심 단어 설명 및 풀이
         Key Expression 단원별 핵심 숙어 및 관용어 설명
         Word Power 반대 또는 비슷한 뜻 단어 배우기
         English Dictionary 영어로 배우는 영어 단어

Step2   실력평가 단원별 수시평가 대비 주관식, 객관식 문제풀이

Step3   서술형 대비 학업성취도 및 수행능력평가 대비 서술형 문제풀이

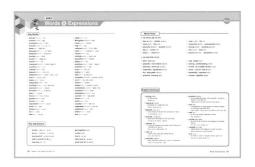

Conversation

Step1   핵심 의사소통 소통에 필요한 주요 표현 방법 요약
         핵심 Check 기본적인 표현 방법 및 활용능력 확인

Step2   대화문 익히기 교과서 대화문 심층 분석 및 확인

Step3   교과서 확인학습 빈칸 채우기를 통한 문장 완성 능력 확인

Step4   기본평가 시험대비 기초 학습 능력 평가

Step5   실력평가 단원별 수시평가 대비 주관식, 객관식 문제풀이

Step6   서술형 대비 학업성취도 및 수행능력평가 대비 서술형 문제풀이

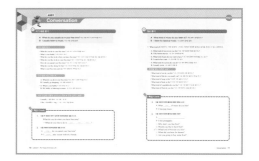

Grammar

Step1   주요 문법 단원별 주요 문법 사항과 예문을 알기 쉽게 설명
         핵심 Check 기본 문법사항에 대한 이해 여부 확인

Step2   기본평가 시험대비 기초 학습 능력 평가

Step3   실력평가 단원별 수시평가 대비 주관식, 객관식 문제풀이

Step4   서술형 대비 학업성취도 및 수행능력평가 대비 서술형 문제풀이

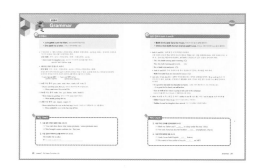

Reading

Step1   구문 분석 단원별로 제시된 문장에 대한 구문별 분석과 내용 설명
         확인문제 문장에 대한 기본적인 이해와 인지능력 확인

Step2   확인학습A 빈칸 채우기를 통한 문장 완성 능력 확인

Step3   확인학습B 제시된 우리말을 영어로 완성하여 작문 능력 키우기

Step4   실력평가 단원별 수시평가 대비 주관식, 객관식 문제풀이

Step5   서술형 대비 학업성취도 및 수행능력평가 대비 서술형 문제풀이
         교과서 구석구석 교과서에 나오는 기타 문장까지 완벽 학습

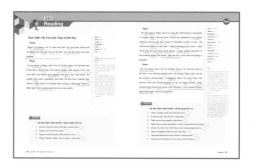

Composition

|영역별 핵심문제|

단어 및 어휘, 대화문, 문법, 독해 등 각 영역별 기출문제의 출제 유형을 분석하여 실전에 대비하고 연습할 수 있도록 문제를 배열

|단원별 예상문제|

기출문제를 분석한 후 새로운 시험 출제 경향을 더하여 새롭게 출제될 수 있는 문제를 포함하여 시험에 완벽하게 대비할 수 있도록 준비

|서술형 실전 및 창의사고력 문제|

학교 시험에서 점차 늘어나는 서술형 시험에 집중 대비하고 고득점을 취득하는데 만전을 기하기 위한 학습 코너

|단원별 모의고사|

영역별, 단계별 학습을 모두 마친 후 실전 연습을 위한 모의고사

INSIGHT on the textbook

교과서 파헤치기

- **단어Test1~3** 영어 단어 우리말 쓰기, 우리말을 영어 단어로 쓰기, 영영풀이에 해당하는 단어와 우리말 쓰기
- **대화문Test1~2** 대화문 빈칸 완성 및 전체 대화문 쓰기
- **본문Test1~5** 빈칸 완성, 우리말 쓰기, 문장 배열연습, 영어 작문하기 복습 등 단계별 반복 학습을 통해 교과서 지문에 대한 완벽한 습득
- **구석구석지문Test1~2** 지문 빈칸 완성 및 전문 영어로 쓰기

Lesson 3

Stories of English Words and Expressions

 의사소통 기능

- 설명 요청하기
  A: What does that mean?
  B: It means "It's raining a lot."

- 반복 설명 요청하기
  Can you say that again?

 언어 형식

- '계속적 용법'의 관계대명사
  The word *shampoo* comes from the Hindi word *chāmpo*, **which** means "to press."

- It is[was] ~ that 가주어, 진주어 구문
  It is interesting **that** the idea of using the word *robot* didn't come from Karel Čapek himself.

교과서
Words & Expressions

Key Words

- **advanced** [ədvǽnst] 형 진보한, 발전된
- **anger** [ǽŋɡər] 동 화나게 하다
- **borrow** [bárou] 동 빌리다
- **British** [brítiʃ] 형 영국인의
- **cause** [kɔːz] 동 초래하다 명 원인
- **century** [séntʃəri] 명 세기, 100년
- **civilization** [sìvəlizéiʃən] 명 문명
- **contact** [kántækt] 명 접촉
- **create** [kriéit] 동 창조하다
- **culture** [kʌ́ltʃər] 명 문화
- **decide** [disáid] 동 결심하다
- **design** [dizáin] 동 설계하다
- **example** [igzǽmpl] 명 사례
- **experience** [ikspíəriəns] 동 경험하다
- **explorer** [iksplɔ́ːrər] 명 탐험가
- **expression** [ikspréʃən] 명 표현
- **factory** [fǽktəri] 명 공장
- **flood** [flʌd] 명 홍수
- **German** [dʒə́ːrmən] 명 독일어
- **hurricane** [hə́ːrəkèin] 명 허리케인
- **include** [inklúːd] 동 포함하다
- **introduce** [ìntrədjúːs] 동 소개하다
- **invent** [invént] 동 발명하다
- **judge** [dʒʌdʒ] 명 재판관, 판사 동 재판하다
- **justice** [dʒʌ́stis] 명 정의
- **law** [lɔː] 명 법
- **language** [lǽŋɡwidʒ] 명 언어

- **massage** [məsáːʒ] 명 마사지, 안마
- **Mayan** [máːjən] 형 마야 사람의
- **mean** [miːn] 동 의미하다
- **meaning** [míːniŋ] 명 의미
- **myth** [miθ] 명 신화
- **nervous** [nə́ːrvəs] 형 불안한
- **origin** [ɔ́ːrədʒin] 명 기원, 유래
- **originally** [ərídʒənəli] 부 원래, 본래
- **originate** [ərídʒənèit] 동 유래하다
- **present** [préznt] 형 현재의
- **press** [pres] 동 누르다
- **produce** [prədjúːs] 동 생산하다
- **science fiction** 공상과학
- **shampoo** [ʃæmpúː] 명 샴푸
- **shortly** [ʃɔ́ːrtli] 부 곧, 즉시
- **slave** [sleiv] 명 노예
- **slice** [slais] 명 얇게 썬 조각; 한 조각
- **soap** [soup] 명 비누
- **special** [spéʃəl] 형 특별한
- **Spanish** [spǽniʃ] 형 스페인의
- **storm** [stɔːrm] 명 폭풍
- **suggest** [səɡdʒést] 동 제안하다
- **tool** [tuːl] 명 도구
- **trader** [tréidər] 명 상인, 거래자
- **universe** [júːnəvə̀ːrs] 명 우주, 은하계
- **weather** [wéðər] 명 날씨
- **yoga** [jóuɡə] 명 요가

Key Expressions

- **be in hot water** 곤경에 처하다
- **be late for ~** ~에 지각하다
- **be made into ~** ~로 만들어지다
- **break a leg** 행운을 빌다
- **call ~ after ...** ...을 본떠 ~의 이름을 부르다
- **come from ~** ~에서 오다, 유래하다
- **cup of tea** [부정어와 함께; one's ~] 기호[취미]에 맞는 사람[물건]
- **It's a piece of cake.** 그것은 식은 죽 먹기이다.
- **keep in touch** 연락하다
- **keep one's fingers crossed** 행운을 빌다
- **look like ~** ~처럼 보이다

- **Lunch is on me.** 점심은 제가 사겠습니다.
- **make a long face** 우울한 얼굴을 하다
- **not ~ at all** 전혀 ~가 아니다
- **originate from** ~에서 비롯되다
- **pass through** 거쳐 지나가다
- **pick up** ~을 익히게 되다
- **pig out** 돼지 같이 먹다
- **pull one's leg** 놀리다
- **rain cats and dogs** 비가 세차게 내리다
- **see eye to eye** 의견을 같이하다
- **under the weather** 몸이 안 좋은
- **watch out** 조심하다

Word Power

※ 서로 비슷한 뜻을 가진 어휘

- □ **borrow** 빌리다 : **rent** 임대하다
- □ **trader** 상인, 거래자 : **merchant** 상인
- □ **tool** 도구 : **device** 장치
- □ **design** 설계하다 : **devise** 고안하다

- □ **example** 사례 : **instance** 사례
- □ **origin** 기원 : **source** 근원
- □ **present** 현재의 : **current** 현재의
- □ **decide** 결심하다 : **determine** 결정하다

※ 서로 반대의 뜻을 가진 어휘

- □ **borrow** 빌리다 ↔ **lend** 빌려주다
- □ **produce** 생산하다 ↔ **consume** 소비하다

- □ **include** 포함하다 ↔ **exclude** 제외하다
- □ **special** 특별한 ↔ **general** 일반적인

※ 동사 – 명사

- □ **decide** 결심하다 – **decision** 결심
- □ **introduce** 소개하다 – **introduction** 소개
- □ **originate** 유래하다 – **origination** 유래
- □ **suggest** 제안하다 – **suggestion** 제안

- □ **express** 표현하다 – **expression** 표현
- □ **produce** 생산하다 – **production** 생산
- □ **create** 창조하다 – **creation** 창조
- □ **invent** 발명하다 – **invention** 발명

※ 나라 이름 – 형용사/언어

- □ **Spain** 스페인 – **Spanish** 스페인어
- □ **Germany** 독일 – **German** 독일어

- □ **Italy** 이탈리아 – **Italian** 이탈리아어
- □ **Korea** 한국 – **Korean** 한국어

English Dictionary

- □ **anger** 화나게 하다
  → to make someone angry 다른 사람을 화나게 만들다
- □ **borrow** 빌리다
  → to use something that belongs to someone else and that you must give back to them later
  누군가에게 속한 것을 사용하고 나중에 되돌려 주어야만 하다
- □ **century** 세기, 100년
  → a period of a hundred years 백년의 기간
- □ **contact** 접촉
  → communication between people, countries either by talking or writing
  말이나 글로 사람이나 나라 간의 의사소통
- □ **civilization** 문명
  → a society that is well organized and developed
  잘 정돈되고 발전된 사회
- □ **expression** 표현
  → something you say, write, or do that shows what you think or feel 생각과 감정을 보여주는 말, 글, 행동
- □ **flood** 홍수
  → a lot of water that covers land that is usually dry
  평상시 마른 땅을 뒤덮는 많은 물

- □ **originally** 원래
  → in the beginning, before other things happened
  처음에, 다른 일이 일어나기 전에
- □ **present** 현재의
  → happening or existing now 지금 일어나거나 존재하는
- □ **shortly** 곧, 즉시
  → in a short time; soon 짧은 시간에, 곧
- □ **slave** 노예
  → someone who is owned by another person and works for them for no money
  돈을 받지 않고 다른 사람에게 소유되어 그들을 위하여 일하는 사람
- □ **suggest** 제안하다
  → to tell someone you think he or she should do something 무엇을 해야 하는지를 누군가에게 말하다
- □ **trader** 무역업자
  → someone who buys and sells goods
  상품을 사고파는 사람
- □ **universe** 우주, 은하계
  → all of space, including all the stars and planets
  항성과 행성을 포함한 모든 공간

01 다음 짝지어진 단어의 관계가 같도록 빈칸에 알맞은 말은?

source – origin : determine – _____

① present
② cause
③ judge
④ produce
⑤ decide

서답형

02 다음 주어진 영어 설명에 맞게 빈칸에 알맞은 말을 쓰시오.

He presented a new concept of the beginning of the _____.

<영어 설명> all of space, including all the stars and planets

➡ _____

03 다음 〈보기〉의 단어를 사용하여 자연스러운 문장을 만들 수 <u>없는</u> 것은?

┌─ 보기 ─┐
justice   suggest   civilization   present

① Our _____ situation is difficult, but we'll do our best.
② My teacher _____ed that we should read newspapers every day.
③ If you want to be a good judge, be in _____ to a person!
④ The Inca Empire was a very developed _____.
⑤ Like any great _____ or legend, the question still remains.

04 다음 빈칸에 들어갈 알맞은 말을 고르시오.

The _____ of the hamburger is uncertain.

① origin
② contact
③ flood
④ expression
⑤ soap

05 다음 중 밑줄 친 부분의 의미가 <u>잘못된</u> 것은?

① The movie's title <u>originated from</u> a Latin expression. (~에서 비롯되었다)
② I want to <u>keep in touch</u> with you but I don't know how. (연락하다)
③ I think I can <u>introduce</u> some new companies to you. (소개하다)
④ We don't <u>produce</u> the model any longer. (파괴하다)
⑤ They <u>called</u> their first daughter <u>after</u> her grandmother. (…을 본떠 ~의 이름을 불렀다)

06 다음 빈칸에 알맞은 말이 바르게 짝지어진 것을 고르시오.

• Horror movies are just not my cup of _____.
• The actor told me to break a _____.

① tea – leg
② tea – arm
③ cake – leg
④ cake – arm
⑤ coffee – foot

01 다음 영영풀이에 알맞은 어휘를 〈보기〉에서 찾아 쓰시오.

> ┌ 보기 ┐
>
> suggest   slave   borrow   flood

(1) a lot of water that covers land that is usually dry

(2) someone who is owned by another person and works for them for no money

(3) to tell someone you think he or she should do something

(4) to use something that belongs to someone else and that you must give back to them later

➡ (1) _____ (2) _____ (3) _____

(4) _____

02 다음 짝지어진 두 단어의 관계가 같도록 빈칸에 알맞은 말을 쓰시오.

(1) China : Chinese = Italy : _____

(2) decide : decision = suggest : _____

03 다음 우리말에 맞도록 빈칸에 알맞은 말을 쓰시오.

(1) 요새 건강이 안 좋으시다니 안타깝네요.

→ I'm sorry to hear that you've been under the _____ lately.

(2) 나는 너를 안 믿으니까 나를 그만 놀리시지.

→ I don't believe you, so stop _____ my leg.

(3) 그녀는 언어를 정말 쉽게 습득한다.

→ She _____ up languages really easily.

(4) 우리는 여기에 머무르지 않고 지나갈 것입니다.

→ We're not staying here, we're just _____ through.

04 다음 우리말에 맞게 한 단어를 추가하여 주어진 단어를 알맞게 배열하시오.

(1) 그 학생의 버릇없음에 선생님은 화가 났다.

(rudeness, the teacher, the student's, angered, by)

➡ _____

_____

(2) 문화 차이를 경험한 적이 있나요?

(differences, you, experienced, cultural, ever)

➡ _____

_____

(3) 컴퓨터를 켜고 싶다면, 이 빨간 버튼을 누르세요. (the computer, button, you, this, turn, press, want, red, if, to)

➡ _____

_____

(4) 그는 법학 대학원을 들어가기 위한 시험을 통과했다. (the exam, he, school, entering, passed, a, for)

➡ _____

_____

Conversation

교과서

1 설명 요청하기

> **A** What does that mean? 그게 무슨 뜻이니?
> **B** It means "It's raining a lot." 그것은 "비가 아주 많이 내린다."라는 뜻이야.

- 상대방이 한 말의 의미를 설명해 달라고 요청할 때 쓰는 표현은 "What does that mean?(그것이 무슨 뜻입니까?)", "What do you mean by that?(그것이 무슨 뜻이니?)", "What is the meaning of that?(그것의 의미가 무엇이니?)" 등이 있다. that은 상대방이 말한 내용을 언급하는 대명사이고, by that은 "그 말로써, 그것으로"라는 뜻으로, 직역하면 "그 말로써 너는 무엇을 의미하니?"라는 뜻이다.

- 상대방에게 설명을 요청할 때는 "설명하다, 말하다"의 의미를 가지는 동사 explain, tell이나 give information, be specific 등의 표현을 사용하여 "Could you explain the meaning of it?", "Could you tell me more about them?" 등의 표현을 사용하기도 한다. Could 대신 Would, Can, Will 등을 사용할 수 있고, "Do you mind if I ask you to explain ~?"이라고 말할 수도 있다.

- 상대방의 말을 알아듣지 못했을 때는 "I'm not following you.(잘 못 알아듣겠습니다.)", "I don't get it.(제대로 이해를 못하겠어요.)" 등의 표현을 사용하여 상대방이 다시 설명을 하도록 요청할 수도 있다.

설명 요청하기

- What does that mean? 그게 무슨 뜻이죠?
- What do you mean by that? 그게 무슨 말이야?
- Could you give me more information? 좀 더 정보를 주시겠습니까?
- Can you explain more in detail? 좀 더 자세히 설명해 주시겠습니까?
- Could you be more specific? 좀 더 구체적으로 말해 주시겠습니까?
- What is the meaning of that exactly? 정확하게 그게 무슨 뜻입니까?
- Could you explain what it means? 그게 무엇을 의미하는지 설명 좀 해 주시겠습니까?

핵심 Check

1. 다음 우리말과 일치하도록 주어진 어휘를 이용하여 빈칸에 알맞은 말을 쓰시오.

A: It's raining cats and dogs.

B: Excuse me, but can you please say that again?

A: I said, "It's raining cats and dogs."

B: _____? (그게 무슨 뜻이니?) (what, mean)

A: It means "It's raining a lot."

② 반복 설명 요청하기

• **Can you say that again?** 다시 한 번 말해 줄래?

■ 상대방의 말을 잘 듣지 못했거나, 이해하지 못해서 다시 한 번 반복해서 말해줄 것을 요청하고 싶을 때 "Can you (please) say that again?(다시 한 번 말씀해 주시겠습니까?)" 또는 "Excuse me(, but I'm not following you)?(죄송하지만 잘 못 알아들었어요.)" "Can you repeat that?", "What did you say?" 등을 사용한다. 이렇게 요청받고 반복해서 말해 줄 때는 "I said "~."(저는 ~라고 말했습니다.)"라는 표현을 사용한다.

■ 일상적으로 부담 없이 상대방에게 반복을 요청하는 표현은 "What?(뭐라고 하셨죠?)" "What did you say?(뭐라고 말씀하셨는지요?)", "(I beg your) Pardon?(다시 한 번 말씀해 주시겠습니까?)" "Excuse me?(실례지만 잘 못 알아들었습니다.)" 등이 있는데 이런 표현은 의문의 뜻으로 억양을 올려서 말한다.

■ 좀 더 공손해야 할 필요가 있을 때는 "(Sorry, I'm afraid) I don't know what you mean[meant]." "Will you say that again, please? (다시 한 번 말씀해 주시겠어요?)"와 같은 표현을 쓰거나 아주 격식을 갖출 필요가 있을 때는 "I am afraid I am not quite clear what you mean by that.(죄송합니다만, 말씀하신 내용이 명확하게 이해가 되지 않습니다.)"라고 말하고 다시 이야기해 달라고 말하거나, "I didn't quite follow what you said, please repeat it.(말씀하신 것을 잘 알아듣지 못했는데, 다시 한 번 말씀해 주세요.)"라고 한다.

설명 요청하기

• Can you please say that again? 다시 한 번 말씀해 주시겠습니까?

• Will you say that again, please? 다시 한 번 말씀해 주시겠어요?

• Excuse me, but I'm not following you. 죄송하지만 잘 못 알아들었어요.

• Pardon? / Pardon me? 잘 못 알아들었습니다. / 뭐라고요?

• I beg your pardon? 다시 한 번 말씀해 주시겠어요?

• Sorry? 뭐라고 하셨는지요?   • Excuse me? 잘 못 알아들었습니다.

• I didn't quite follow what you said. 말씀하신 것을 잘 알아듣지 못했습니다.

핵심 Check

2. 주어진 문장 다음에 이어질 (A)~(D)를 바르게 배열하시오.

A: I'm under the weather.

(A) It means "I don't feel well."   (B) I said, "I'm under the weather."

(C) What do you mean by that?   (D) Excuse me, but I'm not following you.

➡ _____

 Listen and Talk A 1

G: Look. ❶It's raining cats and dogs.

B: Raining cats and dogs? ❷What does that mean?

G: It means "It's raining ❸a lot."

B: Oh. Don't worry. I have an umbrella in my backpack.

G: 봐. 고양이와 개처럼 비가 내려.

B: 고양이와 개처럼 비가 내린다고? 그게 무슨 뜻이니?

G: 그것은 "비가 아주 많이 내린다."라는 뜻이야.

B: 오, 걱정 마. 내 배낭에 우산이 있어.

❶ 'rain cats and dogs'는 '비가 많이 온다'라는 뜻이다.
❷ 상대방이 한 말의 의미를 설명해 달라고 요청할 때 쓰는 표현이다. "What do you mean by that?", "What is the meaning of that?" 등으로 바꿔 쓸 수 있다.
❸ 'a lot'은 부사구로 사용되었다.

Check(√) True or False

(1) The boy knew the meaning of "raining cats and dogs." T ☐ F ☐

(2) The girl is explaining the meaning of "raining cats and dogs." T ☐ F ☐

 Listen and Talk C

G: Thank you for everything, Jiho. ❶I had a great time in Korea.

B: My pleasure. Please ❷come visit me again, Lucy.

G: I'd love to, but before I do, I'd like to invite you to visit me in London.

B: Thanks. Anyway, it's too bad that you can't come to my soccer game tomorrow.

G: I'm sorry that I can't stay longer. I'll ❸keep my fingers crossed for you.

B: ❹Excuse me, but can you please say that again?

G: I said, "I'll keep my fingers crossed for you." It means "I wish you good luck."

B: Oh. Thanks. Have a nice trip.

G: Thanks. I'll ❺keep in touch.

G: 지호야. 모든 게 고마웠어. 한국에서 정말 좋은 시간을 보냈어.

B: 천만에. 다음에 또 와줘. Lucy.

G: 그러고 싶지만, 그 전에 난 런던으로 널 초대하고 싶어.

B: 고마워. 어쨌든, 내일 네가 내 축구 시합에 올 수 없어서 너무 안타깝다.

G: 나도 더 오래 머물 수 없어서 유감이야. 너를 위해 내 손가락을 교차할게.

B: 미안한데, 다시 한 번 말해 줄래?

G: 나는 "너를 위해 내 손가락을 교차할게."라고 말했어. 그것은 "행운을 빌게."라는 뜻이야.

B: 아, 고마워. 즐거운 여행이 되길 바랄게.

G: 고마워. 연락할게.

❶ 'have a good[great] time'은 '좋은[재미있는] 시간을 보내다'라는 의미이다.
❷ 'come visit'은 'come and visit' 또는 'come to visit'으로도 쓸 수 있다.
❸ 'keep one's fingers crossed'는 '행운을 빌다'라는 뜻이다.
❹ 반복해서 설명해 줄 것을 요청하는 표현이다.
❺ 'keep in touch'는 '연락하다'를 의미한다.

Check(√) True or False

(3) Lucy is leaving for London. T ☐ F ☐

(4) Jiho is glad that Lucy will come to his soccer game. T ☐ F ☐

Listen and Talk A 2

G: ❶This juice is on me, Suho.

B: Excuse me? ❷Can you say that again?

G: I said, "This juice is on me." It means "I'll pay for the juice."

B: Oh. Thanks a lot.

G: ❸You're welcome.

G: 수호야, 이 주스는 내 위에 있어.
B: 뭐라고 했어? 다시 한 번 말해 줄래?
G: "이 주스는 내 위에 있어."라고 했어. 그것은 "내가 그 주스를 낼게."라는 뜻이야.
B: 오. 정말 고마워.
G: 천만에.

❶ '~ is on me.'는 '~은 내가 내겠다.'라는 의미이다.
❷ 반복해서 설명해 줄 것을 요청할 때 쓰는 표현이다. 'Pardon me?', 'Can you repeat that?', 'What did you say?' 등으로 바꿔 쓸 수 있다.
❸ '천만에요.'라는 뜻으로 'Don't mention it.', 'Not at all.', 'No problem.', 'My pleasure.' 등으로도 말할 수 있다.

Check(√) True or False

(5) The girl will pay for Suho's juice.

T ☐ F ☐

(6) Suho wants to buy the juice for the girl.

T ☐ F ☐

Listen and Talk A 3

B: Everything ❶looks delicious.

G: Yes. ❷Would you like some of my spaghetti?

B: No, thanks. Spaghetti is ❸not my cup of tea.

G: ❹Not your cup of tea? What does that mean?

B: It means "I don't like ❺something."

G: Oh, ❻I see. You don't like spaghetti.

B: 모든 것이 맛있어 보여.
G: 응. 내 스파게티 좀 먹을래?
B: 괜찮아. 스파게티는 나의 차 한 잔이 아니야.
G: 네 차 한 잔이 아니라고? 그게 무슨 뜻이니?
B: 그것은 "난 무언가를 좋아하지 않아."라는 뜻이야.
G: 오, 알겠어. 넌 스파게티를 좋아하지 않는구나.

❶ look+형용사: ~하게 보이다
❷ 'Would you like ~?'는 'Do you want ~?'와 같은 의미로 공손히 말할 때 쓰는 표현이다.
❸ 'not my cup of tea'는 '좋아하지 않는 것[사람]'이라는 뜻이다.
❹ 끝을 올려 읽어서 의문문 대용으로 사용한다.
❺ 부정문이지만 'something'이 사용됐음에 주의한다.
❻ '알겠다.'라는 뜻이다.

Check(√) True or False

(7) The boy doesn't like spaghetti.

T ☐ F ☐

(8) The girl will drink a cup of tea.

T ☐ F ☐

Listen and Talk A 4

G: I feel ❶under the weather.

B: Excuse me, but ❷can you please say that again?

G: I said, "I feel under the weather." It means "I don't feel well." I think I ❸have a cold.

B: Oh. ❹Why don't you buy some medicine before you get on the plane? You can get medicine at the store over there.

G: I guess ❺I should.

❶ 'under the weather'는 '몸이 안 좋은'이라는 의미이다.
❷ 반복해서 설명해 줄 것을 요청할 때 쓰는 표현이다.
❸ have a cold = catch a cold: 감기에 걸리다
❹ 'Why don't you ~?'는 '권유'하는 표현으로 'How about ~?', 'What about ~?', 'What do you say to ~?' 등으로 바꿔 쓸 수 있다. 'Why don't we ~'는 '제안'할 때 쓰는 것이므로 서로 혼동하지 않도록 주의한다.
❺ 뒤에 'get medicine at the store'가 생략되어 있다.

 Review 2

W: ❶I feel under the weather.

M: Excuse me, but can you please say that again?

W: I said, "I feel under the weather."

M: ❷What does that mean?

W: It means "I don't feel well." I think I have a cold.

M: Oh. ❸Why don't you buy some medicine? You can get medicine at the store over there.

W: OK, I will.

❶ 'under the weather'는 '몸이 안 좋은'이라는 의미이다.
❷ 상대방이 한 말의 의미를 설명해 달라고 요청할 때 쓰는 표현이다.
❸ Why don't you ~?는 '권유'하는 표현이다.

 Listen and Talk B

M: ❶Break a leg.

W: ❷Excuse me, but can you please say that again?

M: I said, "Break a leg."

W: ❸What does that mean?

M: It means "Good luck."

❶ '행운을 빈다.'라는 뜻이다.
❷ 반복해서 말해 줄 것을 요청할 때 쓰는 표현이다.
❸ 상대방이 한 말의 의미를 설명해 달라고 요청할 때 쓰는 표현이다.

 Review 3

M: Look. It's raining cats and dogs.

W: ❶Can you say that again?

M: It's raining cats and dogs.

W: What does ❷that mean?

M: It means "It's raining a lot."

❶ 반복해서 말해 줄 것을 요청하고 있다.
❷ that은 'It's raining cats and dogs.'를 받고 있다.

 Review 1

G: ❶I'll keep my fingers crossed for you.

B: ❷I'm sorry, but can you please say that again?

G: I said, "I'll keep my fingers crossed for you." It means "I wish you good luck."

❶ 'keep one's fingers crossed'는 '행운을 빌다'라는 뜻이다.
❷ 반복해서 설명해 줄 것을 요청할 때 쓰는 표현이다.

 Review 4

G: ❶This pizza is on me, Suho.

B: ❷What does that mean?

G: It means "I'll ❸pay for the pizza."

❶ 피자 값을 자기가 지불하겠다는 표현이다.
❷ 상대방이 한 말의 의미를 설명해 달라고 요청할 때 쓰는 표현이다.
❸ 'pay for'는 '~에 대한 값을 지불하다'라는 뜻이다.

● 다음 우리말과 일치하도록 빈칸에 알맞은 말을 쓰시오.

 해석

Listen and Talk A 1

G: Look. It's raining _____ _____ _____.

B: Raining _____ _____? What does _____ _____?

G: It _____ "It's raining _____ _____."

B: Oh. Don't _____. I have an umbrella in my backpack.

> **G:** 봐. 고양이와 개처럼 비가 내려.
> **B:** 고양이와 개처럼 비가 내린다고? 그게 무슨 뜻이니?
> **G:** 그것은 "비가 아주 많이 내린다."라는 뜻이야.
> **B:** 오, 걱정 마. 내 배낭에 우산이 있어.

Listen and Talk A 2

G: This juice is _____ _____, Suho.

B: _____ _____? _____ you _____ _____ again?

G: I said, "This juice is _____ _____." It means "I'll _____ the juice."

B: Oh. Thanks _____ _____.

G: _____ _____.

> **G:** 수호야, 이 주스는 내 위에 있어.
> **B:** 뭐라고 했어? 다시 한 번 말해 줄래?
> **G:** "이 주스는 내 위에 있어."라고 했어. 그것은 "내가 그 주스를 낼게."라는 뜻이야.
> **B:** 오. 정말 고마워.
> **G:** 천만에.

Listen and Talk A 3

B: Everything looks _____.

G: Yes. _____ you _____ _____ _____ of my spaghetti?

B: No, thanks. Spaghetti is _____ my cup of _____.

G: _____ your cup of _____? What does that mean?

B: It means "I _____ _____ _____."

G: Oh, I _____. You don't like spaghetti.

> **B:** 모든 것이 맛있어 보여.
> **G:** 응. 내 스파게티 좀 먹을래?
> **B:** 괜찮아. 스파게티는 나의 차 한 잔이 아니야.
> **G:** 네 차 한 잔이 아니라고? 그게 무슨 뜻이니?
> **B:** 그것은 "난 무언가를 좋아하지 않아." 라는 뜻이야.
> **G:** 오, 알겠어. 넌 스파게티를 좋아하지 않는구나.

Listen and Talk A 4

G: I feel _____ _____ _____.

B: _____ _____, but _____ you please _____ _____ _____?

G: I said, "I feel _____ _____ _____." It means "I _____ _____ _____." I think I have a cold.

B: Oh. _____ _____ _____ buy some medicine before you _____ on the plane? You can _____ medicine at the store over there.

G: I guess I _____.

> **G:** 난 날씨 아래 있는 기분이야.
> **B:** 미안하지만 다시 한 번 말해 줄래?
> **G:** "나는 날씨 아래 있는 기분이야."라고 말했어. 그것은 "몸이 좋지 않아."라는 뜻이야. 난 감기에 걸린 것 같아.
> **B:** 오, 비행기 타기 전에 약을 좀 사는 게 어때? 저기에 있는 가게에서 약을 살 수 있어.
> **G:** 그래야겠다.

Listen and Talk B 1

A: Don't _____ _____ _____ _____.

B: _____ _____, but _____ _____ _____
_____ _____?

A: I said, "Don't _____ _____ _____ _____."

B: _____ _____ _____ _____ _____?

A: It means "Don't _____ _____."

A: 얼굴을 길쭉하게 만들지 마.
B: 미안하지만 다시 한 번 말해 줄래?
A: "얼굴을 길쭉하게 만들지 마."라고 했어.
B: 그게 무슨 뜻이니?
A: 그것은 "슬퍼하지 마."라는 뜻이야.

Listen and Talk B 2

M: _____ _____ _____ _____.

W: _____ _____, but _____ _____ _____
_____ ?

M: I said, "_____ _____ _____ _____."

W: _____ _____ _____ _____ ?

M: It means "_____ _____ _____."

M: 다리를 부러뜨려.
W: 미안하지만 다시 한 번 말해 줄래?
M: "다리를 부러뜨려."라고 했어.
W: 그게 무슨 뜻이니?
M: 그것은 "행운을 빌어."라는 뜻이야.

Listen and Talk B 3

M: I feel _____ _____ _____.

W: _____ _____, but _____ _____ _____
_____ _____ ?

M: I said, "I feel _____ _____ _____."

W: _____ _____ _____ _____ ?

M: It means "I don't feel well."

M: 나는 날씨 아래 있는 기분이야.
W: 미안하지만 다시 한 번 말해 줄래?
M: "나는 날씨 아래 있는 기분이야."라고 했어.
W: 그게 무슨 뜻이니?
M: 그것은 "난 몸이 좋지 않아."라는 뜻이야.

Listen and Talk C

G: Thank you for everything, Jiho. I _____ _____ _____
_____ in Korea.

B: _____ _____. Please _____ _____ me again, Lucy.

G: I'd _____ _____, but before I do, I'd _____ _____
_____ you to visit me in London.

B: Thanks. Anyway, _____'s too bad _____ you can't _____ to
my soccer game tomorrow.

G: I'm sorry that I can't stay _____. I'll _____ _____
_____ for you.

B: _____ _____, but _____ _____ please _____
_____ ?

G: I said, "I'll _____ _____ _____ _____ _____ for you." It means
"I _____ _____ _____ _____."

B: Oh. Thanks. _____ a nice _____.

G: Thanks. I'll _____ _____ _____.

G: 지호야, 모든 게 고마웠어. 한국에서 정말 좋은 시간을 보냈어.
B: 천만에. 다음에 또 와줘, Lucy.
G: 그러고 싶지만, 그 전에 난 런던으로 널 초대하고 싶어.
B: 고마워. 어쨌든, 내일 네가 내 축구 시합에 올 수 없어서 너무 안타깝다.
G: 나도 더 오래 머물 수 없어서 유감이야. 너를 위해 내 손가락을 교차할게.
B: 미안한데, 다시 한 번 말해 줄래?
G: 나는 "너를 위해 내 손가락을 교차할게."라고 말했어. 그것은 "행운을 빌게."라는 뜻이야.
B: 아, 고마워. 즐거운 여행이 되길 바랄게.
G: 고마워. 연락할게.

Review 1

G: I'll _____ _____ _____ _____ _____ for you.

B: I'm sorry, but _____ _____ _____ _____ _____ _____ _____ ?

G: I said, "I'll _____ _____ _____ _____ _____ for you." It means "I _____ _____ _____ _____ _____ ."

Review 2

W: I _____ _____ _____ _____ _____ _____ .

M: Excuse me, but _____ _____ _____ _____ _____ _____ _____ ?

W: I said, "I _____ _____ _____ _____ _____ _____ ."

M: _____ _____ _____ _____ _____ ?

W: It means "I _____ _____ _____ _____ ." I think I have a cold.

M: Oh. _____ _____ _____ _____ some medicine? You can get medicine at the store over there.

W: OK, I _____ .

Review 3

M: Look. It's raining _____ _____ _____ .

W: _____ _____ _____ _____ _____ _____ ?

M: It's raining _____ _____ _____ .

W: _____ _____ _____ _____ ?

M: It means "It's raining _____ _____ ."

Review 4

G: This pizza _____ _____ _____ _____ , Suho.

B: _____ _____ _____ _____ _____ ?

G: It means "I'll _____ _____ the pizza."

해석

G: 너를 위해 내 손가락을 교차할게.
B: 미안하지만 다시 한 번 말해 줄래?
G: "너를 위해 내 손가락을 교차할게."라고 했어. 그것은 "행운을 빌게."라는 뜻이야.

W: 저는 날씨 아래에 있는 기분이에요.
M: 죄송한데, 다시 한 번 말해 주시겠어요?
W: "저는 날씨 아래에 있는 기분이에요."라고 말했어요.
M: 그게 무슨 뜻인가요?
W: 그것은 "몸이 좋지 않다."라는 뜻이에요. 감기에 걸린 것 같아요.
M: 오. 약을 좀 사는 게 어때요? 저기에 있는 가게에서 약을 살 수 있어요.
W: 네, 그럴게요.

M: 봐요. 고양이와 개처럼 비가 내리네요.
W: 다시 한 번 말해 주시겠어요?
M: 고양이와 개처럼 비가 내려요.
W: 그게 무슨 뜻인가요?
M: 그것은 "비가 아주 많이 내린다."라는 뜻이에요.

G: 수호야, 이 피자는 내 위에 있어.
B: 그게 무슨 뜻이니?
G: 그것은 "피자는 내가 살게."라는 뜻이야.

Conversation 시험대비 기본평가

01 다음 빈칸 (A)에 알맞은 문장을 쓰시오.

> M: Look. _____ (A) _____
> W: Can you say that again?
> M: _____ (A) _____
> W: What does that mean?
> M: It means "It's raining a lot."

➡ _____

02 다음 밑줄 친 우리말에 해당하는 영어 문장을 고르시오.

> G: Look. It's raining cats and dogs.
> B: Raining cats and dogs? 그게 무슨 뜻이니?
> G: It means "It's raining a lot."
> B: Oh. Don't worry. I have an umbrella in my backpack.

① Can you say that again? ② Is it on me?
③ Do you feel under the weather? ④ What does that mean?
⑤ Are you pulling my leg?

03 다음 대화의 빈칸에 들어갈 말로 어색한 것은?

> G: This juice is on me, Suho.
> B: Excuse me? Can you say that again?
> G: I said, "This juice is on me." It means "I'll pay for the juice."
> B: Oh. Thanks a lot.
> G: _____

① You're welcome. ② Don't mention it.
③ That's alright. ④ My pleasure.
⑤ Not at all.

04 다음 밑줄 친 우리말을 주어진 단어를 이용해 영작하시오.

> A: You look tired today.
> B: 다시 한 번 말해 줄래? (say, can, that, 5 단어)

➡ _____

01 다음 중 짝지어진 대화가 <u>어색한</u> 것은?

① A: I'll keep my fingers crossed for you.
   B: I'm sorry, but can you please say that again?

② A: What does that mean?
   B: It means "It's raining a lot."

③ A: Excuse me, but can you please say that again?
   B: I said, "I feel under the weather."

④ A: What does that mean?
   B: I said, "It's raining cats and dogs."

⑤ A: Have a nice trip.
   B: Thanks. I'll keep in touch.

[02~05] 다음 대화를 읽고 물음에 답하시오.

> **B:** Everything looks delicious.
> **G:** Yes. Would you like some of my spaghetti?
> **B:** _____(A)_____ Spaghetti is not my cup of tea.
> **G:** Not your cup of tea? (a)그게 무슨 뜻이니?
> **B:** It means "_____(B)_____"
> **G:** Oh, I see. You don't like spaghetti.

02 빈칸 (A)에 알맞은 말을 고르시오.

① Why not?
② No, thanks.
③ I had enough.
④ Thanks a lot.
⑤ You're welcome.

03 위 대화의 빈칸 (B)에 들어갈 말로 알맞을 쓰시오.

➡ _____

04 밑줄 친 (a)의 우리말에 맞게 that을 이용하여 영작하시오.

➡ _____

05 위 대화의 내용과 일치하는 것은?

① The girl and the boy meet for the first time.
② The boy is having spaghetti.
③ The boy likes spaghetti a lot.
④ The girl knows the meaning of 'not my cup of tea.'
⑤ The girl understands what the boy means.

[06~07] 다음 대화를 읽고 물음에 답하시오.

> **A:** Don't make a long face.
> **B:** _____(A)_____
> **A:** I said, "Don't make a long face."
> **B:** What does that mean?
> **A:** It means "_____(B)_____"

06 위 대화의 빈칸 (A)에 들어갈 말로 알맞은 것은?

① I want to make a long face.
② I don't want to make a long face.
③ Do I make a long face?
④ Do you want me to make a long face?
⑤ Excuse me, but can you please say that again?

07 위 대화의 빈칸 (B)에 들어갈 알맞은 말을 쓰시오. (3 words)

➡ _____

08 주어진 문장 사이에 대화가 자연스럽게 연결되도록 (A)~(D)를 순서대로 적절하게 배열한 것은?

> W: I feel under the weather.
> M: Excuse me, but can you please say that again?
> (A) It means "I don't feel well." I think I have a cold.
> (B) What does that mean?
> (C) I said, "I feel under the weather."
> (D) Oh. Why don't you buy some medicine? You can get medicine at the store over there.
> W: OK, I will.

① (B) – (A) – (C) – (D)
② (B) – (C) – (A) – (D)
③ (C) – (B) – (A) – (D)
④ (C) – (B) – (D) – (A)
⑤ (C) – (D) – (B) – (A)

[09~12] 다음 대화를 읽고 물음에 답하시오.

> G: Thank you for everything, Jiho. I had a great time in Korea.
> B: _____(A)_____ Please come visit me again, Lucy.
> G: I'd love to, but before I do, I'd like to invite you to visit me in London.
> B: Thanks. Anyway, it's too bad that you can't come to my soccer game tomorrow.
> G: I'm sorry that I can't stay longer. I'll keep my fingers crossed for you.
> B: Excuse me, but _____(B)_____? (can, please, that)
> G: I said, "I'll keep my fingers crossed for you." It means "(a)행운을 빌게.(wish, good)"
> B: Oh. Thanks. Have a nice trip.
> G: Thanks. _____(C)_____

09 위 대화의 빈칸 (A)에 알맞지 <u>않은</u> 말은?

① You're welcome.
② Don't mention it.
③ My pleasure.
④ You can say that again.
⑤ Not at all.

10 위 대화의 빈칸 (B)에 알맞은 말을 주어진 어휘를 이용하여 쓰시오.

➡ _____

11 위 대화의 빈칸 (C)에 가장 알맞은 말은?

① Welcome!
② I'll keep in touch.
③ Would you like anything else?
④ Don't feel under the weather.
⑤ You can come again.

12 위 대화의 밑줄 친 우리말 (a)에 맞게 주어진 어휘를 이용하여 5 단어로 쓰시오.

➡ _____

13 다음 대화의 밑줄 친 부분의 의도로 알맞은 것은?

> G: I'll keep my fingers crossed for you.
> B: <u>I'm sorry, but can you please say that again?</u>
> G: I said, "I'll keep my fingers crossed for you." It means "I wish you good luck."

① 희망 표현하기　② 경험 묻기
③ 경험 답하기　④ 설명 요청하기
⑤ 다시 말해 달라고 요청하기

[01~03] 다음 대화를 읽고 물음에 답하시오.

G: Thank you for everything, Jiho. I had a great time in Korea.

B: My pleasure. (a)다음에 또 와줘(please, me, visit), Lucy.

G: I'd love to, but before I do, I'd like to invite you to visit me in London.

B: Thanks. Anyway, it's too bad that you can't come to my soccer game tomorrow.

(A) Oh. Thanks. Have a nice trip.

(B) Excuse me, but can you please say that again?

(C) I said, "I'll keep my fingers crossed for you." It means "I wish you good luck."

(D) I'm sorry that I can't stay longer. I'll keep my fingers crossed for you.

G: Thanks. I'll keep in touch.

01 위 대화의 (A)~(D)를 알맞은 순서로 배열하시오.

➡ _____

02 괄호 안에 주어진 어휘를 이용하여 밑줄 친 우리말 (a)에 맞게 5 단어로 쓰시오.

➡ _____

03 Why can't Lucy go to Jiho's soccer game tomorrow? Use the phrase 'It's because'.

➡ _____
_____

[04~06] 다음 대화를 읽고 물음에 답하시오.

G: I feel under the weather.

B: Excuse me, but can you please say that again?

G: I said, "I feel under the weather." It means "_____(A)_____" I think I have a cold.

B: Oh. Why don't you buy some medicine before you get on the plane? You can get medicine at the store over there.

G: I guess I should.

04 위 대화의 빈칸 (A)에 알맞은 말을 쓰시오. (well을 포함해서 4 단어)

➡ _____

05 Why does the girl feel under the weather?

➡ _____

06 Where do you guess they are now?

➡ _____

[07~08] 다음 대화를 읽고 물음에 답하시오.

G: _____(A)_____, Suho.

B: What does that mean?

G: It means "I'll pay __(B)__ the pizza."

07 위 대화의 빈칸 (A)에 알맞은 말을 5 단어로 쓰시오.

➡ _____

08 위 대화의 빈칸 (B)에 알맞은 전치사를 쓰시오.

➡ _____

Grammar

교과서

---

1 '계속적 용법'의 관계대명사 which / who

- This book is about King Sejong, **who** invented Hangeul.
  이 책은 세종대왕에 관한 것이고, 그는 한글을 창제했다.

■ 계속적 용법은, 형태상으로 콤마(,)를 쓰며, 관계대명사가 받는 '선행사의 범위'가 다르다.

- I want to see *the Mona Lisa* **which** Leonardo da Vinci painted. – 콤마(×),
  다빈치가 그린 모나리자를 보고 싶다.(다른 사람이 그린 모나리자도 있을 수 있음) → 제한적 용법
- I want to see *the Mona Lisa*, **which** Leonardo da Vinci painted. – 콤마(○),
  모나리자라는 작품을 보고 싶고(유일한 작품). 그것을 다빈치가 그렸다. → 계속적 용법

■ 계속적 용법의 관계대명사는 '접속사+대명사'로 전환 가능하다. (and, but, for, though 등)

- She bought a laptop, **which** was broken.

  = She bought a laptop, **but it** was broken. 그녀는 노트북 한 대를 구매했지만, 그것은 고장 났다.

  cf. She bought a laptop **which** was broken. 제한적 – 그녀는 고장 난 노트북 한 대를 구매했다.

- The Louvre has thousands of works of art, most of **which** were stolen.

  = The Louvre has thousands of works of art, and most of them were stolen.
  Louvre 박물관은 수천 점의 예술 작품이 있는데. 그것들 대부분은 훔친 것이다.

■ 선행사는 앞에 나온 명사, 대명사 뿐만 아니라, 구, 절, 앞 문장 전체 등이 모두 가능하다.

- Some animals can use tools, **which** I feel amazed at.

  = Some animals can use tools, and I feel amazed at that. 어떤 동물들은 도구를 사용할 수 있고, 나는 그것을
  놀랍다고 느낀다. → 선행사는 앞 문장 전체(어떤 동물들이 도구를 사용할 수 있다는 것)이며, '접속
  사 and와 대명사 it/that'으로 받을 수 있다.

- It is good for the young not to give up their dream, **which** a few think to be natural.

  = It is good for the young not to give up their dream, though a few think it to be natural.
  청년들이 자신들의 꿈을 포기하지 않는 것은 좋은 일이다. 비록 몇몇 소수는 그것[꿈을 포기하는 것]을 당연하다고 생각
  하지만. → 선행사는 준동사구(to give up their dream)이며, 문맥상 '접속사 though와 대명사 it'으
  로 받을 수 있다.

■ that, what은 계속적 용법으로 쓸 수 없고, '전치사+관계대명사'는 관계부사로 바꿀 수 있다.

- They bought the farm, **which** goats lived in. 그들은 그 농장을 구매했는데, 염소들이 그곳에서 살았다.

  = They bought the farm, **in which** goats lived. (= , where)

핵심 Check

1. 다음 괄호 안에서 알맞은 단어를 고르시오.

(1) I visited the British Museum, (that / which) is in London.

(2) Chris only blames his colleagues, (which / who) makes his boss angry.

---

② It is[was] ~ that 주어+동사 (가주어 it – 진주어 that 절)

- **It** is interesting **that** the idea of using the word *robot* didn't come from Karel Capek himself. robot이라는 단어를 사용하려는 생각이 Karel Capek 자신에게서 나오지 않은 것은 흥미롭다.
- **It** is true **that** he was the first president of the club.
  그가 그 클럽의 첫 번째 회장이었다는 것은 사실이다.

■ 접속사 that이 명사절로서 문장의 주어 역할을 할 때, 이렇게 절로 표현된 긴 주어 부분을 뒤로 보내 짧은 형식상 주어로 대체하는 것을 가주어 It이라 부르며, 뒤로 보내진 that 명사절을 진주어라고 한다. 'It+be동사+[형용사/명사]+that+완전한 절'의 형태를 취한다.

- **It** is interesting **that** some animals can use tools. 어떤 동물들이 도구를 쓸 수 있다는 것은 흥미롭다.
- **It** was shocking **that** he lost the race. 그가 경주에서 졌다는 것은 충격적이었다.

■ 목적절로 쓰인 that절을 수동태로 바꿀 때에도, 가주어–진주어 형식으로 표현한다.

- People believe **that** Koreans are very diligent. 사람들은 한국인들이 매우 근면하다고 생각한다.
  → **It is believed that** Koreans are very diligent. 이 경우 that절 안의 주어를 앞으로 보내서 문장 전체의 주어로 변환시키면 to부정사를 활용해서 단문으로 표현 가능하다.
  → Koreans **are believed to be** very diligent.

■ to부정사(구) 또는 의문사절도 진주어가 될 수 있다. 동명사(구)는 흔하지 않지만, 쓸 때도 있다.

- **It** is good for you **to exercise every day**. 당신이 매일 운동하는 것은 좋다.
- **It** is a mystery **why he left us**. 왜 그가 우리를 떠났는지는 미스터리이다.
- **It** is no use **crying over spilt coke**. 엎질러진 콜라를 보며 우는 것은 소용 없다.

■ It ~ that 강조구문과 가주어–진주어 구문은 구조로 쉽게 구분할 수 있다.

- It ~ that 사이에 부사(구/절)이 쓰이면, 무조건 강조구문이다.
- 강조구문에서는 It ~ that 사이에 주로 명사 또는 부사(구/절)이 쓰이고, 가주어–진주어 구문에서는 It ~ that 사이에 주로 형용사/분사 그리고 일부 명사가 쓰인다.
- 강조구문에서 It ~ that 사이에 명사가 쓰이면, that절 뒤는 불완전한데, 가주어–진주어 구문에서는 언제나 접속사 that 뒤가 완전한 절이다.
- 강조구문의 that은 강조 대상에 따라 who, which 등으로 대체 가능하지만, 가주어–진주어 구문의 접속사 that은 다른 단어로 대체 불가능하다.

핵심 Check

2. 다음 괄호 안에서 알맞은 단어를 고르시오.

(1) It is true (if / that) some birds can't fly.

(2) It is thought (that / when) Mom fell in love with Daddy 20 years ago.

01 다음 문장에서 어법상 어색한 단어를 한 개씩만 찾아 고치시오.

(1) He suggested *roboti*, that means "slave workers" in Czech.

_____ ➡ _____

(2) British traders experienced a bath in India, which they introduced it to Britain in the 18th century.

_____ ➡ _____ , _____ ➡ _____

(3) Huracán is one of the gods in Maya, which created humans.

_____ ➡ _____

(4) This is Gimchi, and which is a traditional Korean food.

_____ ➡ _____ , _____ ➡ _____

02 다음 중 밑줄 친 단어의 쓰임이 다른 하나는?

① It is interesting that many birds can use tools.
② It was strange that the man was waiting for the boss.
③ It is worth reading that book written by Arthur Conan Doyle.
④ It was shocking that Mike wrote that musical at 12.
⑤ It is not surprising that she spent all of her money.

03 다음 빈칸에 들어갈 말로 알맞은 것은?

> This is *Sunflowers*, _____ Vincent van Gogh painted.

① and   ② which   ③ that
④ who   ⑤ what

04 다음 밑줄 친 that절을 진주어로 하는, 수동태로 바꿔 다시 쓰시오.

> People think that the origin of the first hamburger is not clear.

➡ _____

01 다음 중 어법상 어색한 것을 <u>모두</u> 골라 기호를 쓰고 알맞게 고치시오.

> ⓐ I want to visit the Louvre, which have about four hundred thousand works of art.
> ⓑ She read about the origin of the word of *shampoo*, who means "pressing something".
> ⓒ A cook in Texas placed a Hamburg-style cheese between two slices of bread, which people started to call such food a hamburger.
> ⓓ The flood destroyed the village, which was shocking to people there.
> ⓔ The play *R.U.R* was written by a Czech writer, which was not a famous author then.

➡ _____

_____

02 다음 중 밑줄 친 부분의 쓰임이 나머지와 <u>다른</u> 것은?

① It is interesting <u>that</u> he originally called the machines *labori*.
② It is Sophia <u>that</u> made such a bad decision.
③ It was true <u>that</u> he was not creative.
④ It is clear <u>that</u> they are still alive.
⑤ It was a mistake <u>that</u> he pushed me.

 서답형

03 다음 대화의 문맥에 맞게 가주어−진주어와 괄호 속 단어를 사용하여 영작하시오. (현재시제로 9 단어로 쓸 것.)

> Sam: Did Mat cheat on the exam?
> Jonathan: Yes, _____. (true)

➡ _____

04 다음 중 어법상 <u>어색한</u> 문장은?

① I don't know where my review is, which I put in the drawer yesterday.
② Yewon helped the old man carry the baggage, who had trouble walking fast.
③ The little girl was playing the piano enthusiastically, which was so moving.
④ Robert had his laptop fixed by the mechanic, who cost him 200 dollars.
⑤ There was a car accident, which killed three people.

05 다음 우리말과 의미가 같도록 주어진 단어를 배열할 때 여섯 번째로 오는 것은?

> robot이라는 단어를 사용하려는 생각이 작가 자신에게서 나온 게 아니었다는 것이 흥미롭다.
> (the idea of, interesting, didn't come, using, it is, that, the word *robot*, himself, from the author).

① the word *robot* ② using
③ the idea of ④ didn't come
⑤ that

[06~07] 다음 중 'that'의 쓰임이 나머지 넷과 <u>다른</u> 것은?

06 ① It is clear <u>that</u> Sejong invented Hangeul.
② It was strange <u>that</u> the police were waiting for her.
③ It is mysterious <u>that</u> Susan doesn't remember me.
④ It was certain <u>that</u> Mary fell in love with the professor at a glance.
⑤ It was a dress <u>that</u> her aunt made Kathy for the Academy Awards.

07
① It was half an hour ago <u>that</u> the train left for Daegu.
② It was at Thomas' house <u>that</u> the party was held.
③ It is playing the cello <u>that</u> Phoebe often enjoys after her dinner.
④ It is surprising to her <u>that</u> her son got promoted to the CEO of the company.
⑤ It was Comet Halley <u>that</u> crossed the night sky yesterday.

서답형
08 다음 우리말을 〈조건〉에 맞게 영작하시오.

> 내 친구들은 Jasmine을 아는데, 그녀에 의해 풀리지 않는 수학 문제들은 없다.

조건
1. can't, math problems, no, solved를 활용할 것.
2. 계속적 용법의 관계대명사 who와 제한적 용법의 관계대명사 that을 반드시 사용할 것.
3. 수동태 표현을 반드시 사용하여 총 13단어로 영작할 것.

➡ _____
_____

09 다음 중 어법상 <u>어색한</u> 문장은?

① People called the food Sandwich, which was named after the Earl Sandwich.
② She said, "I'll keep my fingers crossed", which means "good luck."
③ King Sejong created Hangeul, which is one of the most scientific writing systems.
④ Chris loves Japchae, which is a healthy and tasty Korean food.
⑤ Sunny was born in 1988, which the Olymic games were held in Seoul.

10 다음 문장의 빈칸 (A)~(C)에 들어갈 말로 가장 적절한 것은?

> • The volunteers visited a girl in Buenos Aires, ____(A)____ grew up to be a world famous actress this year.
> • The computer had a button, ____(B)____ let it save electricity when not in use.
> • That was 1517, ____(C)____ the first Spanish contact with the Mayan civilization occurred.

	(A)	(B)	(C)
①	which	which	which
②	who	that	when
③	which	that	which
④	who	who	which
⑤	who	which	when

서답형
11 다음 주어진 문장의 진주어를 that절로 전환하여 같은 의미의 문장으로 바꾸시오.

> It is important for them to learn many words of foreign origin.

➡ _____
_____

12 다음 중 어법상 옳은 문장은?

① It snowed heavily yesterday, that made Brian stay all day long.
② The novels, which Kate borrowed from a neighbor, were so interesting.
③ The writer passed away this morning, who was shocking to me.
④ There was a figure on his desk, of which was made of plastic.
⑤ Koro is a Japanese actor, who often come to Seoul to eat *Bulgogi*.

13 다음 주어진 단어를 모두 배열하여 대화를 완성하시오. (단, 계속적 용법의 관계대명사를 반드시 추가할 것.)

> Becky: I heard that you're traveling to England. Where would you like to go and where is it?
>
> Shanon: _____
>
> (visit, to, in, want, the British Museum, I, is, London)

➡ _____

14 다음 중 밑줄 친 that을 다른 단어로 대체하여 바꿔 쓸 수 있는 문장은?

① It was a mistake that he left his bag at the subway.

② It is no wonder that the clerk was fired for being rude to anyone.

③ It was shocking that the AI machine composed such a great music.

④ It was at the cafeteria that my uncle made pizza for 5 years.

⑤ It is a good luck that I know the man offering me the job opportunity.

15 다음 중 어법상 올바른 문장의 개수는?

> ⓐ Maria saw the kids singing on the street, that made her join them.
> ⓑ Nolan told his brother to wash his shirt, which were dirty with paint marks.
> ⓒ It was surprising which his girlfriend took Michael to the CEO's office.

> ⓓ The young student helped the hurt dog to cross the street, who was so impressive.
> ⓔ Bob met the man living upstairs, and who was the one making a huge noise last night.
> ⓕ It was impossible that all the prisoners escaped from the jail overnight.

① 1개　② 2개　③ 3개　④ 4개　⑤ 5개

16 다음 우리말에 맞게 괄호 안의 단어를 배열하시오. (단, 괄호에 없는, 필요한 두 단어는 직접 써 넣으시오.)

> 그 피자가 Jane에 의해 만들어졌다는 것은 놀라운데, Jane은 이제 겨우 7살이다.
> (the pizza, is only, surprising, by, was made, it is, 7, Jane / 추가 단어 포함 총 14 단어)

➡ _____

17 다음 중 어법상 어색한 문장을 고르면? (3개)

① I read a book about Thomas Edison, who was a great inventor.

② Sarah was found alive, that made all of us relieved.

③ Yulgok was proud of his mother, which was good at writing and painting.

④ It is true that the doctor devoted her life to helping poor people.

⑤ It was impressive that Chris made at the convention.

01 다음 영화의 장면과 그 내용을 설명하는 글을 읽고, 괄호 안에 주어진 단어들을 알맞게 배열하여 요약문을 완성하시오.

Coco, the great grandmother of Miguel, was too old to remember even the names of her family members. One day, while Miguel was singing the song of her childhood, Coco sang along with it. People were amazed at the scene.
→ It is (anything, can't, along, that, who, remember, an old lady, amazing, sings) with her childhood song.

➡ It is _____

_____ with

her childhood song.

02 다음 문장을 관계대명사의 계속적 용법을 이용하여 한 문장으로 만드시오.

(1) • Mom said, "I feel under the weather."
  • It means "I don't feel well."
  ➡ _____
  _____

(2) • Emma is a coffee trader.
  • She buys and sells coffee.
  ➡ _____
  _____

(3) • I learned the expression, "This is on me."
  • That refers to "I'll pay for this."
  ➡ _____
  _____

03 다음 각 문장에서 어법상 어색한 부분을 찾아 바르게 고치시오.

(1) It's impossible of her to do those things all by herself.
  _____ ➡ _____

(2) It was foolish for him to spend all the money given by winning the lottery.
  _____ ➡ _____

(3) It is surprising what the celebrity is waiting for my sister.
  _____ ➡ _____

(4) It is safe of Kate to fasten the seatbelt when her son drives her car.
  _____ ➡ _____

(5) It is excited that I will move to Jeju island.
  _____ ➡ _____

04 다음 우리말에 맞게 괄호 안의 단어를 활용하여 영작하시오.

비버와 같은 몇몇 동물들이 도구를 사용할 수 있다는 것은 흥미롭다.
(animals, beavers, tools, some, such as, can, interesting 사용, 가주어-진주어 형식, 총 12단어)

➡ _____
_____

05 다음 각 문장에서 어법상 <u>어색한</u> 부분을 한 곳씩 찾아 고치시오.

(1) The police officers don't examine all the suspects, but which is a routine.

➡ _____

(2) A cook placed a Hamburg-style steak between two slices of bread, which people started to call such food a hamburger.

➡ _____

(3) Linda broke her arms practicing the yoga movement, who was very important to her.

➡ _____

(4) King Sejong finished working of inventing Hangeul, that made him so happy.

➡ _____

(5) This is the movie *Avatar*, it was popular around the world.

➡ _____

06 다음 그림을 보고, 우리말에 맞게 괄호 안의 단어를 배열하여 영작하되, 한 단어의 형태만 바꾸시오. (대·소문자와는 무관)

많은 영어 단어들이 다른 여러 민족들로부터 왔다는 것은 사실이다.
(words, is, different, came, true, it, English, that, people, many, from)

➡ _____
_____

07 다음 〈보기〉와 같이 두 문장이 같은 의미가 되도록, '접속사+대명사'는 관계대명사로, 관계대명사는 '접속사+대명사'로 바꿔 문장을 다시 쓰시오.

┌─ 보기 ─┐
There are many English words about music and they come from Italia.
→ There are many English words about music, which come from Italia.
└─────┘

(1) Robot comes from *roboti* and it means 'slave workers' in Czech.

➡ _____
_____

(2) Most people in the temple stop working every three hours, and they pray to their god.

➡ _____
_____

(3) Hamburger comes from Hamburg and it is the second-largest city in Germany.

➡ _____
_____

(4) Amy uses shampoo every day to wash her dog, but he doesn't like it.

➡ _____
_____

(5) Wendy received a massage from her aunt, which didn't make her feel better.

➡ _____
_____

(6) The castle looked quite modern, which was built in the 8th century.

➡ _____
_____

(7) Maria loves Spanish food, but actually it is not Spanish but Mayan.

➡ _____
_____

Reading

English Words of Foreign Origin

English has often borrowed words from other cultures or languages.
Here are some examples with interesting stories.

shampoo

The word *shampoo* comes from the Hindi word *chāmpo*, which
means "to press." In India, the word was used for a head massage.
British traders in India experienced a bath with a head massage and
introduced it to Britain in the 18th century.

The meaning of the word *shampoo* changed a few times after it first
entered English around 1762. In the 19th century, *shampoo* got its
present meaning of "washing the hair." Shortly after that, the word
began to be also used for a special soap for the hair.

robot

The word *robot* comes from the play *R.U.R.*, which was written in
1920 by a Czech writer Karel Čapek. In the play, robots are machines
that look like humans. They are designed to work for humans and
are produced in a factory.

It is interesting that the idea of using the word *robot* didn't come
from Karel Čapek himself. He originally called the machines in his
play *labori* from the Latin word for "work." However, his brother
suggested *roboti*, which means "slave workers" in Czech. Karel Čapek
liked the idea and decided to use the word *roboti*. In 1938, the play
was made into a science fiction show on television in Britain.

shampoo 샴푸

press 누르다

massage 마사지, 안마

British 영국인의

trader 상인, 거래자

century 세기, 100년

present 현재의

soap 비누

originally 원래, 본래

suggest 제안하다

slave 노예

📎 확인문제

● 다음 문장이 본문의 내용과 일치하면 T, 일치하지 않으면 F를 쓰시오.

1 English has often borrowed words from other cultures or languages. ☐

2 The Hindi word *chāmpo* means "to wash the hair." ☐

3 In India, *chāmpo* was used for a head massage. ☐

4 The word *robot* comes from the movie *R.U.R.* ☐

5 Karel Čapek originally called the machines in his play *labori*. ☐

hurricane

The word *hurricane* comes from the Spanish word *huracán*, which originates from the name of a Mayan god. In the Mayan creation myth, Huracán is the weather god of wind, storm, and fire, and he is one of the three gods who created humans. However, the first humans angered the gods, so Huracán caused a great flood.

The first Spanish contact with the Mayan civilization was in 1517. Spanish explorers who were passing through the Caribbean experienced a hurricane and picked up the word for it from the people in the area. In English, one of the early uses of *hurricane* was in a play by Shakespeare in 1608.

hamburger

The word *hamburger* originally comes from Hamburg, Germany's second-largest city. *Hamburger* means "people or things from Hamburg" in German.

The origin of the first hamburger is not clear. However, it is believed that the hamburger was invented in a small town in Texas, USA, sometime between 1885 and 1904. A cook placed a Hamburg-style steak between two slices of bread, and people started to call such food a hamburger.

---

hurricane 허리케인

originate from ~에서 비롯되다

Mayan 마야 사람의

flood 홍수

Spanish 스페인의

contact 접촉

civilization 문명

pass through ~을 거쳐 지나가다

pick up ~을 익히게 되다

origin 기원, 유래

slice 얇게 썬 조각, 한 조각

확인문제

• 다음 문장이 본문의 내용과 일치하면 T, 일치하지 않으면 F를 쓰시오.

1 The word *hurricane* comes from the Spanish word *huracán*. ☐

2 The Spanish word *huracán* originates from the name of a Spanish god. ☐

3 The first Spanish contact with the Mayan civilization was in 1517. ☐

4 The word *hamburger* originally comes from Hamburg, Germany's third-largest city. ☐

5 *Hamburger* means "people or things from Hamburg" in German. ☐

6 The origin of the first hamburger is clear. ☐

● 우리말을 참고하여 빈칸에 알맞은 말을 쓰시오.

1 **English Words of** _____ _____

2 English has often _____ _____ from _____ _____ or languages.

3 Here are some examples _____ _____ _____ .

shampoo

4 The word *shampoo* comes _____ the Hindi word *chāmpo*, which means "_____ _____ ."

5 In India, the word _____ _____ for a head massage.

6 British traders in India experienced a bath _____ _____ _____ _____ and introduced it to Britain in the 18th century.

7 The meaning of the word *shampoo* changed _____ _____ _____ after it first _____ English around 1762.

8 In the 19th century, *shampoo* got its _____ meaning of "_____ _____ _____ ."

9 _____ _____ _____ , the word began _____ _____ _____ _____ for a special soap for the hair.

robot

10 The word *robot* comes from the play *R.U.R.*, which _____ _____ in 1920 by a Czech writer Karel Čapek.

11 In the play, robots are machines that _____ _____ humans.

12 They _____ _____ to work for humans and _____ _____ in a factory.

13 It is interesting that _____ _____ _____ _____ the word *robot* didn't come from Karel Čapek _____ .

14 He originally called the machines in his play *labori* _____ the Latin word _____ "work."

1 외국어에서 유래된 영어 단어

2 영어는 종종 다른 문화나 언어에서 단어를 빌려왔다.

3 여기 재미있는 이야기가 있는 몇 개의 예가 있다.

샴푸

4 *shampoo*라는 단어는 힌디어 *chāmpo*에서 왔고, '누르다'라는 의미이다.

5 인도에서 그 단어는 머리 마사지라는 의미로 쓰였다.

6 인도에 있는 영국 상인들은 머리 마사지를 함께하는 목욕을 경험했고 마사지를 18세기에 영국에 소개했다.

7 *shampoo*라는 단어의 의미는 그 단어가 1762년쯤 영어에 처음으로 들어온 이후 몇 번 바뀌었다.

8 19세기에, *shampoo*는 '머리 감기'라는 현재의 의미를 갖게 되었다.

9 그 후 얼마 지나지 않아, 그 단어는 머리에 사용하는 특별한 비누에도 쓰이기 시작했다.

로봇

10 *robot*이라는 단어는 "*R.U.R.*"에서 왔는데, 그 연극은 1920년 체코의 작가 Karel Čapek에 의해 쓰였다.

11 그 연극에서 로봇은 인간처럼 생긴 기계이다.

12 그들은 인간을 위해 일하도록 설계되고, 공장에서 생산된다.

13 *robot*이라는 단어를 사용하려는 생각이 Karel Čapek 자신에게서 나온 게 아니었다는 것이 흥미롭다.

14 그는 원래 자신의 연극에서 그 기계들을 '일'을 의미하는 라틴어에서 온 *labori*라고 불렀다.

15 _____, his brother suggested *roboti*, which means "slave workers" _____ _____.

16 Karel Čapek liked the idea and decided _____ _____ the word *roboti*.

17 In 1938, the play _____ _____ _____ a science fiction show on television in Britain.

hurricane

18 The word *hurricane* comes from the Spanish word *huracán*, which _____ _____ the name of a Mayan god.

19 In the Mayan _____ _____, Huracán is the weather god of wind, storm, and fire, and he is one of the three _____ who _____ humans.

20 However, the first humans _____ the gods, _____ Huracán _____ a great flood.

21 The first _____ _____ _____ the Mayan civilization was in 1517.

22 Spanish explorers who were _____ _____ the Caribbean experienced a hurricane and _____ _____ the word _____ _____ from the people in the area.

23 _____ _____, one of the early _____ of *hurricane* was in a play _____ Shakespeare in 1608.

hamburger

24 The word *hamburger* _____ comes from Hamburg, Germany's _____ city.

25 *Hamburger* means "people or things from Hamburg" _____ _____.

26 The origin of the first hamburger _____ _____ _____.

27 However, _____ _____ _____ _____ the hamburger was invented in a small town in Texas, USA, sometime _____ 1885 _____ 1904.

28 A cook _____ a _____ steak between _____ _____ _____, and people started to call _____ _____ a hamburger.

15 하지만, 그의 형이 *roboti*를 제안했는데, *roboti*는 체코어로 '노예 근로자들'을 의미한다.

16 Karel Čapek은 그 아이디어가 마음에 들어 *roboti*라는 단어를 사용하기로 결정했다.

17 1938년에 그 연극은 영국 TV에서 공상 과학물로 만들어졌다.

태풍

18 *hurricane*이라는 단어는 스페인어 단어 *huracán*에서 왔고, 그것은 마야 신의 이름에서 유래한다.

19 마야의 창조 신화에서, Huracán은 바람, 폭풍우, 그리고 불에 관한 날씨의 신이며, 그는 인간을 창조한 세 명의 신들 중 한 명이다.

20 하지만, 최초의 인간들이 신들을 화나게 해서 Huracán은 거대한 홍수를 일으켰다.

21 스페인이 마야 문명과 했던 첫 접촉은 1517년이었다.

22 카리브 제도를 지나던 스페인 탐험가들이 허리케인을 겪었고, 그 지역 사람들로부터 그것을 의미하는 단어를 듣게 되었다.

23 영어에서 일찍이 *hurricane*을 사용한 것 중 하나는 1608년 셰익스피어에 의한 희곡에서였다.

햄버거

24 *hamburger*라는 단어는 원래 독일에서 두 번째로 큰 도시인 함부르크에서 왔다.

25 *hamburger*는 독일어로 '함부르크 출신의 사람 또는 사물'을 의미한다.

26 최초의 햄버거의 기원은 분명하지 않다.

27 하지만 햄버거는 1885년에서 1904년 사이의 언젠가 미국 텍사스에 있는 작은 마을에서 발명되었다고 믿어진다.

28 한 요리사가 빵 두 조각 사이에 함부르크 스타일의 스테이크를 넣었고, 사람들은 그런 음식을 햄버거라고 부르기 시작했다.

● 우리말을 참고하여 본문을 영작하시오.

1 외국어에서 유래된 영어 단어

➡ _____

2 영어는 종종 다른 문화나 언어에서 단어를 빌려왔다.

➡ _____

3 여기 재미있는 이야기가 있는 몇 개의 예가 있다.

➡ _____

shampoo 샴푸

4 shampoo라는 단어는 힌디어 *chāmpo*에서 왔고, '누르다'라는 의미이다.

➡ _____

5 인도에서 그 단어는 머리 마사지라는 의미로 쓰였다.

➡ _____

6 인도에 있는 영국 상인들은 머리 마사지를 함께하는 목욕을 경험했고 마사지를 18세기에 영국에 소개했다.

➡ _____

_____

7 *shampoo*라는 단어의 의미는 그 단어가 1762년쯤 영어에 처음으로 들어온 이후 몇 번 바뀌었다.

➡ _____

8 19세기에, *shampoo*는 '머리 감기'라는 현재의 의미를 갖게 되었다.

➡ _____

9 그 후 얼마 지나지 않아, 그 단어는 머리에 사용하는 특별한 비누에도 쓰이기 시작했다.

➡ _____

robot 로봇

10 robot이라는 단어는 "*R.U.R.*"에서 왔는데, 그 연극은 1920년 체코의 작가 Karel Čapek에 의해 쓰였다.

➡ _____

11 그 연극에서 로봇은 인간처럼 생긴 기계이다.

➡ _____

12 그들은 인간을 위해 일하도록 설계되고, 공장에서 생산된다.

➡ _____

13 robot이라는 단어를 사용하려는 생각이 Karel Čapek 자신에게서 나온 게 아니었다는 것이 흥미롭다.

➡ _____

14 그는 원래 자신의 연극에서 그 기계들을 '일'을 의미하는 라틴어에서 온 *labori*라고 불렀다.

➡ _____

15 하지만, 그의 형이 roboti를 제안했는데, roboti는 체코어로 '노예 근로자들'을 의미한다.

➡ _____

16 Karel Čapek은 그 아이디어가 마음에 들어 roboti라는 단어를 사용하기로 결정했다.

➡ _____

17 1938년에 그 연극은 영국 TV에서 공상 과학물로 만들어졌다.

➡ _____

hurricane 태풍

18 hurricane이라는 단어는 스페인어 단어 huracán에서 왔고, 그것은 마야 신의 이름에서 유래한다.

➡ _____

19 마야의 창조 신화에서, Huracán은 바람, 폭풍우, 그리고 불에 관한 날씨의 신이며, 그는 인간을 창조한 세 명의 신들 중 한 명이다.

➡ _____
_____

20 하지만, 최초의 인간들이 신들을 화나게 해서 Huracán은 거대한 홍수를 일으켰다.

➡ _____

21 스페인이 마야 문명과 했던 첫 접촉은 1517년이었다.

➡ _____

22 카리브 제도를 지나던 스페인 탐험가들이 허리케인을 겪었고, 그 지역 사람들로부터 그것을 의미하는 단어를 듣게 되었다.

➡ _____
_____

23 영어에서 일찍이 hurricane을 사용한 것 중 하나는 1608년 셰익스피어의 희곡에서였다.

➡ _____

hamburger 햄버거

24 hamburger라는 단어는 원래 독일에서 두 번째로 큰 도시인 함부르크에서 왔다.

➡ _____

25 hamburger는 독일어로 '함부르크 출신의 사람 또는 사물'을 의미한다.

➡ _____

26 최초의 햄버거의 기원은 분명하지 않다.

➡ _____

27 하지만 햄버거는 1885년에서 1904년 사이의 언젠가 미국 텍사스에 있는 작은 마을에서 발명되었다고 믿어진다.

➡ _____
_____

28 한 요리사가 빵 두 조각 사이에 함부르크 스타일의 스테이크를 넣었고, 사람들은 그런 음식을 햄버거라고 부르기 시작했다.

➡ _____
_____

[01~03] 다음 글을 읽고 물음에 답하시오.

English has often borrowed words from other cultures or languages. Here are some examples with interesting stories.

shampoo

The word *shampoo* comes ___ⓐ___ the Hindi word *chāmpo*, (A)which means "to press." In India, the word was used for a head massage. British traders in India experienced a bath with a head massage and introduced it ___ⓑ___ Britain in the 18th century.

The meaning of the word *shampoo* changed a few times after it first entered English around 1762. In the 19th century, *shampoo* got its present meaning of "washing the hair." Shortly after that, the word began to be also used for a special soap for the hair.

01 위 글의 빈칸 ⓐ와 ⓑ에 들어갈 전치사가 바르게 짝지어진 것은?

ⓐ	ⓑ		ⓐ	ⓑ
① for	– to		② from	– on
③ in	– at		④ for	– on
⑤ from	– to			

서답형

02 위 글의 밑줄 친 (A)which를 대명사를 포함하여 두 단어로 바꿔 쓰시오.

➡ _____

중요

03 According to the passage, which is NOT true?

① English has many words that it lent to other cultures or languages.

② The word *shampoo* originates in the Hindi word *chāmpo*.

③ In India, the word *chāmpo* was used for a head massage.

④ The word *shampoo* first entered English around 1762.

⑤ Shortly after getting its present meaning of "washing the hair," the word *shampoo* began to be also used for a special soap for the hair.

[04~05] 다음 글을 읽고 물음에 답하시오.

hamburger

The word *hamburger* originally comes from Hamburg, Germany's second-largest city. *Hamburger* means "people or things from Hamburg" in German.

The origin of the first hamburger is not clear. However, it is believed that the hamburger was invented in a small town in Texas, USA, sometime between 1885 and 1904. A cook placed a Hamburg-style steak between two ___ⓐ___ of bread, and people started to call such food a hamburger.

04 위 글의 빈칸 ⓐ에 들어갈 알맞은 말을 고르시오.

① sheets　　② lumps　　③ bars
④ slices　　⑤ pounds

서답형

05 위 글의 내용과 일치하도록 다음 빈칸 (A)와 (B)에 알맞은 단어를 쓰시오.

(A)_____ is the name of Germany's second-largest city and the word (B)_____ means "people or things from (C)_____" in German.

[06~08] 다음 글을 읽고 물음에 답하시오.

robot

The word *robot* comes from the play *R.U.R.*, which was written in 1920 by a Czech writer Karel Čapek. In the play, ⓐ로봇은 인간처럼 생긴 기계이다. They are designed to work for humans and are produced in a factory.

ⓑIt is interesting that the idea of using the word *robot* didn't come from Karel Čapek himself. He originally called the machines in his play *labori* from the Latin word for "work." However, his brother suggested *roboti*, which means "slave workers" in Czech. Karel Čapek liked the idea and decided to use the word *roboti*. In 1938, the play was made into a science fiction show on television in Britain.

서답형

06 위 글의 밑줄 친 ⓐ의 우리말에 맞게 주어진 어휘를 이용하여 7 단어로 영작하시오.

> that, like

➡ _____

07 위 글의 밑줄 친 ⓑIt과 문법적 쓰임이 같은 것을 고르시오.

① I make it a rule to jog after dinner.
② How's it going with you?
③ It was three weeks later that he heard the news.
④ Look! It's going up that tree.
⑤ It will be difficult for him to come so early.

서답형

08 What were the machines that looked like humans called in the play *R.U.R.*? Answer in English in a full sentence. (4 words)

➡ _____

[09~11] 다음 글을 읽고 물음에 답하시오.

hurricane

The word *hurricane* comes from the Spanish word *huracán*, which originates from the name of a Mayan god. ①In the Mayan creation myth, Huracán is the weather god of wind, storm, and fire, and he is one of the three gods who created humans. ②Every year the hurricane damages many areas near the Caribbean. ③However, the first humans angered the gods, so Huracán caused a great flood.

④The first Spanish contact with the Mayan civilization was in 1517. ⑤Spanish explorers who were passing through the Caribbean experienced a hurricane and picked up the word for it from the people in ⓐthe area. In English, one of the early uses of *hurricane* was in a play by Shakespeare in 1608.

중요

09 위 글의 ①~⑤ 중에서 전체 흐름과 관계 없는 문장은?

①   ②   ③   ④   ⑤

서답형

10 위 글의 내용과 일치하도록 다음 빈칸 (A)와 (B)에 알맞은 단어를 쓰시오.

> According to the Mayan creation myth, Huracán, who is the (A)_____ god and one of the three gods who created humans, caused a (B)_____ _____ as the first humans angered the gods.

서답형

11 위 글의 밑줄 친 ⓐthe area가 가리키는 것을 본문에서 찾아 쓰시오.

➡ _____

[12~14] 다음 글을 읽고 물음에 답하시오.

English ⓐhas often borrowed words from other cultures or languages. Here are some examples with interesting stories.

shampoo

The word *shampoo* comes from the Hindi word *chāmpo*, which means "to press." In India, ⓑthe word was used for a head massage. British traders in India experienced a bath with a head massage and introduced it to Britain in the 18th century.

The meaning of the word shampoo changed a few times after it first entered English around 1762. In the 19th century, *shampoo* got its present meaning of "washing the hair." Shortly after that, the word began to be also used for a special soap for the hair.

12 위 글의 밑줄 친 ⓐ와 현재완료의 용법이 같은 것을 모두 고르시오.

① He has gone to Paris.
② Have you ever been to Jeju Island?
③ I have lived in Seoul for 10 years.
④ She has already finished dinner.
⑤ How many times have you seen it?

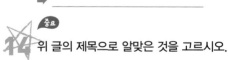

13 위 글의 밑줄 친 ⓑthe word가 가리키는 것을 본문에서 찾아 쓰시오.

➡ _____

14 위 글의 제목으로 알맞은 것을 고르시오.

① The Influence of Other Cultures or Languages
② Do You Know the Behind Stories of Various Cultures?
③ Let Me Tell You the Interesting Story of the Word *Shampoo*

④ How about a Bath with a Head Massage?
⑤ Wow! This is a Really Special Soap for the Hair!

[15~17] 다음 글을 읽고 물음에 답하시오.

robot

The word *robot* comes from the play *R.U.R.*, which was written in 1920 by a Czech writer Karel Čapek. In the play, robots are machines that look like humans. They are designed to work for humans and are produced in a factory.

It is interesting that the idea (A)of using the word *robot* didn't come from Karel Čapek himself. He originally called the machines in his play *labori* from the Latin word _____ⓐ_____ "work." However, his brother suggested *roboti*, which means "slave workers" _____ⓑ_____ Czech. Karel Čapek liked the idea and decided to use the word *roboti*. In 1938, the play was made into a science fiction show on television in Britain.

15 위 글의 빈칸 ⓐ와 ⓑ에 들어갈 전치사가 바르게 짝지어진 것은?

	ⓐ	ⓑ		ⓐ	ⓑ
①	in	from	②	for	in
③	for	from	④	in	at
⑤	on	in			

16 위 글의 밑줄 친 (A)of와 문법적 쓰임이 같은 것을 고르시오.

① I didn't know the fact of your meeting him.
② He is a man of ability.
③ Look at the house built of brick.
④ He was robbed of his money on his way home.
⑤ She comes of a good family.

17 위 글을 읽고 *labori*에 대해 알 수 <u>없는</u> 것을 고르시오.

① Where was the word *labori* used?

② What did the word *labori* indicate?

③ Who used the word *labori*?

④ How long was the word *labori* used?

⑤ What does the word *labori* mean in Latin?

20 다음 중 위 글의 밑줄 친 ①~⑤가 가리키는 것에 대한 설명이 옳지 <u>않은</u> 것을 고르시오.

① the Spanish word *huracán*

② a Mayan god Huracán

③ the three gods who created humans

④ *huracán*

⑤ the Caribbean

[18~20] 다음 글을 읽고 물음에 답하시오.

hurricane

The word *hurricane* comes from the Spanish word *huracán*, ①<u>which</u> originates from the name of a Mayan god. In the Mayan creation myth, Huracán is the weather god of wind, storm, and fire, and ②<u>he</u> is one of the three gods who created humans. However, the first humans angered ③<u>the gods</u>, (A)[as / so] Huracán caused a great flood.

The first Spanish contact with the Mayan civilization was in 1517. Spanish explorers who (B)[was / were] passing through the Caribbean experienced a hurricane and picked up ④<u>the word</u> for ⑤<u>it</u> from the people in the area. In English, one of the early uses of *hurricane* (C)[was / were] in a play by Shakespeare in 1608.

[21~22] 다음 글을 읽고 물음에 답하시오.

hamburger

The word *hamburger* originally comes from Hamburg, ⓐ독일에서 두 번째로 큰 도시. *Hamburger* means "people or things from Hamburg" in German.

The origin of the first hamburger is not clear. However, it is believed that the hamburger was invented in a small town in Texas, USA, sometime between 1885 and 1904. A cook placed a Hamburg-style steak between two slices of bread, and people started to call such food a hamburger.

서답형

21 위 글의 밑줄 친 ⓐ의 우리말에 맞게 3 단어로 영작하시오.

➡ _____

서답형

18 What's the origin of the Spanish word *huracán*? Answer in English in a full sentence. (7 words)

➡ _____

 22 위 글의 주제로 알맞은 것을 고르시오.

① the origin of the word *hamburger* and the first hamburger

② to introduce the place where a hamburger was invented

③ to introduce the time when a hamburger was invented

④ to introduce the creativity of a cook

⑤ the popularity of a hamburger in America

서답형

19 위 글의 괄호 (A)~(C)에서 문맥이나 어법상 알맞은 낱말을 골라 쓰시오.

➡ (A) _____ (B) _____ (C) _____

[01~03] 다음 글을 읽고 물음에 답하시오.

hurricane

The word *hurricane* comes from the ___@___ word *huracán*, which originates from the name of a Mayan god. In the Mayan creation myth, Huracán is the weather god of wind, storm, and fire, and he is one of the three gods who created humans. However, the first humans angered the gods, so Huracán caused a great flood.

The first ___ⓑ___ contact with the Mayan civilization was in 1517. ___ⓒ___ explorers who were passing through the Caribbean experienced a hurricane and picked up the word for it from the people in the area. In English, ⓓ일찍이 *hurricane*을 사용한 것 중 하나는 was in a play by Shakespeare in 1608.

⭐중요

01 위 글의 빈칸 @~ⓒ에 공통으로 들어갈 Spain의 알맞은 형태를 쓰시오.

➡ _____

02 위 글의 밑줄 친 ⓓ의 우리말에 맞게 주어진 어휘를 이용하여 7 단어로 영작하시오.

early

➡ _____

03 다음 빈칸 (A)~(C)에 알맞은 단어를 넣어 마야어, 스페인어, 영어에서 쓰이는 huracán이라는 단어와 관련된 내용을 완성하시오.

(1) In Mayan: (A)_____, a Mayan god, is the weather god in the Mayan creation myth.

(2) In Spanish: The Spanish word (B)_____ was picked up by Spanish explorers from the people in the Caribbean for the hurricane they experienced while passing through the area.

(3) In English: The word (C)_____ comes from the word *huracán*, and in 1608, the word *hurricane* was used by Shakespeare in his play.

⭐중요

04 다음 글을 읽고 주어진 글의 빈칸 (A)와 (B)에 알맞은 단어를 넣어 햄버거의 발명에 대한 소개를 완성하시오.

hamburger

The word *hamburger* originally comes from Hamburg, Germany's second-largest city. *Hamburger* means "people or things from Hamburg" in German.

The origin of the first hamburger is not clear. However, it is believed that the hamburger was invented in a small town in Texas, USA, sometime between 1885 and 1904. A cook placed a Hamburg-style steak between two slices of bread, and people started to call such food a hamburger.

A cook in a small town in Texas, USA, invented the (A)_____ _____ sometime between 1885 and 1904 by placing a (B)_____ _____ between two slices of bread.

[05~07] 다음 글을 읽고 물음에 답하시오.

English has often (A)[borrowed / lent] words from other cultures or languages. Here are some examples with interesting stories.

shampoo

The word *shampoo* comes from the Hindi word *chāmpo*, which means "to press." In India, the word was used for a head (B)[massage / message]. British traders in India experienced a bath with a head massage and introduced it to Britain in the 18th century.

The meaning of the word *shampoo* changed a few (C)[hours / times] after it first entered English around 1762. In the 19th century, *shampoo* got its present meaning of "washing the hair." Shortly after that, the word began to be also used for a special soap for the hair.

05 위 글의 괄호 (A)~(C)에서 문맥상 알맞은 낱말을 골라 쓰시오.

➡ (A) _____ (B) _____ (C) _____

06 다음 문장에서 위 글의 내용과 <u>다른</u> 부분을 찾아서 고치시오.

> The meaning of the word *shampoo* did not change at all after it first entered English around 1762.

_____ ➡ _____

07 위 글의 내용과 일치하도록 다음 빈칸 (A)와 (B)에 알맞은 단어를 쓰시오.

> The Hindi word *chāmpo* means "(A)_____ _____," and in India, people used the word for a (B)_____ .

[08~10] 다음 글을 읽고 물음에 답하시오.

robot

The word *robot* comes from the play *R.U.R.*, ⓐwhich was written in 1920 by a Czech writer Karel Čapek. In the play, robots are machines that look like humans. They are designed to work for humans and are produced in a factory.

It is interesting that ⓑthe idea of using the word *robot* didn't come from Karel Čapek himself. He originally called the machines in his play *labori* from the Latin word for "work." However, his brother suggested *roboti*, which means "slave workers" in Czech. Karel Čapek liked the idea and decided to use the word *roboti*. In 1938, the play was made into a science fiction show on television in Britain.

08 위 글의 밑줄 친 ⓐ를 능동태로 고치시오.

➡ _____

09 위 글의 밑줄 친 ⓑthe idea가 가리키는 것을 본문에서 찾아 쓰시오.

➡ _____

10 다음 빈칸 (A)~(C)에 알맞은 단어를 넣어 *robot*이라는 단어가 생기게 된 과정을 완성하시오.

> (1) In 1920, in the play *R.U.R.*, a Czech writer Karel Čapek called the machines that looked like humans (A)_____ .
> (2) Karel's brother suggested using the word (B)_____ instead of *labori*.
> (3) In 1938, the play *R.U.R.* was made into a (C)_____ _____ on television in Britain.

교과서

구석구석

After You Read A

Online Dictionary

English words from other cultures or languages

shampoo: It comes from the Hindi word *chāmpo*, which means "to press."
= originates from   = and it

robot: It comes from *roboti*, which means "slave workers" in Czech.
체코어로

hurricane: It comes from Spanish word, *huracán*, which originates from the
that(×)   = comes from
name of a Mayan god.
Maya의 형용사

hamburger: It comes from Hamburg, the second-largest city in Germany.
Hamburg와 the second-largest city in Germany는 동격 관계

구문해설 • from: (출처, 기원) ~에서 온 • press: 누르다 • slave: 노예 • hurricane: 허리케인
• Spanish: 스페인의 • originate from: ~에서 비롯되다 • Mayan: 마야 사람의

Around the World

1. Many English words about law come from French. Examples include words
~에서 오다   France의 형용사/언어   → exclude
like judge and justice.
전치사(= such as)

2. There are many English words about music that come from Italian. For
주격 관계대명사
example, piano and violin come from Italian.
Italy의 형용사/언어

3. Many English words for vegetables come from Spanish. For example,
Spain의 형용사/언어   = for instance
tomato comes from *tomate* and potato comes from *patata* in Spanish.

구문해설 • include: 포함하다 • judge: 판사 • justice:정의

Think and Write Step 2

The Origin of the Word *Sandwich*

The word *sandwich* comes from John Montagu, who was the 4th Earl of
관계대명사 계속적 용법(= and he)
Sandwich. He enjoyed eating meat between two slices of bread because he
enjoy+동명사 목적어   빵(물질명사)은 slice 등의 단위로 수를 셈
could play a card game while he was eating. People thought that it was a great
(= playing a card game while eating)
idea and began to call such food a sandwich after him.
= began calling   전치사+대명사 목적격

구문해설 • origin: 기원 • earl: 백작 • slice: (얇은) 조각
• call A after B: B의 이름을 따라서 A를 부르다

해석

온라인 사전

다른 문화나 언어에서 온 영어 단어들

샴푸: 그것은 힌디어 *chāmpo*에서 왔는데, '누르다'를 의미한다.

로봇: 그것은 *roboti*에서 왔는데, *roboti*는 체코어로 '노예 근로자들'을 의미한다.

허리케인: 그것은 스페인어 *huracán*에서 왔는데, 마야 신의 이름에서 유래된다.

햄버거: 그것은 독일에서 두 번째로 큰 도시인 함부르크에서 왔다.

1. 법에 관한 많은 영어 단어들은 프랑스어에서 왔다. **judge**(판사)와 **justice**(정의)와 같은 단어들을 예로 들 수 있다.
2. 이탈리아어에서 온 음악에 관한 많은 영어 단어들이 있다. 예를 들어, **piano**(피아노)와 **violin**(바이올린) 등이 있다.
3. 채소에 관한 많은 영어 단어들은 스페인어에서 왔다. 예를 들어, **tomato**(토마토)는 *tomate*에서 왔고, **potato**(감자) 는 *patata*에서 왔다.

단어 sandwich의 유래

단어 sandwich는 John Montagu에게서 유래했는데, 그는 샌드위치 백작 4세였다. 그는 먹는 동안에 카드 게임을 할 수 있었기 때문에 빵 두 조각 사이에 고기를 끼워서 먹는 것을 즐겼다. 사람들은 그것을 좋은 생각이라고 여겼고, 그의 이름을 따서 그런 음식을 샌드위치라고 부르기 시작했다.

Words & Expressions

01 〈보기〉의 밑줄 친 어휘와 같은 의미로 쓰이지 <u>않은</u> 것을 고르시오.

┌─── 보기 ───
Did you know that the word *tea* <u>originates</u> from Chinese?
└──────────

① When did the idea <u>originate</u> in your mind?
② Where did this wonderful tradition <u>originate</u>?
③ Yoga <u>originated</u> from India.
④ Many of the sandstorms <u>originate</u> in Mongolia.
⑤ From which country does spam mail <u>originate</u>?

02 다음 대화의 빈칸에 〈영영풀이〉에 해당하는 단어를 쓰시오.

A: This cake is so delicious.
B: I _____ _____ tips from this book and made it.

〈영영풀이〉 to learn a new skill or start a habit without intending to

➡ _____

03 괄호 안에 주어진 어휘를 이용하여 빈칸에 알맞게 쓰시오.

• The _____ directly bought goods from producers. (trade)
• My family _____ comes from Mexico. (origin)

04 다음 영영풀이에 해당하는 단어를 주어진 철자로 시작하여 빈칸에 쓰고, 알맞은 것을 골라 문장을 완성하시오.

• l_____ : a system of rules that a society or government develops in order to deal with crime etc.
• o_____ : the beginning, cause, or source of something

(1) All men are equal in the eye of the _____.

(2) The _____ of the rings of Saturn is still unknown.

05 다음 대화의 빈칸 (A)～(C)에 알맞은 말을 쓰시오.

A: Where are you from?
B: I'm from Vietnam. I'm (A)_____.
C: I'm from France. I'm (B)_____.
D: I'm from Ireland. I'm (C)_____.

Conversation

[06~07] 다음 대화를 읽고 물음에 답하시오.

B: Everything looks delicious.
(A) It means "I don't like something."
(B) No, thanks. Spaghetti is not my cup of tea.
(C) Not your cup of tea? What does that mean?
(D) Yes. (a)Would you like some of my spaghetti?
G: Oh, I see. You don't like spaghetti.

06 주어진 두 문장 사이에 이어질 대화의 순서로 알맞은 것은?

① (B) – (A) – (C) – (D)
② (C) – (B) – (A) – (D)
③ (C) – (B) – (D) – (A)
④ (D) – (B) – (A) – (C)
⑤ (D) – (B) – (C) – (A)

07 위 대화의 밑줄 친 (a)와 같은 뜻의 문장을 괄호 안에 주어진 어휘를 이용하여 영어로 쓰시오.

➡ _____

(will, have)

➡ _____

(do, want)

08 다음 중 짝지어진 대화가 <u>어색한</u> 것은?

① A: It means "I don't like something."
　B: Oh, I see. You don't like spaghetti.
② A: I feel under the weather.
　B: Excuse me, but can you please say that again?
③ A: Oh. Why don't you buy some medicine before you get on the plane? You can get medicine at the store over there.
　B: I guess you should.
④ A: I said, "Break a leg."
　B: What does that mean?
⑤ A: Thank you for everything, Jiho. I had a great time in Korea.
　B: My pleasure. Please come visit me again, Lucy.

[09~10] 다음 대화를 읽고 물음에 답하시오.

G: Look. It's raining cats and dogs.
B: Raining cats and dogs? What does that mean?

G: It means "＿＿＿＿＿(A)＿＿＿＿＿"
B: Oh. Don't worry. I have an umbrella in my backpack.

09 위 대화의 빈칸 (A)에 알맞은 말을 쓰시오. (4 words)

➡ _____

10 Why does the boy tell the girl not to worry? (8 words)

➡ _____

[11~13] 다음 대화를 읽고 물음에 답하시오.

G: This juice is on me, Suho. (①)
B: Excuse me? (②) Can you say that again? (③)
G: I said, "This juice is on me." (④)
B: (⑤) Oh. Thanks a lot.
G: You're welcome.

11 ①~⑤ 중 주어진 문장이 들어갈 곳은?

It means "I'll pay for the juice."

①　　②　　③　　④　　⑤

12 Who will pay for the juice? Answer in English with a full sentence.

➡ _____

13 위 대화의 내용과 일치하는 것은?

① 수호는 'This juice is on me.'의 의미를 알고 있었다.
② 수호는 미안해하고 있다.
③ 수호는 주스를 소녀에게 쏟았다.
④ 그들은 주스를 마셨다.
⑤ 그들은 서로 환영하고 있다.

Grammar

14 다음 중 어법상 올바른 문장은?

① My grandmother had four sons, that all became businessmen.

② Jenny likes the cell phone what Peter got her from Paris.

③ The one in the middle of the picture is Eddy, which is the most famous scientist in his country.

④ A word derived from a person's name is sandwich, which was the name of the 4th Earl of Sandwich.

⑤ The word *shampoo*, what is commonly used when washing hair, is from the Hindi word *chāmpo*.

15 다음 중 우리말을 영작한 것이 <u>어색한</u> 것을 <u>고르면</u>?

① 누가 최초의 햄버거를 만들었는지는 확실하지 않다.
→ It is not clear that who made the first hamburger.

② 그 단어를 쓰는 아이디어가 작가의 동생으로부터 왔다는 것은 흥미롭다.
→ It is interesting that the idea of using the word came from the author's brother.

③ 그 단어가 마사지를 의미하는 것은 놀랍다.
→ It is amazing that the word means a massage.

④ 영어 단어의 70%가 다른 언어에서 유래했다는 것은 사실이다.
→ It is true that 70 percent of English words come from other languages.

⑤ 내가 그녀를 기다리는 것은 낯설다.
→ It is strange that I'm waiting for her.

[16~17] 주어진 우리말을 알맞게 영작할 때 어법상 옳은 문장을 고르시오.

16

> George는 Sarah가 내게서 빌린 펜과 똑같은 펜을 가지고 있다.

① George has a pen, and it is the same as the one what Sarah borrowed from me.

② George has a pen, which is the same as the one which Sarah borrowed it from me.

③ George has a pen which the same as the one that Sarah borrowed from me.

④ George has a pen, which is the same as what Sarah borrowed from me.

⑤ George has a pen, and which is the same as the one that Sarah borrowed from me.

17

> 그 백작이 포커를 좋아한다는 것은 그의 많은 친구들이 다 알고 있다.

① The earl likes poker, and all of whose many friends know it.

② The earl likes poker, which all of his many friends know it.

③ The earl likes poker, which all of his many friends know.

④ All of his many friends know which the earl likes poker.

⑤ The earl has many friends, all of whom knows he likes poker.

18 다음 중 밑줄 친 that의 쓰임이 나머지와 다른 하나는?

① It was a pizza that my family often ordered through the app.

② It is very strange that Susan forgot my name.

③ It was not surprising that he spent all the money fixing his computer.

④ It is true that he became rich by marrying the girl.

⑤ It is a bad idea that we should throw the garbage away into the river.

19 다음 중 밑줄 친 부분의 쓰임이 〈보기〉와 같지 않은 것은?

┌─── 보기 ───┐

Minjoo worked out harder despite her injury, which worsened her health.

└───────────┘

① Yewon tried to stay awake during the boring lecture, which didn't work.

② Susan doesn't remember her daughter, which is so strange.

③ Mom ordered beef for me, which was not a usual thing.

④ We saw the crows use tools, which was quite interesting.

⑤ The princess had difficulty choosing which prince she would marry.

20 다음 주어진 세 문장을 관계대명사의 계속적 용법과 제한적 용법을 활용하여, 〈조건〉에 맞게 한 문장으로 표현하시오.

- My father made a family motto.
- The motto would remind us the love between family members.
- The love between family members had never been thought of before.

┌─── 조건 ───┐

that과 which를 반드시 사용할 것. 본문에 있는 표현만을 활용할 것. (변형 불가)

└───────────┘

➡ _____

_____

_____

21 다음 중 어법상 어색한 문장은?

① Many people lost their houses, which was because of the flood.

② Martha saw the map of Washington, which would be her second home.

③ The Mayan civilization, which is in Central America, was very advanced.

④ He is a tea trader, who buy and sell tea around the world.

⑤ Did you throw away my sandwich, which I brought home four days ago?

Reading

[22~24] 다음 글을 읽고 물음에 답하시오.

shampoo

The word *shampoo* comes from the Hindi word *chāmpo*, ①which means "to press." In India, the word ⓐ_____ for a head massage. British traders in India experienced a bath with a head massage and introduced ②it to Britain in the 18th century.

The meaning of the word *shampoo* changed a few times after it first entered English around 1762. In the 19th century, *shampoo* got its present meaning of "washing the hair." ③ Shortly after that, ④the word began ⑤to be also used for a special soap for the hair.

22 위 글의 빈칸 ⓐ에 use를 알맞은 형태로 쓰시오.

➡ _____

23 다음 중 위 글의 밑줄 친 ①~⑤에 대한 설명을 바르게 하지 못한 사람을 고르시오.

① 지연: which는 계속적 용법의 관계대명사이기 때문에 that으로 바꿔 쓸 수 없어.

② 민호: it은 바로 앞에 나온 a bath with a head massage를 가리키는 거야.

③ 규빈: Shortly는 '간단히'라는 뜻이야.

④ 재성: the word는 shampoo를 가리키는 거야.

⑤ 덕수: 그 단어는 머리에 사용하는 특별한 비누에도 쓰이기 시작했다고 해야 하므로 to부정사의 수동태로 쓰는 것이 옳아.

24 위 글의 주제로 알맞은 것을 고르시오.

① the meaning of the word *chāmpo*

② the origin and the meaning of the word *shampoo*

③ the experience of a bath with a head massage in India

④ the explanation of the time when the word *shampoo* entered English

⑤ the research on the special soap for the hair

[25~27] 다음 글을 읽고 물음에 답하시오.

robot

The word *robot* comes from the play *R.U.R.*, which was written in 1920 by a Czech writer Karel Čapek. In the play, robots are machines that look like humans. They are designed to work for humans and are produced in a factory.

It is (A)[interesting / interested] that the idea of using the word *robot* didn't come from Karel Čapek ⓐhimself. He originally called the machines in his play *labori* from the Latin word for "work." However, his brother suggested *roboti*, which means "slave workers" in Czech. Karel Čapek liked the idea and decided (B)[using / to use] the word *roboti*. In 1938, the play was made (C)[by / into] a science fiction show on television in Britain.

25 위 글의 괄호 (A)~(C)에서 어법상 알맞은 낱말을 골라 쓰시오.

➡ (A) _____ (B) _____ (C) _____

26 위 글의 밑줄 친 ⓐhimself와 문법적 쓰임이 같은 것을 고르시오.

① He went there by himself.

② He killed himself.

③ He himself made it.

④ He seated himself on the chair.

⑤ He made it for himself.

27 According to the passage, which is NOT true?

① A Czech writer Karel Čapek wrote the play *R.U.R.* in 1920.

② In the play *R.U.R.*, robots are machines that look like humans.

③ In his play *R.U.R.*, Karel Čapek originally called the machines *labori*.

④ Karel's brother suggested *roboti*, which means "work" in Latin.

⑤ The play *R.U.R.* was made into a science fiction show on television in Britain in 1938.

출제율 95%

01 다음 중 짝지어진 단어의 관계가 나머지와 <u>다른</u> 것은?

① trader – merchant
② include – exclude
③ present – current
④ suggest – propose
⑤ design – devise

출제율 95%

02 다음 중 밑줄 친 부분의 의미로 알맞지 <u>않은</u> 것은?

① He stole a car and <u>is in hot water</u> with the law. (곤경에 처하다)
② My mom made all the things I loved, so I <u>pigged out</u>. (돼지 같이 먹었다)
③ I've heard the course was <u>a piece of cake</u>. (힘든 일)
④ I'll <u>keep my fingers crossed</u> for your new business. (행운을 빌다)
⑤ They do not <u>see eye to eye</u> with each other. (의견을 같이하다)

출제율 90%

03 다음 빈칸에 공통으로 들어갈 알맞은 말을 쓰시오.

> • We _____d difficult times because of the flood.
> • Hemingway later wrote about his _____ in Italy.

출제율 100%

04 다음 주어진 우리말에 맞게 빈칸을 채우시오. (철자가 주어진 경우 주어진 철자로 시작할 것)

(1) 나는 피자 한 조각을 먹고 싶다.
➡ I would like to have a s_____ of pizza.

(2) Lincoln은 미국의 노예를 해방하는 것을 도왔다.
➡ Lincoln helped set _____ in the US free.

(3) 홍수로 건물들이 파괴되었다.
➡ The _____ destroyed the buildings.

[05~07] 다음 대화를 읽고 물음에 답하시오.

> G: I feel under the weather.
> B: Excuse me, but can you please say that again?
> G: I said, "I feel under the weather." It means "I don't feel well." I think I have a cold.
> B: Oh. _____(A)_____ some medicine before you __(B)__ on the plane? You can __(C)__ medicine at the store over there.
> G: I guess I should.

출제율 90%

05 위 대화의 빈칸 (A)에 '사는 게 어때'라는 의미의 말을 쓰시오. (4 단어)

➡ _____

출제율 95%

06 위 대화의 빈칸 (B)와 (C)에 공통으로 들어갈 알맞은 말을 쓰시오.

➡ _____

07 위 대화를 읽고 대답할 수 <u>없는</u> 질문을 고르시오.

① Why does the girl feel under the weather?

② What does the boy ask the girl to say again?

③ What does the boy suggest to the girl?

④ What will the girl do after getting on the plane?

⑤ Where are the boy and the girl now?

[08~09] 다음 대화의 빈칸 (A)에 알맞은 말을 쓰시오.

출제율 90%

08
A: I'm in hot water.
B: Can you please say that again?
A: I said, "I'm in hot water."
B: What does that mean?
A: It means "_____(A)_____" (3 words)

➡ _____

출제율 95%

09
A: I'm in hot water. We pigged out.
B: Can you please say that again?
A: I said, "We pigged out."
B: What does that mean?
A: It means "_____(A)_____" (4 words)

➡ _____

출제율 100%

10 다음 중 어법상 <u>어색한</u> 문장은?

① There are some English words, which originate from other cultures.

② The rabbit provided Alice with some pizza, which made her small.

③ Genie was reading a book about Rome, which she visited last year.

④ Mike had his phone stolen, which his mother bought it for him as a graduation gift.

⑤ This is Makgully, which is a traditional Korean drink.

출제율 90%

11 다음 각 문장에 사용된 어법 사항을 <보기>에서 골라 기호를 괄호 안에 쓰시오.

┌─── 보기 ───
ⓐ It(가주어) ~ that(진주어) 구문 문장
ⓑ It ~ that 강조 구문 문장
└───────────

(1) It is Mona Lisa that Leonardo da Vinci painted in 1503. (_____)

(2) Is it possible that Hangeul was invented by the King's warm heart? (_____)

(3) It was by her sacrifice that all the villagers got happy. (_____)

(4) It is wonderful that Peter will get a scholarship. (_____)

(5) It is only when you work hard that you experience the real success. (_____)

출제율 95%

12 다음 중 밑줄 친 관계대명사가 가리키는 것으로 바르지 <u>않은</u> 것은?

① The actor remembered the band's title song, <u>which</u> was related to the first love.
(→ the band's title song)

② Maria became the manager of the restaurant, <u>which</u> was her first work place.
(→ the restaurant)

③ They should have taken the subway line 2, <u>which</u> runs through Seoul City.
(→ the subway line 2)

④ Seohyeon is a student at Balsan middle school, <u>which</u> is situated in Ilsan.
(→ Balsan middle school)

⑤ Jim is not afraid of fire, <u>which</u> enabled him to be a fire fighter.
(→ fire)

13 다음 그림을 보고, 우리말에 맞게 괄호 안의 단어를 배열하되, 어법에 맞게 한 단어만 추가하여 영작하시오.

출제율 90%

당나귀가 자기의 주인을 속인 것은 어리석었다.
(the donkey, foolish, deceive, was, master, to, its, it)

➡ _____

[14~16] 다음 글을 읽고 물음에 답하시오.

hamburger

The word *hamburger* originally comes from Hamburg, Germany's second-largest city. *Hamburger* means "people or things from Hamburg" in German.

The origin of the first hamburger is not clear. However, it is believed that the hamburger was invented in a small town in Texas, USA, sometime between 1885 and 1904. A cook placed a Hamburg-style steak between two slices of bread, and people started to call ⓐ such food a hamburger.

14 위 글의 밑줄 친 ⓐsuch food가 가리키는 것을 우리말로 쓰시오.

출제율 95%

➡ _____

15 According to the passage, which is NOT true?

출제율 100%

① The word *hamburger* originally comes from Hamburg.

② Hamburg is Germany's second-largest city.

③ "People or things from Hamburg" can be called *hamburger* in German.

④ The origin of the first hamburger is clear.

⑤ People believe that the hamburger was invented in a small town in Texas, USA, sometime between 1885 and 1904.

16 Why did people start to call a food made by placing a Hamburg-style steak between two slices of bread a hamburger? Fill in the blanks (A) and (B) with suitable words.

출제율 90%

It's because *hamburger* means "people or things from (A)_____" in German and this food was made by placing a (B)_____ steak between two slices of bread.

[17~19] 다음 글을 읽고 물음에 답하시오.

robot

The word *robot* comes from the play *R.U.R.*, which was written in 1920 by a Czech writer Karel Čapek. In the play, robots are machines (A)that look like humans. They ___ⓐ___ to work for humans and ___ⓑ___ in a factory.

It is interesting (B)that the idea of using the word robot didn't come from Karel Čapek himself. He originally called the machines in his play *labori* from the Latin word for "work." However, his brother suggested *roboti*, which means "slave workers" in Czech. Karel Čapek liked the idea and decided to use the word *roboti*. In 1938, the play was made into a science fiction show on television in Britain.

17 위 글의 빈칸 ⓐ와 ⓑ에 design과 produce를 각각 알맞은 형태로 쓰시오.

➡ ⓐ _____ ⓑ _____

18 다음 〈보기〉 중에서 위 글의 밑줄 친 (A)that, (B)that과 문법적 쓰임이 같은 것을 각각 고르시오.

┌─── 보기 ───┐

① She said that she was tired.

② It's the best novel that I've ever read.

③ This is the house that the poet was born in.

④ The trouble is that we are short of money.

⑤ Is this the letter that came yesterday?

➡ (A)that과 같은 것: _____
(B)that과 같은 것: _____

19 본문의 내용과 일치하도록 다음 빈칸 (A)와 (B)에 알맞은 단어를 쓰시오.

In the play *R.U.R.*, the machines that looked like humans were originally called (A)_____, which was changed into (B)_____.

[20~22] 다음 글을 읽고 물음에 답하시오.

shampoo

The word *shampoo* ⓐcomes from the Hindi word *chāmpo*, which means "to press." (①) British traders in India experienced a bath with a head massage and introduced ⓑit to Britain in the 18th century. (②)

The meaning of the word *shampoo* changed a few times after it first entered English around 1762. (③) In the 19th century, shampoo got its present meaning of "washing the hair." (④) Shortly after that, the word began to be also used for a special soap for the hair. (⑤)

20 위 글의 흐름으로 보아, 주어진 문장이 들어가기에 가장 적절한 곳은?

In India, the word was used for a head massage.

① ② ③ ④ ⑤

21 위 글의 밑줄 친 ⓐcomes from과 바꿔 쓸 수 있는 말을 모두 고르시오.

① happens ② originates in

③ occurs to ④ comes up with

⑤ originates from

22 위 글의 밑줄 친 ⓑit이 가리키는 것을 본문에서 찾아 쓰시오.

➡ _____

[23~24] 다음 글을 읽고 물음에 답하시오.

The Origin of the Word *Sandwich*

The word *sandwich* comes from John Montagu, who was the 4th Earl of Sandwich. He enjoyed eating meat between two slices of bread because he could play a card game while he was eating. People thought that it was a great idea, and began to call such food a sandwich ⓐ_____ him.

23 위 글의 빈칸 ⓐ에 들어갈 알맞은 전치사를 고르시오.

① to ② after ③ for

④ as ⑤ into

24 위 글의 내용과 일치하도록 다음 빈칸 (A)와 (B)에 알맞은 단어를 쓰시오.

The word *sandwich* comes from the 4th Earl of Sandwich because he enjoyed eating meat (A)_____ _____ _____ _____ in order to play (B)_____ _____ _____ while eating.

[01~03] 다음 대화를 읽고 물음에 답하시오.

G: Thank you for everything, Jiho. I had a great time in Korea.

B: My pleasure. Please come visit me again, Lucy.

G: I'd love to, but before I do, I'd like to invite you to visit me in London.

B: Thanks. Anyway, it's too bad that you can't come to my soccer game tomorrow.

G: I'm sorry that I can't stay longer. I'll keep my fingers crossed for you.

B: _____(A)_____, but can you please say that again?

G: I said, "I'll keep my fingers crossed for you." It means "I wish you good luck."

B: Oh. Thanks. Have a nice trip.

G: Thanks. I'll keep in touch.

01 다음 영영풀이에 해당하는 말을 빈칸 (A)에 쓰시오.

This is used before you do or say something that might annoy somebody.

➡ _____

02 Where does Lucy invite Jiho?

➡ _____

03 What is Jiho doing at the airport? Use the word, 'off.' (5 words)

➡ _____

04 다음 대화를 읽고, 빈칸에 들어갈 알맞은 말을 괄호 안에 주어진 어휘를 이용하여 쓰시오. (필요할 경우 변형 가능.)

Jiho: It's too bad that you can't come to my soccer game tomorrow.

Lucy: I'm sorry that I can't stay longer. I'll keep my fingers crossed for you.

Jiho: Wait. Mom, can you please explain that expression to me?

Mom: She said, "I'll keep my fingers crossed for you," _____, Jiho. (you, mean, luck, which, good, wish, she)

Jiho: Oh, thanks, Mom. Thanks, Lucy. Have a nice trip.

➡ _____

05 다음 그림을 보고, 괄호 안에 주어진 단어를 활용하여 밑줄 친 우리말에 맞게 영작하시오. (단, 반드시 가주어-진주어 표현을 써야 함.)

The origin of the first hamburger is not clear. However, 햄버거는 미국 텍사스에 있는 작은 마을에서 발명되었다고 믿어진다. A cook placed a Hamburg-style steak between two slices of bread, and people started to call such food a hamburger.

(in a small town / invent / believe / in Texas, USA / that / is / was / 총 15 단어)

➡ _____

_____

shampoo

The word *shampoo* comes from the Hindi word *chāmpo*, which means "to press." In India, the word was used for a head massage. British traders in India experienced a bath with a head massage and introduced it to Britain in the 18th century.

ⓐThe meaning of the word *shampoo* changed a few times after it first entered into English around 1762. In the 19th century, *shampoo* got its present meaning of "washing the hair." Shortly after that, the word began to be also used for a special soap for the hair.

06 위 글의 밑줄 친 ⓐ에서 어법상 틀린 부분을 찾아 고치시오.

_____ ➡ _____

07 In India, what word did people use for a head massage? Fill in the blanks with suitable words.

➡ They used _____ _____ _____
for a head massage.

08 다음 빈칸 (A)~(C)에 알맞은 단어를 넣어 *shampoo*라는 단어가 현재의 의미를 가지게 된 과정을 완성하시오.

(1) In the 18th century, British traders who experienced a bath with (A)_____ _____ _____ (*chāmpo*) in India introduced it to Britain.

(2) In the 19th century, *shampoo* got its present meaning of "(B)_____ _____."

(3) Shortly after that, the word began to be also used for (C)_____ _____ _____.

robot

The word *robot* comes from the play *R.U.R.*, which was written in 1920 by a Czech writer Karel Čapek. In the play, robots are machines that look like humans. They are designed to work for humans and are produced in a factory.

It is interesting that the idea of using the word *robot* didn't come from Karel Čapek himself. He originally called the machines in his play *labori* from the Latin word for "work." However, his brother suggested *roboti*, which means "slave workers" in Czech. Karel Čapek liked the idea and decided to use the word *roboti*. In 1938, the play was made into a science fiction show on television in Britain.

09 다음 문장에서 위 글의 내용과 다른 부분을 찾아서 고치시오. (두 군데)

In the play *R.U.R.*, Karel Čapek called the machines that looked like humans *roboti*, but his brother suggested calling them *labori*.

➡ _____, _____

10 위 글의 내용과 일치하도록 다음 빈칸 (A)와 (B)에 알맞은 단어를 쓰시오.

Labori means "work" in (A)_____, and *roboti* means "(B)_____ _____" in Czech.

창의사고력 서술형 문제

01 (A)와 (B)의 표현을 이용하여 〈보기〉와 같이 다음 대화의 빈칸에 알맞은 말을 쓰시오.

> Do you know what the expression "_____" means?
> It means "_____."

보기

> Do you know what the expression "I feel under the weather" means?
> It means "I don't feel well."
> (A) I feel under the weather. / He hit the ceiling again. / He pulled my leg. / It's a piece of cake.
> (B) feel well / angry again / make fun of / very easy

(1) _____

(2) _____

(3) _____

02 다음 대화를 바탕으로 단어 sandwich의 유래를 설명하는 글을 쓰시오.

> A: Who's that man?
> B: He's John Montagu, the 4th Earl of Sandwich.
> A: What's he eating?
> B: He's eating meat between two slices of bread. I think he's enjoying it.
> A: What a great idea! That way, he can play a card game while he's eating.
> B: Yes. Let's call such food a sandwich after him.

> **The Origin of the Word *Sandwich***
> The word *sandwich* comes from John Montagu, who was (A)_____. He enjoyed eating meat (B)_____ because he could (C)_____ while he was (D)_____. People thought that it was a great idea, and began to call such food (E)_____ after him.

단원별 모의고사

01 다음 짝지어진 단어의 관계가 같도록 빈칸에 알맞은 말을 쓰시오.

> special – general : lend – _____

02 주어진 영어 설명에 맞게 문장의 빈칸에 알맞은 말을 쓰시오.

> The castle was built in the middle of the 8th _____.

> <영어 설명> a period of a hundred years

➡ _____

03 다음 빈칸에 알맞은 말로 짝지어진 것을 고르시오.

> • There is no _____ against loving her.
> • He sent her roses as an _____ of his love.

① rare – invention
② row – creation
③ raw – depression
④ low – impression
⑤ law – expression

[04~05] 다음 영영풀이에 해당하는 어휘를 주어진 철자로 시작하여 쓰시오.

04
> c_____ : to make something happen

05
> p_____ : to push something strongly

06 다음 영영풀이를 참고하여 빈칸에 알맞은 말을 쓰시오.

> a society that is well organized and developed

> The Orient closed the door against to Western _____.

07 다음 빈칸에 알맞은 말이 바르게 짝지어진 것은?

> • I _____ yoga twice a week.
> • I _____ up some useful English expressions from this book.

① do – picked
② make – made
③ get – pressed
④ take – meant
⑤ have – included

[08~10] 다음 대화를 읽고 물음에 답하시오.

> G: I feel under the __(A)__ .
> B: ⓐI'm sorry, but can you please say that again?
> G: I said, "I feel under the __(A)__ ."
> B: What does that mean?
> G: It means "I don't feel well." I think I ⓑcatch a cold.
> B: Oh. Why don't you ⓒpurchase some medicine. You can ⓓdose medicine at the store over there.
> G: OK, I ⓔwill.

08 다음 영영풀이에 해당하는 어휘를 빈칸 (A)에 쓰시오.

> the condition of the atmosphere in one area at a particular time

➡ _____

09 밑줄 친 ⓐ~ⓔ 중 어색한 것은?

① ⓐ   ② ⓑ   ③ ⓒ   ④ ⓓ   ⑤ ⓔ

10 What does the boy suggest to the girl? (9 words)

➡ _____

[11~13] 다음 대화를 읽고 물음에 답하시오.

G: Thank you for everything, Jiho. I had a great time in Korea.

B: My pleasure. Please come visit me again, Lucy.

G: I'd love to, but before I do, I'd like to invite you to visit me in London.

B: Thanks. Anyway, it's too bad that you can't come to my soccer game tomorrow.

G: I'm sorry that I can't stay longer. I'll keep my fingers crossed for you.

B: Excuse me, but can you please say that again?

G: I said, "I'll keep my fingers crossed for you." It means "I wish you good luck."

B: Oh. Thanks. _____ (A) _____

G: Thanks. I'll keep in touch.

11 위 대화의 빈칸 (A)에 알맞은 말을 4 단어로 쓰시오.

➡ _____

12 What does Jiho ask Lucy to do? (8 words)

➡ _____

13 What does Lucy ask Jiho to do? (8 words)

➡ _____

14 다음 우리말에 맞게 괄호 안에 주어진 어구를 배열하시오.

(1) 여우는 그 포도들을 먹으려고 애썼지만, 그것들은 너무 높이 있었다.

(the fox, were, which, to eat, tried, too, the grapes, high)

➡ _____

(2) 그 포도들은 여우가 닿기에는 너무 높이 있어서, 여우는 그것들이 맛이 시큼할 거라고 여겼다.

(the grapes, the fox, were, considered, so, sour, high, for, who, them)

➡ _____
_____

15 다음 밑줄 친 부분과 어법상 쓰임이 같은 것은?

> Miranda said the pizza was on her, <u>which</u> means she would pay for the pizza.

① Hurricane was named by Spanish explorers, <u>who</u> were passing by the sea.

② The farmers figured out <u>which</u> products they would sell.

③ This is the play in <u>which</u> the word *robot* first showed up.

④ What Jenny eats doesn't bother me but the way in <u>which</u> she eats it annoys me.

⑤ If the accident happened to you, <u>which</u> do you choose to save?

16 다음 내용을 읽고, 질문에 대한 답을 조건에 맞게 영작하시오.

> • I watched *Frozen 2* with my friends.
> • The movie is the second episode of *Frozen*.
> • Taeyeon sang its Korean version OST.
> • As a huge fan of hers, I was surprised with the fact that she joined the movie.

(1) What did I watch and what is it specifically? ('계속적' 용법의 관계대명사 which와 the movie, episode를 반드시 사용할 것, 총 12 단어 - 영화 제목은 1 단어로 취급)

➡ _____

_____

(2) What did you think of the fact that Taeyeon sang the OST? (sang, Korean version OST, surprising, its, Taeyeon을 반드시 사용할 것, 가주어-진주어 구문으로 영작할 것, 총 10 단어)

➡ _____

_____

17 다음 밑줄 친 부분의 쓰임이 <u>다른</u> 하나를 고르면?

① It is believed <u>that</u> she created them.
② It wasn't true <u>that</u> he was a genius.
③ It seemed <u>that</u> she hated the boss.
④ It was my fault <u>that</u> the baby got burnt.
⑤ It was Peter <u>that</u> cheated on her.

18 다음 우리말을 주어진 어구를 활용하여 조건에 맞게 영작하시오. (어형 변화 가능)

(1) 그 문어 미술가는 손이 많은데, 그것이 한꺼번에 그림을 그리는 데 도움이 된다.
(help, at, the octopus artist, many hands, has, her, once, draw, which 활용, 총 12 단어)

➡ _____

_____

(2) 음악 천재들 중 하나가 바로 모차르트인데, 그는 여덟 살에 교향곡을 작곡했다.
(the musical geniuses, the age, one of, is, Mozart, a symphony, eight, at, of, write, who 활용, 총 16 단어)

➡ _____

_____

[19~21] 다음 글을 읽고 물음에 답하시오.

> **shampoo**
>
> The word *shampoo* comes from the Hindi word *chāmpo*, which means "to press." In India, the word was used for a head massage. British traders in India experienced a bath with a head massage and introduced it to Britain in the 18th century.
>
> The meaning of the word *shampoo* changed a few times after it first entered English ⓐ <u>around</u> 1762. In the 19th century, *shampoo* got its present meaning of "washing the hair." Shortly after that, the word began to be also used for a special soap for the hair.

19 Who introduced a bath with a head massage to Britain in the 18th century? Fill in the blanks with suitable words.

> _____ _____ who experienced a bath with a head massage in India introduced it to Britain in the 18th century.

20 위 글의 밑줄 친 @around와 같은 의미로 쓰인 것을 고르시오.

① I heard laughter all around.
② Our house is just around the corner.
③ He arrived around five o'clock.
④ We were all running around trying to get ready in time.
⑤ The house was built around a central courtyard.

21 위 글의 내용과 일치하도록 다음 빈칸 (A)와 (B)에 알맞은 단어를 쓰시오.

> The original meaning of the word *shampoo* was "to press," but since the 19th century, it has been used not only for "(A)_____ _____ _____" but also for "(B)_____ _____ _____ for the hair."

[22~23] 다음 글을 읽고 물음에 답하시오.

robot

The word *robot* comes from the play *R.U.R.*, which was written in 1920 by a Czech writer Karel Čapek. (①) In the play, robots are machines that look like humans. (②) They are designed @to work for humans and are produced in a factory.

(③) It is interesting that the idea of using the word *robot* didn't come from Karel Čapek himself. (④) However, his brother suggested *roboti*, which means "slave workers" in Czech. (⑤) Karel Čapek liked the idea and decided to use the word *roboti*. In 1938, the play was made into a science fiction show on television in Britain.

22 위 글의 흐름으로 보아, 주어진 문장이 들어가기에 가장 적절한 곳은?

> He originally called the machines in his play *labori* from the Latin word for "work."

①   ②   ③   ④   ⑤

23 아래 〈보기〉에서 위 글의 밑줄 친 @to work와 to부정사의 용법이 다른 것의 개수를 고르시오.

> ┤ 보기 ├
> ① It's possible for robots to work without stopping.
> ② My hope is to work for Apple Inc.
> ③ He must be tired to work till late at night.
> ④ Is it normal to work 60 hours a week?
> ⑤ I was glad to work with her as a team.

① 1개   ② 2개   ③ 3개   ④ 4개   ⑤ 5개

[24~25] 다음 글을 읽고 물음에 답하시오.

hurricane

The word *hurricane* comes from the Spanish word *huracán*, which originates from the name of a Mayan god. In the Mayan creation myth, Huracán is the weather god of wind, storm, and fire, and he is one of the three gods who created humans. However, the first humans angered the gods, so Huracán caused a great flood.

The first Spanish contact with the Mayan civilization was in 1517. Spanish explorers who were passing through the Caribbean experienced a hurricane and picked up the word for it from the people in the area. In English, one of the early uses of *hurricane* was in a play by Shakespeare in 1608.

24 위 글의 제목으로 알맞은 것을 고르시오.

① Have You Heard of the Mayan Creation Myth?

② The Origin of the Word *Hurricane*

③ The Anger of the Three Gods

④ The Spanish Contact with the Mayan Civilization

⑤ The Hurricane in the Caribbean

25 According to the passage, which is NOT true?

① The word *hurricane* originates from the Spanish word *huracán*.

② The Spanish word *huracán* comes from the name of a Mayan god.

③ In the Mayan creation myth, Huracán is the weather god and caused a great earthquake.

④ In 1517, the first Spanish contact with the Mayan civilization was established.

⑤ In English, Shakespeare used the word *hurricane* in his play in 1608.

[26~27] 다음 글을 읽고 물음에 답하시오.

1. Many English words about ⓐlaw come from French. Examples ⓑexclude words like judge and justice.

2. There are many English words about ⓒmusic that come from Italian. For example, piano and violin come from Italian.

3. Many English words for ⓓvegetables come from Spanish. ⓔFor example, tomato comes from *tomate* and potato comes from *patata* in Spanish.

26 위 글의 밑줄 친 ⓐ~ⓔ에서 문맥상 낱말의 쓰임이 적절하지 <u>않은</u> 것을 찾아 알맞게 고치시오.

_____ ➡ _____

27 다음 빈칸에 알맞은 단어를 넣어 위 글에 대한 소개를 완성하시오.

The contents of the text above are about some English words of foreign _____.

[28~29] 다음 글을 읽고 물음에 답하시오.

hurricane

The word *hurricane* comes from the Spanish word *huracán*, which originates from the name of a Mayan god. In the Mayan creation myth, Huracán is the weather god of wind, storm, and fire, and he is one of the three gods who created humans. ___ⓐ___, the first humans angered the gods, so Huracán caused a great flood.

The first Spanish contact with the Mayan civilization was in 1517. Spanish explorers who were passing through the Caribbean experienced a hurricane and picked up the word for it from the people in the area. In English, one of the early uses of *hurricane* was in a play by Shakespeare in 1608.

28 위 글의 빈칸 ⓐ에 들어갈 알맞은 말을 고르시오.

① Moreover   ② However
③ Therefore   ④ For example
⑤ Similarly

29 다음 빈칸 (A)~(C)에 알맞은 단어를 넣어 huracán이라는 단어가 스페인어에 들어오게 된 과정을 완성하시오.

> (1) In the (A)_____ creation myth, Huracán, the weather god, caused a great flood as the first humans angered the gods who were their creators.
> (2) In 1517, the explorers from Spain experienced (B)_____ _____ while passing through the Caribbean and (C)_____ _____ the word for it from the people in the area.

[30~31] 다음 글을 읽고 물음에 답하시오.

Online   ⓐ

English words from other cultures or languages

shampoo: It ⓑ<u>comes from</u> the Hindi word *chāmpo*, which means "to press."
robot: It comes from *roboti*, which means "slave workers" in Czech.
hurricane: It comes from Spanish word, *huracán*, which originates from the name of a Mayan god.
hamburger: It comes from Hamburg, the second-largest city in Germany.

30 위 글의 빈칸 ⓐ에 들어갈 알맞은 단어를 쓰시오.

➡ _____

31 위 글의 밑줄 친 ⓑ<u>comes from</u>과 바꿔 쓸 수 있는 말을 본문에서 찾아 쓰시오.

➡ _____

Lesson 4

Be a Smart Spender

🎤 의사소통 기능

- 교환 요청하기
  I'd like to exchange this bag.

- 환불 요청하기
  I'd like to get a refund for this bag.

🎤 언어 형식

- 현재완료진행형
  I think you**'ve been spending** too much.

- 의문사+to부정사
  I don't know **how to solve** this problem.

Words & Expressions

Key Words

- **advice** [ædváis] 명 충고
- **allowance** [əláuəns] 명 용돈
- **already** [ɔːlrédi] 부 이미, 벌써
- **although** [ɔːlðóu] 접 비록 ~이지만
- **balance** [bǽləns] 명 균형, 통장의 잔액
- **budget** [bʌ́dʒit] 명 예산
- **by** [bai] 전 ~쯤에는, ~가 되었을 때
- **case** [keis] 명 사례, 경우
- **charity** [tʃǽrəti] 명 자선 단체
- **comfortable** [kʌ́mfərtəbl] 형 편안한
- **correct** [kərékt] 동 바로 잡다
- **couch** [kautʃ] 명 소파
- **divide** [diváid] 동 나누다
- **donate** [dóuneit] 동 기부하다
- **effort** [éfərt] 명 노력
- **exchange** [ikstʃéindʒ] 명 교환 동 교환하다
- **gift** [gift] 명 선물
- **however** [hauévər] 부 그러나
- **instead** [instéd] 부 그 대신에
- **item** [áitəm] 명 물품
- **lastly** [lǽstli] 부 마지막으로
- **loose** [luːs] 형 헐렁한, 느슨한

- **majority** [mədʒɔ́ːrəti] 명 대다수
- **manage** [mǽnidʒ] 동 관리하다
- **medicine** [médəsn] 명 의약품
- **native** [néitiv] 명 원주민
- **paper money** 지폐
- **pocket money** 용돈
- **price** [prais] 명 가격, 가치
- **rainy** [réini] 형 비가 내리는
- **receipt** [risíːt] 명 영수증
- **receive** [risíːv] 동 받다
- **recently** [ríːsntli] 부 최근에
- **refund** [rífʌnd] 명 환불 동 환불받다
- **remaining** [riméiniŋ] 형 남아 있는
- **result** [rizʌ́lt] 명 결과
- **return** [ritə́ːrn] 동 반품하다
- **save** [seiv] 동 저축하다, 구하다
- **survey** [sərvéi] 명 설문조사
- **tight** [tait] 형 빠듯한, 꽉 조이는[딱 붙는]
- **weekly** [wíːkli] 형 매주의, 주간의 부 매주
- **while** [hwail] 접 ~하는 동안, ~하는 반면에
- **work** [wəːrk] 동 작동하다
- **worry** [wə́ːri] 명 걱정 동 걱정하다

Key Expressions

- **be gone** 사라지다, 없어지다
- **carry around** 가지고 다니다
- **change one's mind** 마음을 바꾸다
- **for example** 예를 들면
- **get an exchange** 교환받다
- **get a refund** 환불받다
- **go camping** 캠핑하러 가다
- **have difficulty (in) - ing** ~하는 데 어려움을 겪다
- **have money back** 돈을 돌려받다
- **Here you are.** 여기 있습니다.
- **Let's see.** 어디 보자. (무엇인가 생각하면서 하는 말)

- **look for** ~을 찾다
- **make a budget plan** 예산 계획을 세우다
- **on sale** 할인 중인, 판매되는
- **on the spot** 그 자리에서, 현장에서
- **right away** 즉시
- **spending habit** 소비 습관
- **take care of** ~을 돌보다, ~을 처리하다
- **take effort** 노력을 필요로 하다
- **use up** 다 쓰다, 완전히 소모하다
- **would like to** ~하기를 원하다, ~을 좋아하다

Word Power

※ 서로 비슷한 뜻을 가진 어휘

- ☐ **case** 사례, 경우 : **example** 사례
- ☐ **paper money** 지폐 : **bill** 지폐
- ☐ **recently** 최근에 : **lately** 최근에

- ☐ **lastly** 마지막으로 : **finally** 마지막으로
- ☐ **pocket money** 용돈 : **allowance** 용돈
- ☐ **result** 결과 : **outcome** 결과

※ 서로 반대의 뜻을 가진 어휘

- ☐ **easy** 쉬운 ↔ **difficult** 어려운
- ☐ **loose** 헐렁한 ↔ **tight** 꽉 조이는[딱 붙는]
- ☐ **smart** 현명한 ↔ **foolish** 어리석은

- ☐ **expensive** 값비싼 ↔ **cheap** 값싼
- ☐ **same** 같은 ↔ **different** 다른
- ☐ **true** 진실인 ↔ **false** 거짓인

※ 동사 – 명사

- ☐ **advise** 충고하다 – **advice** 충고
- ☐ **divide** 나누다 – **division** 나누기

- ☐ **correct** 바로 잡다 – **correction** 수정
- ☐ **donate** 기부하다 – **donation** 기부

English Dictionary

- ☐ **advice** 충고
  → an opinion you give someone about what they should do 누군가에게 무엇을 해야 할지 말해 주는 의견

- ☐ **allowance** 용돈
  → money given by parents to a child regularly that the child can spend
  부모에 의해 아이에게 규칙적으로 주어지는 아이가 쓸 수 있는 돈

- ☐ **balance** 잔액
  → the amount of money that you have in your bank account 통장에 남아 있는 금액

- ☐ **budget** 예산
  → an amount money that a person or company can spend 개인이나 회사가 쓸 수 있는 금액

- ☐ **charity** 자선 단체
  → an organization that gives money, goods, or help to people who are poor, sick, etc.
  가난하거나 아픈 사람에게 돈, 물품 또는 도움을 주는 단체

- ☐ **correct** 바로 잡다
  → to make something right or to make it work the way it should
  무엇인가를 제대로 되도록 하거나 원래의 방식대로 작동하게 만들다

- ☐ **couch** 소파
  → a comfortable piece of furniture big enough for two or three people to sit on
  두, 세 사람이 앉을 만큼 충분히 크고 편안한 가구

- ☐ **donate** 기부하다
  → to give money to a group that needs help
  도움이 필요한 단체에 돈을 주다

- ☐ **effort** 노력
  → hard work that you do when you are trying to achieve something
  어떤 것을 이루려고 애쓸 때 하는 힘든 일

- ☐ **exchange** 교환
  → the act of giving someone something and receiving something else from them
  누군가에게 무엇인가를 주고 그들로부터 다른 어떤 것을 받는 행위

- ☐ **loose** 느슨한
  → not firmly fastened in place
  단단히 제자리에 고정되어 있지 않은

- ☐ **majority** 대다수
  → most of the people or things in a group
  한 그룹 내의 대부분의 사람이나 물건

- ☐ **medicine** 의약품
  → a substance used for treating illness
  질병을 치료하기 위하여 사용되는 물질

- ☐ **native** 원주민
  → a person who was born in a particular place
  특정한 장소에서 태어난 사람

- ☐ **receipt** 영수증
  → a piece of paper that shows you have paid for something 어떤 것의 대가를 지불했음을 보여주는 종이 조각

- ☐ **refund** 환불
  → a sum of money which is returned to you
  반환되는 돈의 총액

- ☐ **remaining** 남아 있는
  → left over after a part has been taken, used, or lost
  일부가 제거되거나 사용되거나 분실된 후에 남아 있는

Words & Expressions 시험대비 실력평가

01 다음 짝지어진 단어의 관계가 같도록 빈칸에 알맞은 말은?

easy – difficult : true – _____

① happy
② convenient
③ hard
④ proud
⑤ false

 서답형

02 주어진 영어 설명에 맞게 문장의 빈칸에 알맞은 말을 쓰시오.

Only a small portion of the _____ is spent on books.

<영어 설명> an amount money that a person or company can spend

➡ _____

중요

03 밑줄 친 부분의 의미로 알맞지 <u>않은</u> 것은?

① He took a look at the car and decided to buy it <u>on the spot</u>. (즉석에서)
② There is no chance that he will <u>change his mind</u>. (결정하다)
③ I have a few things I have to <u>take care of</u>. (처리하다)
④ I'm <u>having difficulties understanding</u> your point about needing to finish the production by this week. (이해하는 데 어려움을 겪다)
⑤ I'm trying to <u>get a refund</u> for this ticket. (환불받다)

04 다음 빈칸에 들어갈 알맞은 말을 고르시오.

I bought something 20 days ago, but I don't have the _____.

① receipt
② refund
③ price
④ couch
⑤ majority

중요

05 다음 <보기>의 단어를 사용하여 자연스러운 문장을 만들 수 없는 것은? (대 · 소문자 무시)

┌─ 보기 ─┐
loose   donate   result   refund

① They will announce the _____ of the vote tonight.
② The clerk is going to _____ my money.
③ These pants are a little _____ for me.
④ _____ to preserve the peace have failed.
⑤ He _____d money to the school in Africa.

06 다음 빈칸에 알맞은 말이 바르게 짝지어진 것을 고르시오.

• The shirts are on _____ at up to 40 percent off.
• It will _____ time and effort.

① expansion – take
② expansion – need
③ sale – take
④ sale – hide
⑤ increase – need

01 다음 영영풀이에 알맞은 어휘를 〈보기〉에서 찾아 쓰시오.

┌─ 보기 ─┐
majority　remaining　correct　effort

(1) to make something right or to make it work the way it should

(2) hard work that you do when you are trying to achieve something

(3) left over after a part has been taken, used, or lost

(4) most of the people or things in a group

➡ (1) _____ (2) _____ (3) _____
　　(4) _____

02 다음 짝지어진 두 단어의 관계가 같도록 빈칸에 알맞은 말을 쓰시오.

(1) same : different = _____ : tight

(2) donate : donation = advise : _____

03 다음 우리말에 맞도록 빈칸에 알맞은 말을 쓰시오. (철자가 주어진 경우 그 철자로 시작할 것.)

(1) 사람들은 해변을 깨끗하게 하기 위해 노력했다.
　→ People made an _____ to clean the beach.

(2) 그들은 이번 주에 일정이 빠듯하다.
　→ They have a t_____ schedule this week.

(3) 그 가수는 그의 팬들로부터 많은 선물을 받았다.
　→ The singer r_____ lots of gifts from his fans.

(4) 나와 우리 가족은 크리스마스에 서로 선물을 교환한다.
　→ My family and I _____ presents on Christmas.

04 우리말에 맞게 한 단어를 추가하여 주어진 단어를 알맞게 배열하시오.

(1) Mike는 그의 새로운 카메라를 사용하는 데 어려움이 있다. (Mike, his, camera, difficulty, has, new)
　➡ _____
　　_____

(2) 나는 모자를 사기 위해 용돈을 모았다. (buy, I, saved, my, have, to, a hat)
　➡ _____
　　_____

(3) Justin은 즉석에서 기타 연주를 했다. (Justin, guitar, the, the, played, on)
　➡ _____
　　_____

(4) 인터넷으로 당신의 통장 잔고를 확인하기는 쉽다. (the Internet, is, check, easy, bank, your, balance, on, to)
　➡ _____
　　_____

Conversation

교과서

1 교환 요청하기

> • **I'd like to exchange this bag.** 이 가방을 교환하고 싶습니다.

■ 구입한 물건을 교환해야 할 때는 'exchange(교환; 교환하다)'를 사용한다. 자신이 산 물건을 교환해 달라는 말은 'I would like to exchange this.' 또는 'Can I exchange this?', 'I would like to get an exchange.'라고 한다.

■ 교환을 요청할 때는 'I'd like to exchange … for ~.' 또는 'Can I exchange … for ~?'라고 말한다. 교환할 특정 물건이 있는 경우에는 exchange 뒤에 교환하고 싶은 자신의 물건을, for 뒤에 교환 받고 싶은 새로운 특정 물건을 넣어서 말한다.

> • A: Can I exchange this bag for that hat? 이 가방을 저 모자로 교환할 수 있나요?
> B: Sure. 물론이죠.

교환 요청하기

- I would like to exchange this. 이것을 교환하고 싶습니다.
- Can I exchange this? 이것을 교환할 수 있나요?
- I would like to get an exchange. 교환하고 싶어요.
- Why don't we get an exchange? 교환하는 것이 어때요?
- I would like to exchange A for B. A를 B로 교환하고 싶어요.
- Can I exchange A for B? A를 B로 교환할 수 있나요?

핵심 Check

1. 다음 대화의 빈칸에 들어갈 말로 알맞은 것을 고르시오.

A: Hello. Are you looking for anything special?
B: No, I'm not. _____ It's too small.
A: Sure. What size would you like?
B: Large, please.

① I would like to buy this T-shirt.
② I hope you would like this T-shirt.
③ Did you sell this T-shirt here?
④ I'd like to exchange this T-shirt.
⑤ Can I get a refund for this T-shirt?

2 환불 요청하기

> • I'd like to get a refund for this bag. 이 가방을 환불받고 싶습니다.

■ 구입한 물건을 반품하고, 환불을 요청할 때는 보통 'return(반품)'이나 'refund(환불)'를 사용한다. 환불을 위하여 반품을 할 때는 'I would like to return ~.'이라고 한다. 반품하고 물건의 환불을 요청할 때는 'I would like to return this for refund.'라고 한다.

■ 환불을 요청하는 영어 표현은 'I'd like to get a refund for ~.'라고 말하거나 'Can I get a refund for ~?'라고 말할 수 있다. 같은 의미로 'Can I have money back?'이라고 물을 수도 있다. 전액 환불을 강조하는 경우에는 'a full refund'라고 하기도 한다.

> • A: I'd like to get a refund for this bag. 이 가방을 환불받고 싶어요.
>
> B: I'm sorry, you can't. 죄송하지만 안 됩니다.

환불 요청하기

- I'd like a refund. 환불을 원합니다.
- I'd like my money back. 돈을 돌려주시기 바랍니다.
- I'd like to get a refund. 환불 받고 싶습니다.
- Can I get a refund for ~? ~에 대해서 환불 받을 수 있을까요?
- Can I have my money back? 돈을 돌려받을 수 있을까요?
- Is it possible to get a refund for ~? ~에 대하여 환불을 받을 수 있습니까?

핵심 Check

2. 다음 우리말 의미와 같도록 주어진 어구를 바르게 배열하여 문장을 완성하시오.

저는 이 가방을 환불받고 싶습니다. (I'd, get, like, a refund, for, this bag, to)

➡ _____

3. 다음 대화의 빈칸에 들어갈 말로 알맞은 것을 고르시오.

A: Hello. May I help you?

B: Yes, please. I'd like to get a refund for this watch.

A: OK. Was there anything wrong with it?

B: _____ Can I get my money back?

A: OK. I'll take care of it right away.

① Yes, it was really interesting.　② Yes, the watch was very good.

③ No, I just changed my mind.　④ No, I want to get the one over there.

⑤ I'd like to exchange this for that one.

Listen and Talk A 1

W: Hello. ❶May I help you?

B: Yes, please. ❷I'd like to get a refund for this watch.

W: OK. Was there ❸anything wrong with it?

B: No, I just changed my mind. Can I ❹get my money back?

W: OK. I'll take care of it right away.

W: 안녕하세요. 무엇을 도와드릴까요?

B: 네, 이 손목시계를 환불받고 싶어서요.

W: 알겠습니다. 시계에 무슨 문제가 있었나요?

B: 아니요. 그냥 마음이 바뀌었어요. 돈을 돌려받을 수 있을까요?

W: 네. 지금 바로 처리해드리겠습니다.

❶ '도와드릴까요?'라는 의미로 상대방에게 도움을 제공하겠다는 뜻을 나타내는 표현이다.
❷ 환불을 요청할 때 쓰는 표현이다.
❸ wrong이 anything을 뒤에서 수식하고 있다.
❹ 'get my money back'은 '돈을 돌려받다'라는 뜻이다.

Check(√) True or False

(1) The boy wants to get a refund for a watch.　　　　T ☐ F ☐

(2) Something was wrong with the watch.　　　　T ☐ F ☐

Listen and Talk C

M: Hello. May I help you?

G: Yes, please. ❶I'd like to get a refund for this cap.

M: Do you have the receipt?

G: No, I don't. I received ❷it as a gift.

M: If you don't have the receipt, then, ❸it's not possible to get a refund.

G: I see. Then, can I ❹exchange it for something else?

M: Yes, you can. What would you like to get?

G: I want to get this blue bag.

M: ❺Let me see .... The price is the same, so you can just take it.

G: Thank you.

M: 안녕하세요. 도와드릴까요?

G: 네. 이 모자를 환불받고 싶어요.

M: 영수증을 가지고 있나요?

G: 아니요. 선물로 받았어요.

M: 영수증이 없으면, 환불은 가능하지 않아요.

G: 알겠어요. 그럼, 다른 것으로 교환할 수 있나요?

M: 네, 가능해요. 어떤 것을 원하시나요?

G: 이 파란색 가방을 갖고 싶어요.

M: 한번 볼게요…. 가격이 같으니까 그것을 가져가셔도 돼요.

G: 고맙습니다.

❶ 'I'd like to'는 'I want to'와 같은 의미이다. 'get a refund for ∼'는 '∼에 대해 환불받다'라는 뜻이다.
❷ 'it'은 'this cap'을 가리킨다.
❸ 'it'은 가주어이고 'to get a refund'는 진주어이다.
❹ exchange A for B: A를 B로 바꾸다
❺ 'Let me see'는 '글쎄, 어디 보자' 정도의 뜻으로 무엇인가 생각하면서 하는 말이다.

Check(√) True or False

(3) The girl received the cap as a gift.　　　　T ☐ F ☐

(4) The man lets the girl get a refund for the cap.　　　　T ☐ F ☐

Listen and Talk A 2

W: Hello. ❶Do you need some help?

B: Yes. ❷I'd like to return this smartphone case.

W: ❸Let's see. Do you have the receipt with you?

B: Here it is. I bought ❹it three days ago.

W: Oh, then ❺it's possible.

W: 안녕하세요. 도움이 필요하
신가요?

B: 네. 이 스마트폰 케이스를 환
불받고 싶어요.

W: 잠시만요. 영수증을 가지고
계시나요?

B: 여기 있습니다. 3일 전에 구
매했어요.

W: 아, 그렇다면 가능합니다.

❶ 'May[Can] I help you?'와 같은 의미이다.
❷ 환불을 요청하는 말로 쓰였으며 return은 '반환하다'라는 의미이다.
❸ 'Let's see.'는 '어디 보자.' 정도의 뜻으로 생각을 하거나 무엇을 기억하려 하면서 하는 말이다.
❹ it은 'the smartphone case'를 가리킨다.
❺ it은 'to return the smartphone case'를 가리킨다.

Check(√) True or False

(5) The boy wants to return the smartphone case.   T ☐ F ☐

(6) The woman says that he cannot return the smartphone case.   T ☐ F ☐

Listen and Talk A 3

W: Hello. ❶Are you looking for anything special?

B: No, ❷I'm not. ❸I'd like to exchange this T-shirt. It's too small.

W: Sure. ❹What size would you like?

B: Large, please.

W: ❺Here you are.

B: Thank you.

W: 안녕하세요. 특별히 찾으시
는 것 있으세요?

B: 아니요. 저는 이 티셔츠를 교
환하고 싶어서요. 너무 작아
요.

W: 네. 어떤 사이즈를 원하세
요?

B: Large 사이즈요.

W: 여기 있습니다.

B: 감사합니다.

❶ 보통 점원이 손님을 응대하면서 하는 말이다. anything을 special이 뒤에서 수식하고 있다.
❷ 'Are you ~?'로 물었으므로 'I'm not.'으로 답한다. don't를 쓰면 안 되는 것에 유의한다.
❸ 교환을 요청하는 표현이다.
❹ What size would you like?: 'What size do you want?'를 보다 공손하게 표현하고 있다.
❺ 'Here you are.'는 '여기 있습니다.'라는 의미이다.

Check(√) True or False

(7) The boy is looking for something special.   T ☐ F ☐

(8) The boy wants a large size.   T ☐ F ☐

Listen and Talk A 4

W: Hello. ❶What can I do for you?

B: ❷Can I ❸exchange this black umbrella for a different color?

W: Sure. ❹What color would you like?

B: ❺I'd like a yellow ❻one, please.

W: OK. Here you are.

❶ 'May I help you?', 'Can I help you?' 또는 'Do you need some help?'와 바꿔 쓸 수 있는 표현이다.
❷ Can은 '허가'의 의미로 쓰였다.
❸ 'exchange A for B'는 'A를 B로 바꾸다'라는 의미이다.
❹ What은 의문형용사로 color를 수식하고 있다.
❺ 'I'd like ~'는 'I want ~'를 보다 공손하게 표현하고 있다.
❻ one은 부정대명사로 umbrella를 받고 있다.

 Listen and Talk B 1

A: Hello. May I help you?

B: Yes, please. ❶I'd like to exchange this bag.

A: ❷Sure. What would you like to exchange it for?

B: ❸I'd like to exchange it for a cap.

A: OK.

❶ 교환을 요청하는 표현으로 뒤에 'for something else' 따위가 생략되어 있다.
❷ 긍정의 답으로 'OK.'라고 할 수도 있다.
❸ 'I want to exchange it for a cap.'과 바꿔 쓸 수 있다.

 Listen and Talk B 2

A: Hello. May I help you?

B: Yes, please. ❶I'd like to get a refund for this bag.

A: Sure. Do you have the receipt?

B: Yes, ❷I do. ❸Here it is.

❶ 환불을 요청하는 표현이다.
❷ do는 'have the receipt'를 대신하는 대동사이다.
❸ 'Here it is.'는 '여기 있습니다.'라는 의미이다.

 Review 1

W: Hello. May I help you?

B: Yes, please. ❶I'd like to return this baseball glove.

W: OK. Was there anything wrong with ❷it?

B: No, I just changed my mind. ❸Can I have my money back?

W: OK. ❹Here's your money.

❶ '반품하고 싶다'는 표현이며 return은 '반환하다'라는 의미이다.
❷ it은 'the baseball glove'를 가리킨다.
❸ 'Can I get my money back?'으로 쓸 수도 있다.
❹ 'Here it is.'나 'Here you are.'로 바꿔 쓸 수 있다.

 Review 2

M: Hello. Can I help you?

W: Yes, please. I'd like to exchange this yellow T-shirt. It's ❶too small for me.

M: Sure. ❷What size would you like to exchange it for?

W: Medium size, please. Oh! Can I have ❸it in red?

M: OK. ❹Here you are.

❶ too는 small을 수식하는 부사이다.
❷ 'exchange A for B'는 'A를 B로 바꾸다'라는 의미이다.
❸ it은 'the medium size T-shirt'를 가리킨다.
❹ 'Here it is.'로 바꿔 쓸 수 있다.

 Review 3

M: Hello. May I help you?

G: Yes, please. Can I get a refund for this hat?

M: ❶I'm afraid you can't.

G: Then, can I exchange this hat for the gloves ❷over there?

M: Yes, you ❸can.

❶ 'I'm afraid ~'는 유감스러운 내용을 말할 때 예의상 덧붙이는 표현으로 '~할 것 같다, (유감이지만) ~이다' 정도의 뜻이다.
❷ over there: 저기에
❸ can 뒤에는 'exchange the hat for the gloves'가 생략되어 있다.

 Review 4

A: Hello. May I help you?

B: ❶I'd like to get a refund for this cap.

A: Sure. Do you have the receipt?

B: Yes, I do. ❷Here it is.

❶ 환불을 요청하는 말이다.
❷ 'Here it is.'는 '여기 있습니다.'라는 의미이다

● 다음 우리말과 일치하도록 빈칸에 알맞은 말을 쓰시오.

Listen and Talk A 1

W: Hello. May I _____ _____?

B: Yes, please. I'd like to get a _____ for this watch.

W: OK. Was there anything _____ with it?

B: No, I just changed my mind. Can I _____ my money _____?

W: OK. I'll _____ _____ _____ it right away.

W: 안녕하세요. 무엇을 도와드릴까요?
B: 네, 이 손목시계를 환불받고 싶어서요.
W: 알겠습니다. 시계에 무슨 문제가 있었나요?
B: 아니요, 그냥 마음이 바뀌었어요. 돈을 돌려받을 수 있을까요?
W: 네. 지금 바로 처리해드리겠습니다.

Listen and Talk A 2

W: Hello. Do you _____ _____ _____?

B: Yes. I'd like to _____ this smartphone case.

W: _____ _____. Do you have the _____ with you?

B: _____ _____ _____. I bought _____ three days ago.

W: Oh, then _____ _____.

W: 안녕하세요. 도움이 필요하신가요?
B: 네. 이 스마트폰 케이스를 환불받고 싶어요.
W: 어디 봅시다. 영수증을 가지고 계시나요?
B: 여기 있습니다. 3일 전에 구매했어요.
W: 아, 그렇다면 가능합니다.

Listen and Talk A 3

W: Hello. Are you _____ _____ anything _____?

B: No, I'm not. I'd like to _____ this T-shirt. It's too small.

W: Sure. What size _____ _____ _____?

B: Large, please.

W: _____ _____ _____.

B: Thank you.

W: 안녕하세요. 특별히 찾으시는 것 있으세요?
B: 아니요. 저는 이 티셔츠를 교환하고 싶어서요. 너무 작아요.
W: 네. 어떤 사이즈를 원하세요?
B: 큰 사이즈로 주세요.
W: 여기 있습니다.
B: 감사합니다.

Listen and Talk A 4

W: Hello. _____ can I _____ _____?

B: Can I exchange this black umbrella _____ a different color?

W: Sure. _____ color _____ you _____?

B: _____ _____ a yellow _____, please.

W: OK. _____ _____ _____.

W: 안녕하세요. 무엇을 도와드릴까요?
B: 이 검은색 우산을 다른 색으로 교환할 수 있을까요?
W: 물론이죠. 어떤 색을 원하세요?
B: 저는 노란색을 원해요.
W: 알겠습니다. 여기 있습니다.

Listen and Talk B 1

A: Hello. _____ _____ _____ _____ ?

B: Yes, please. _____ _____ _____ exchange this bag.

A: Sure. _____ would you like to exchange _____ _____ ?

B: I'd like to exchange _____ _____ a cap.

A: OK.

A: 안녕하세요. 무엇을 도와드릴까요?
B: 네. 이 가방을 교환하고 싶어요.
A: 네. 무엇으로 교환하고 싶으세요?
B: 저는 모자로 교환하고 싶어요.
A: 알겠습니다.

Listen and Talk B 2

A: Hello. _____ _____ help you?

B: Yes, please. I'd like to _____ _____ _____ _____ this bag.

A: Sure. Do you have the _____ ?

B: Yes, I _____ . _____ _____ _____ .

A: 안녕하세요. 무엇을 도와드릴까요?
B: 네. 이 가방을 환불받고 싶어요.
A: 물론이죠. 영수증을 가지고 계시나요?
B: 네. 여기 있습니다.

Listen and Talk C

M: Hello. _____ _____ _____ _____ ?

G: Yes, please. I'd like to _____ _____ _____ _____ this cap.

M: Do you have the _____ ?

G: No, I _____ . I received _____ _____ a gift.

M: If you don't have the receipt, then, _____ not possible _____ _____ a refund.

G: _____ _____ . Then, can I _____ it _____ _____ _____ ?

M: Yes, you _____ . What _____ _____ _____ _____ ?

G: I _____ _____ _____ this blue bag.

M: _____ _____ _____ .... The price is the same, so you can just _____ _____ .

G: Thank you.

M: 안녕하세요. 도와드릴까요?
G: 네. 이 모자를 환불받고 싶어요.
M: 영수증을 가지고 있나요?
G: 아니요. 선물로 받았어요.
M: 영수증이 없으면, 환불은 가능하지 않아요.
G: 알겠어요. 그럼, 다른 것으로 교환할 수 있나요?
M: 네, 가능해요. 어떤 것을 원하시나요?
G: 이 파란색 가방을 갖고 싶어요.
M: 한번 볼게요…. 가격이 같으니까 그것을 가져가셔도 돼요.
G: 고맙습니다.

Listen and Talk D

G: I bought this red skirt last week. I like the skirt, but my sister says that the color doesn't _____ _____ _____ me. I wonder _____ I should _____ _____ _____ a different color.

B: It's _____ _____ you but I think it's fine.

G: 나는 지난주에 이 빨간색 치마를 샀어. 나는 치마가 마음에 드는데 내 여동생은 색깔이 나에게 잘 어울리지 않는대. 이걸 다른 색으로 교환을 해야 할지 고민이야.
B: 네가 하고 싶은 대로 하렴. 하지만 내 생각엔 괜찮은 것 같아.

Talk and Play

A: _____ _____ . I'd like to _____ this T-shirt _____ these pants.
B: OK. Is there _____ _____ with it?
A: I don't like the color.
B: I see.

A: _____ _____ . I'd like to _____ _____ _____ _____ this cap.
B: OK. Is there _____ _____ with it?
A: I don't like the color.
B: I see.

Review 1

W: Hello. _____ _____ _____ _____ ?
B: Yes, please. _____ _____ _____ _____ this baseball glove.
W: OK. Was there _____ _____ _____ it?
B: No, I just changed my mind. Can I _____ my money _____ ?
W: OK. _____ _____ _____ .

Review 2

M: Hello. _____ _____ _____ _____ ?
W: Yes, please. _____ _____ _____ _____ this yellow T-shirt. It's too small for me.
M: Sure. What size _____ _____ _____ _____ _____ _____ _____ ?
W: Medium size, please. Oh! Can I _____ _____ _____ red?
M: OK. _____ _____ _____ .

Review 3

M: Hello. May I help you?
G: Yes, please. Can I _____ _____ _____ _____ this hat?
M: I'm _____ _____ _____ .
G: Then, can I _____ this hat _____ the gloves over there?
M: Yes, you _____ .

Review 4

A: Hello. May I help you?
B: I'd like to _____ _____ _____ _____ this cap.
A: Sure. Do you have the _____ ?
B: Yes, I _____ . _____ _____ _____ .

해석

A: 실례합니다. 이 티셔츠를 이 바지로 교환하고 싶어요.
B: 네. 티셔츠에 무슨 문제가 있나요?
A: 색이 마음에 들지 않아요.
B: 알겠습니다.

A: 실례합니다. 저는 이 모자를 환불받고 싶어요.
B: 네. 모자에 무슨 문제가 있나요?
A: 색이 마음에 들지 않아요.
B: 알겠습니다.

W: 안녕하세요. 무엇을 도와드릴까요?
B: 네. 이 야구 글러브를 환불받고 싶어서요.
W: 알겠어요. 그것에 무슨 문제가 있었나요?
B: 아니요. 그냥 마음이 바뀌었어요. 제 돈을 돌려받을 수 있을까요?
W: 네. 여기 있습니다.

M: 안녕하세요. 무엇을 도와드릴까요?
W: 네. 이 노란색 티셔츠를 교환하고 싶어요. 저에게는 너무 작네요.
M: 네. 어떤 사이즈로 교환하고 싶으신가요?
W: 중간 사이즈로 주세요. 오! 빨간색 티셔츠로 바꿀 수 있을까요?
M: 네. 여기 있습니다.

M: 안녕하세요. 무엇을 도와드릴까요?
G: 네. 이 모자를 환불받을 수 있을까요?
M: 죄송하지만 안 됩니다.
G: 그렇다면 이 모자를 저기에 있는 장갑으로 교환할 수 있을까요?
M: 네. 가능합니다.

A: 안녕하세요. 무엇을 도와드릴까요?
B: 네. 이 모자를 환불받고 싶어요.
A: 물론이죠. 영수증을 가지고 계시나요?
B: 네. 여기 있습니다.

01 다음 빈칸 (A)에 알맞은 문장은?

> W: Hello. May I help you?
>
> B: Yes, please. ＿＿＿＿＿＿ (A) ＿＿＿＿＿＿
>
> W: OK. Was there anything wrong with it?
>
> B: No, I just changed my mind. Can I get my money back?
>
> W: OK. I'll take care of it right away.

① What would you like?

② I would like to get an exchange.

③ I'd like to get a refund for this watch.

④ Can I exchange it for something else?

⑤ Can I exchange this?

02 주어진 어휘를 이용하여 밑줄 친 우리말을 영작하시오.

> B: Excause me. I'd like to return this baseball glove.
>
> W: OK. Was there anything wrong with it?
>
> B: No, I just changed my mind. 제 돈을 돌려받을 수 있을까요?
>
> W: OK. Here's your money.

➡ ＿＿＿＿＿＿＿＿＿＿＿＿＿＿＿＿＿＿＿＿ (can, have, my)

[03~04] 다음 대화를 읽고 물음에 답하시오.

> W: Hello. (A)Do you need some help?
>
> B: Yes. I'd like to return this smartphone case.
>
> W: Let's see. Do you have the ＿(a)＿ with you?
>
> B: Here it is. I bought it three days ago.
>
> W: Oh, then it's possible.

03 다음 영영풀이를 참고하여 대화의 빈칸 (a)에 알맞은 말은?

> a piece of paper that shows you have paid for something

① return　② refund　③ receipt　④ exchange　⑤ allowance

04 May를 이용하여 밑줄 친 (A)와 같은 뜻의 말을 4 단어 쓰시오.

➡ ＿＿＿＿＿＿＿＿＿＿＿＿＿＿＿＿＿＿＿＿

01 다음 중 짝지어진 대화가 <u>어색한</u> 것은?

① A: Hello. May I help you?
  B: Yes, please.
② A: Can I have it in red?
  B: OK. Here you are.
③ A: I'd like to get a refund for this cap.
  B: Sure.
④ A: Do you have the receipt?
  B: I'd like to exchange this T-shirt.
⑤ A: What would you like?
  B: I'd like the blue tie.

[02~05] 다음 대화를 읽고 물음에 답하시오.

M: Hello. _____(A)
G: Yes, please. I'd like to get a refund for this cap.
M: Do you have the receipt?
G: No, I don't. I received it as a gift.
M: If you don't have the receipt, then, (a)환불은 가능하지 않아요(it, get, refund).
G: I see. Then, _____(B)_____?
M: Yes, you can. What would you like to get?
G: I want to get this blue bag.
M: Let me see .... The price is the same, so you can just take it.
G: Thank you.

02 빈칸 (A)에 알맞은 말을 고르시오.

① What has brought you here?
② Do I know you?
③ May I help you?
④ Why do you like it?
⑤ Can it be all right?

03 위 대화의 빈칸 (B)에 들어갈 알맞은 말을 주어진 어휘를 배열하여 쓰시오.

(I, it, something, exchange, can, else, for)

➡ _____

04 밑줄 친 (a)의 우리말에 맞게 주어진 어휘를 이용하여 영작하시오.

➡ _____

05 소녀에 관한 위 대화의 내용과 일치하는 것은?

① The girl wants to give a refund for the cap.
② The girl gave the cap as a gift.
③ The girl has the receipt.
④ The girl will receive her money back.
⑤ The girl can take a blue bag.

[06~07] 다음 대화를 읽고 물음에 답하시오.

W: Hello. Are you looking for (a)[something / anything] special?
B: No, (b)[I'm not / I don't]. I'd like to (c)[change / exchange] this T-shirt. It's too small.
W: Sure. What size would you like?
B: Large, please.
W: _____(A)
B: Thank you.

06 위 대화의 빈칸 (A)에 들어갈 말로 알맞은 것을 <u>모두</u> 고르시오.

① Here they go.
② Here it is.
③ Excuse me, but can you repeat that again?
④ Here you are.
⑤ Enjoy them, please.

07 위 대화의 괄호 (a)~(c)에서 알맞은 것을 골라 바르게 짝지은 것은?

	(a)	(b)	(c)
①	anything	I'm not	exchange
②	anything	I don't	exchange
③	anything	I'm not	change
④	something	I don't	exchange
⑤	something	I'm not	change

08 주어진 문장 다음에 대화가 자연스럽게 연결되도록 (A)~(D)를 순서대로 가장 적절하게 배열한 것은?

> M: Hello. Can I help you?
> (A) Medium size, please. Oh! Can I have it in red?
> (B) Yes, please. I'd like to exchange this yellow T-shirt. It's too small for me.
> (C) Sure. What size would you like to exchange it for?
> (D) OK. Here you are.

① (B) – (A) – (C) – (D)
② (B) – (C) – (A) – (D)
③ (B) – (C) – (D) – (A)
④ (C) – (B) – (D) – (A)
⑤ (C) – (D) – (B) – (A)

[09~10] 다음 대화를 읽고 물음에 답하시오.

> A: Hello. May I help you?
> B: Yes, please. _____ (A)
> A: Sure. What would you like to exchange it __(B)__ ?
> B: I'd like to exchange it __(B)__ a cap.
> A: OK.

09 위 대화의 빈칸 (A)에 알맞은 말은?

① Do you have a cap?
② I want to have my money back.
③ I'd like to exchange this bag.
④ Where can I get an exchange?
⑤ How can I find the way to the shop?

10 위 대화의 빈칸 (B)에 공통으로 들어갈 알맞은 말은?

① with   ② at   ③ on
④ for   ⑤ by

11 다음 대화의 밑줄 친 부분의 의도로 가장 적절한 것은?

> A: Hello. May I help you?
> B: Yes, please. I'd like to get a refund for this bag.
> A: Sure. Do you have the receipt?
> B: Yes, I do. Here it is.

① 권유하기   ② 희망 표현하기
③ 교환 요청하기   ④ 설명 요청하기
⑤ 환불 요청하기

[12~13] 다음 대화를 읽고 물음에 답하시오.

> W: Hello. What can I do for you?
> B: Can I exchange this black umbrella for a different color?
> W: Sure. What color would you like?
> B: I'd like a yellow (A)one, please.
> W: OK. Here you are.

서답형

12 What does the boy want?

➡ _____

서답형

13 밑줄 친 (A)one이 가리키는 것을 쓰시오.

➡ _____

[01~05] 다음 대화를 읽고 물음에 답하시오.

M: Hello. May I help you?
G: Yes, please. (a)I'd like to get a refund for this cap.
M: Do you have the receipt?
G: No, I don't. I received it as a gift.
M: (b)영수증이 없으면, 환불은 가능하지 않아요. (it, refund, possible, get, then, if)
(A) I want to get this blue bag.
(B) Let me see .... The price is the same, so you can just take it.
(C) Yes, you can. What would you like to get?
(D) I see. Then, can I exchange it for something else?
G: Thank you.

중요

01 위 대화의 (A)~(D)를 알맞은 순서로 배열하시오.

➡ _____

02 괄호 안에 주어진 어휘를 이용하여 밑줄 친 (a)를 12 단어로 쓰시오.

➡ _____

(it, possible)

고난이도

03 Why can't the girl get a refund for the cap? Use the phrase 'It's because' and 'since.'

➡ _____
_____

04 What does the girl finally get?

➡ _____

고난이도

05 괄호 안에 주어진 어휘를 이용하여 밑줄 친 우리말 (b)에 맞게 14 단어로 쓰시오.

➡ _____
_____

[06~08] 다음 대화를 읽고 물음에 답하시오.

W: Hello. (a)특별히 찾으시는 것 있으세요? (look)
B: No, I'm not. I'd like to exchange this T-shirt. It's too small.
W: Sure. What size would you like?
B: Large, please.
W: _____ (A)
B: Thank you.

중요

06 위 대화의 빈칸 (A)에 알맞은 말을 you를 포함하여 3 단어로 쓰시오.

➡ _____

07 Why does the boy want to exchange the T-shirt? Use the phrase 'It's because'.

➡ _____

중요

08 괄호 안에 주어진 어휘를 이용하여 밑줄 친 우리말 (a)에 맞게 6 단어로 쓰시오.

➡ _____

고난이도

09 다음 대화의 빈칸에 주어진 <영영풀이>에 해당하는 어휘를 쓰시오.

A: Hello. May I help you?
B: Yes, please. I'd like to get a _____ for this watch.

a sum of money which is returned to you

➡ _____

Grammar

교과서

① 현재완료진행시제

> • My aunts **have been watching** TV for two hours. 내 이모들은 두 시간 동안 TV를 보고 있다.
> • He **has been feeling** sick since yesterday. 그는 어제부터 몸이 좋지 않다.

■ 과거에 시작한 일이 현재까지 계속 진행되고 있는 경우를 나타낼 때 사용한다.

• Carter **has been teaching** English since 2010. Carter는 2010년부터 영어를 가르쳐 오고 있다.
• The Typhoon **has been heading** to Japan since last week. 태풍이 지난주부터 일본을 향해 가고 있다.

■ 현재완료의 '계속' 용법과 유사하다. 현재완료진행은 '상태'가 아닌, '동작'을 나타낸다.

• Linda and Jane **have known** each other since their childhood. Linda와 Jane은 어린 시절부터 서로 알고 지내 왔다. (상태의 계속 – 현재완료진행 불가)
• Linda and Jane **have been reading** books for three hours. Linda와 Jane은 세 시간 동안 책을 읽어 왔다. (동작의 계속 – 현재완료진행 가능)

■ 현재완료진행형과 자주 쓰는 부사구는 'for(~ 동안)'와 'since(~ 이후로)'이다.

• Miranda **has been studying** in Paris **since** last year. Miranda는 작년부터 파리에서 공부하고 있다.
• Mom and Dad **have been talking** on my future plan **for** three hours. 엄마와 아빠가 내 미래 계획에 대해 세 시간 동안 얘기하고 있다.

■ 현재완료진행형은 의미상 두 문장으로 나누어 쓸 수 있다. (과거의 시작+현재의 진행형)

• The teachers **have been doing** volunteer work since 2002.
  → The teachers **began** to do volunteer work **in 2002**. (과거형)
      + They're **still** doing it. (현재진행형)

■ 현재완료시제는 과거에서 현재까지 동작의 완료, 경험, 결과, 계속을 의미한다.

• Leon **hasn't completed** his application form yet. Leon은 아직 그의 지원서 작성을 완료하지 못했다. 〈완료〉
• **Has** she ever **been** to the Dessert Fair? 그녀가 디저트 박람회에 가 본 적이 있나요? 〈경험〉
• Tom **has lost** his wallet. Tom은 그의 지갑을 잃어버렸다. 〈결과–현재 없음〉
• The Smiths **have lived** in Seoul for 30 years. Smith씨 가족은 30년간 서울에서 살아 왔다. 〈계속〉

핵심 Check

1. 다음 괄호 안에서 알맞은 단어를 고르시오.

(1) It has been raining cats and dogs (for / since) last September.

(2) Marie has been learning Spanish (for / since) almost two years.

② 의문사 + to부정사

> • Sarah didn't know **what to do**. Sarah는 무엇을 해야 할지 몰랐다.
> • I asked him **where to go** shopping. 나는 그에게 어디로 쇼핑을 가야 할지 물어봤다.

■ '의문사 + to부정사'는 명사구로서 주로 목적어 역할을 한다.

- I don't know **how to make** shikhye. 나는 어떻게 식혜를 만드는지 모른다.
- Let me know **when to press** the button. 언제 버튼을 눌러야 할지 알려 주세요.

■ 의문대명사는 내용상 to부정사의 목적어 역할을 한다.

- She wants to find out **whom to ask** for help. 그녀는 누구에게 도움을 청할지 알고 싶다.
- Mike hasn't decided **which to buy**. Mike는 어느 것을 살지 결정하지 못했다.
- Mom doesn't know **what to say**. 엄마는 무슨 말을 할지 모른다.

■ 의문부사 뒤에는 to부정사의 목적어가 나오며, 'why + to부정사' 형태는 쓸 수 없다.

- The signal tells **when to push the button**. 그 신호는 언제 버튼을 누를지 말해준다.
- Let me know **where to drop you off**. 당신을 어디에 내려줄지 알려 주세요.
- David told me **how to persuade consumers** to buy the products. David는 나에게 어떻게 소비자를 설득해서 제품을 사게 할지 말해줬다.

■ 의문형용사 which와 what은 수식받는 명사를 뒤에 쓴 후에 to부정사가 온다.

- She didn't decide **which dress to put on**. 그녀는 어느 드레스를 입을지 결정하지 못했다.
- Robert wanted to know **what route to take** so that he could arrive as soon as possible. Robert는 가능한 한 빨리 도착할 수 있도록 어떤 경로를 택해야 할지 알고 싶었다.

■ '의문사 + to부정사'는 '의문사+주어+should[can]+동사원형'으로 바꿀 수 있다.

- She didn't know **how to stop buying** unnecessary things.
  = She didn't know **how she could stop buying** unnecessary things. 그녀는 필요하지 않은 물건을 사는 것을 어떻게 멈출지 알지 못했다.
- Can you tell him **when to turn left**?
  = Can you tell him **when he should turn left**? 언제 좌회전해야 할지 그에게 말해 줄 수 있나요?

핵심 Check

2. 다음 우리말에 맞게 주어진 단어를 배열하시오.

(1) 점심으로 무엇을 먹을지 결정합시다. (decide, eat, let's, to, lunch, for, what)

➡ _____

(2) 그녀는 자전거를 어떻게 탈지 모른다. (how, she, a bike, know, to, doesn't, ride)

➡ _____

Grammar 시험대비 기본평가

01 다음 두 문장의 뜻이 같게 빈칸을 채우시오.

(1) Tell her where she should go.

　→ Tell her _____ _____ _____.

(2) Sam didn't know which book he should choose.

　→ Sam didn't know _____ _____ _____ _____.

(3) George hasn't decided what he should buy for her.

　→ George hasn't decided _____ _____ _____ _____

　　_____.

(4) Let me know how to get to the bus station.

　→ Let me know _____ _____ _____ _____ _____

　　the bus station.

02 다음 우리말에 맞게 주어진 단어를 바르게 배열하시오. (필요하면 어형을 바꿀 것.)

(1) Marie는 네 시간 동안 컴퓨터 게임을 하고 있다. (Marie, four hours, have been, games, play, for, computer)

　➡ _____

(2) Susan과 그녀의 친구들은 두 시간 동안 드라마를 시청하고 있다. (a drama, for, have been, and, Susan, watch, two hours, her friends)

　➡ _____

03 다음 우리말에 맞게 빈칸에 알맞은 단어를 쓰시오.

> 이 노트북을 사용하는 법을 알려 주세요.

➡ Let me know _____ _____ _____ this lap top.

= Let me know _____ _____ _____ _____ this lap top.

04 다음 중 어법상 바르지 <u>않은</u> 것은?

① My friends have been watching movies for three hours.

② They have been knowing each other since last year.

③ Squirrels have been digging the hole to spend winter.

④ Amy has been using her smartphone for a day.

⑤ Mark has been shouting since 10 minutes ago.

01 다음 빈칸에 알맞은 것은?

> Lynn began composing a song three weeks ago, and she is still composing it now.
> = Lynn _____ a song since three weeks ago.

① has composing
② has begun composing
③ has been composing
④ has been beginning composing
⑤ has been composed

서답형

02 다음 두 문장을 한 문장으로 표현할 때, 빈칸에 들어갈 알맞은 말을 쓰시오.

> • Riley started to solve the puzzle yesterday.
> • She's still solving the puzzle now.

➡ R i l e y _____ _____ _____
_____ yesterday.

서답형

03 다음 예시와 같이 두 문장을 '의문사+to부정사'를 활용해 한 문장으로 만들 때, 빈칸에 알맞은 말을 넣으시오.

> The girl was wondering. What should she see in London?
> → The girl was wondering what to see in London.

(1) Let the guests know. When should they visit the palace?
→ Let the guests know _____
_____.

(2) Elsa hasn't decided. Which color should she use to describe the scenery?
→ Elsa hasn't decided _____
to describe the scenery.

중요

04 다음 대화의 빈칸 (A), (B), (C)에 들어갈 말로 가장 적절한 것은?

> (1) A: Could you tell me ___(A)___ buy?
>   B: I think the large one is better.
> (2) A: Do you know ___(B)___ fix the bike?
>   B: Sorry, I don't know a thing about it.
> (3) A: I wonder ___(C)___ stay in Paris.
>   B: How about a guest house?

	(A)	(B)	(C)
①	which to	how to	where to
②	which to	how to	what to
③	which to	when to	how to
④	where to	what to	how to
⑤	where to	how to	what to

서답형

05 다음 문장에서 어법상 틀린 부분을 한군데 찾아 바르게 고쳐 쓰시오.

> He asked me that to buy for his wife.

_____ ➡ _____

중요

06 다음 주어진 문장과 의미가 같은 것은?

> The participants haven't decided what to eat for dinner.

① The participants haven't decided what they were eating for dinner.
② The participants haven't decided what they should eat for dinner.
③ The participants haven't decided what did they eat for dinner.
④ The participants haven't decided what they ate for dinner.
⑤ The participants haven't decided what eating for dinner.

07 다음 괄호 안의 어휘들을 활용하여, 총 8단어로 우리말을 영작할 때 5번째로 들어갈 단어는?

> 언제 회의를 시작할지 그녀에게 알려 주세요.
> (when, the, meeting, let, know, to)

① her   ② the   ③ to
④ start   ⑤ when

08 다음 우리말을 바르게 영작한 것은?

① 우리는 경주를 세 번 방문했다.
　→ We have visiting Gyoungju three times.
② 영화 기생충을 본 적이 있습니까?
　→ Have you ever see the movie *Parasite*?
③ 그들은 부산에서 15년 동안 살고 있다.
　→ They have been living in Busan for 15 years.
④ 그녀는 3시간 동안 책을 읽고 있다.
　→ She has been reading a book since three hours.
⑤ Minsu는 전에 이탈리아 음식을 먹어 본 적이 있다.
　→ Minsu has been eating Italian food before.

09 다음 중 어법상 어색한 문장은?

① Has she told her husband what to buy for their parents?
② Does Michael know which to fix the oven?
③ After graduating from college, I couldn't decide what to do.
④ Ask the girl waiting for 3 hours which dress to buy.
⑤ I don't know where to go.

10 다음 중 어법상 옳은 것은?

① The lady has sitting next to the tree since this morning.
② The boy has been riding a bike for over 2 hours.
③ The owner of the shop has been having so much money.
④ Sandra has been losing her first job.
⑤ I have been made a cookie with no one helping me.

서답형

11 다음 대화의 밑줄 친 ⓐ~ⓔ 중 흐름상 어색한 것을 찾아 기호를 쓰고, 고치시오.

> A: ⓐHave you decided what to buy for your daughter's birthday present?
> B: ⓑI can't figure out what I should buy. How about making chocolate cookies?
> A: Wow, that's a great idea. ⓒDo you know how to make them?
> B: ⓓYes, but I don't know when to make the cookies.
> A: How about Peter's office? ⓔLet me ask him when we can use the place.

_____　➡　_____

12 다음 중 밑줄 친 부분의 쓰임이 〈보기〉와 같은 것은?

> ─┤ 보기 ├─
> Yumi <u>has been</u> to New York before.

① Emma's kids <u>have gone</u> to Egypt.
② Daniel <u>has not finished</u> his homework yet.
③ <u>Have</u> you and your family <u>lived</u> in Seoul since 1999?
④ Bob <u>has lost</u> all his money in gambling.
⑤ Park <u>has been elected</u> mayor twice.

13 다음 〈보기〉에서 어법상 옳은 문장은 모두 몇 개인가?

> ┤ 보기 ├
>
> a. Mom doesn't know what should say to her.
> b. Would you tell me why to come here?
> c. We don't know who to elect as chairman.
> d. They wondered where to going.
> e. Noah didn't know when to breathe while doing the swimming moves.
> f. Elephants know how to draw the flower.

① 1개   ② 2개   ③ 3개   ④ 4개   ⑤ 5개

14 다음 문장의 빈칸에 들어갈 말로 가장 알맞은 것은?

> The Amazon rainforest _____ for weeks due to a 'record number of fires' since September 12.

① burned
② is burning
③ was burning
④ has been burnt
⑤ has been burning

서답형

15 다음 〈보기〉에서 알맞은 동사를 한 번씩만 선택하여, 현재완료진행형으로 빈칸을 채워 문장을 완성하시오.

> ┤ 보기 ├
>
> learn   paint   listen   take   travel

(1) The youth expedition _____ in China since last Spring.
(2) Miranda _____ a foreign language for 5 years.
(3) The patient _____ the pill since she left the hospital last year.
(4) The driver _____ to the traffic radio program for 2 weeks.
(5) The students from the art high school _____ the village walls.

16 다음 문장의 빈칸에 들어갈 수 없는 것을 고르시오.

> The crowds in the square have been dancing to the K-pop _____.

① all this afternoon
② since 2 o'clock
③ up to now
④ for an hour
⑤ until 15 minutes ago

서답형

17 다음 우리말과 일치하도록 빈칸에 들어갈 알맞은 단어를 쓰시오.

(1) Vecky는 그녀의 생일 파티에 누구를 초대할지 결정하지 못했다.
  → Vecky hasn't decided _____ _____ _____ to her birthday party.
(2) 저희 레스토랑에 언제 방문할지 알려 주세요.
  → Let us know _____ _____ _____ our restaurant.
(3) 그녀에게 상황이 더 악화되기 전에 언제 멈출지 말하시오.
  → Tell her _____ _____ _____ before things get any worse.
(4) Mary는 성공하기 위해 누구를 만날지 고민 중이다.
  → Mary is wondering _____ _____ _____ in order to succeed.
(5) 나는 두 가지 중에서 어떤 방법을 선택해야 할지 알아낼 수가 없었다.
  → I couldn't figure out _____ _____ _____ between the two.
(6) Kelly는 왕궁에서 무슨 드레스를 입어야 할지 전혀 알 수 없었다.
  → Kelly had no idea _____ _____ _____ in the palace.

Grammar   **83**

01 각 괄호 안의 어구를 바르게 배열하여, 우리말을 영작하시오.

(1) 주자들은 8시간이 넘도록 체육관에서 계속 운동을 하고 있다.

(out / working / in / eight hours / the gym / been / for / the runners / over / have).

➡ _____

(2) Grace는 점심을 먹고 나서 30분간 계속 껌을 씹고 있는 중이다.

(has / after / a gum / been / Grace / chewing / 30 minutes / lunch / for).

➡ _____

(3) Patrick은 컴퓨터를 처음 산 이후, 계속 온라인으로 작곡을 하고 있다.

(he / Patrick / since / has / composing / first / online / been / a computer / bought).

➡ _____
_____

02 다음 그림을 보고, 우리말에 맞게 빈칸을 채우되, 괄호 안의 어휘를 이용하시오.

Roy has been wondering _____ and _____ _____ _____ between the two beverages.

(Roy는 두 음료 중에서 어느 것을, 그리고 어떻게 마실지 고민하고 있는 중이다.)

03 다음에 주어진 각각의 두 문장을 현재완료진행시제를 이용하여, 한 문장으로 쓰시오. 단, 반드시 전치사 for를 사용할 것.

(1) • Oliver started writing an email at 7:00 a.m. this morning.

• He keeps writing the email until noon.

→ Oliver _____
_____.

(2) • Sam began to learn Chinese in May 2017 for the first time in her life.

• As of May 2019, he is still learning Chinese as usual.

→ Sam _____
_____.

(3) • Mr. Yu started to practice playing the cello 4 months ago.

• He is still practicing these days.

→ Mr. Yu _____
_____.

04 다음 〈보기〉의 단어들을 활용하여 우리말에 맞게 영작하시오. (단, '의문사+to부정사' 형태를 반드시 사용할 것.)

┌─── 보기 ───┐
tell, teach, piano, use, play, laptop
└────────────┘

(1) Mason은 나에게 내 노트북을 사용하는 방법을 말해 주었다.

➡ _____

(2) 피아노를 어떻게 연주하는지 제게 가르쳐 주실 수 있나요?

➡ _____

05 다음 두 문장의 뜻이 자연스럽게 이어지도록 〈보기〉에서 필요한 단어를 선택하여, 조건에 맞게 빈칸을 완성하시오.

┤ 보기 ├

how	tell	play
which	know	read
when	teach	park my car
where	decide	visit

┤ 조건 ├

1. 각 단어는 한 번씩만 사용할 것.
2. 주어진 단어를 사용하여 완전한 문장을 만들되, '의문사+to부정사'를 포함할 것.
3. 문맥상 필요한 단어는 추가할 것.

(1) • I want to read both of the novels.
  • I can't _____ .

(2) • We don't know what time we should visit your office.
  • Please _____ .

(3) • Is there a parking place?
  • I don't _____ .

(4) • She wants to be a famous violinist.
  • Can you _____ ?

06 다음 현재완료진행형 문장을 두 문장으로 나눌 때 빈칸에 적절한 단어를 쓰시오.

(1) Shane has been looking after his mom for three years.
  ➡ • Shane began to _____ _____
  _____
  _____ .
  • Shane is still _____ _____ his mom.

(2) I have been watching birds for an hour.
  ➡ • I started to _____ _____
  _____ _____ .
  • I'm still _____ .

07 다음 세 문장을 〈조건〉에 맞게 한 문장으로 다시 쓰시오.

• Emma, Aiden's daughter, brought home her homework five hours ago.
• As soon as she arrived home, Emma asked her father to do her homework and Aiden started instead of his daughter.
• He is still doing her homework.

┤ 조건 ├

• 현재 Aiden의 상태를 현재완료진행형의 완전한 영어 문장으로 쓸 것.
• 접속사, 연결어, since 등은 사용하지 말 것.
• for / daughter's / Aiden을 반드시 포함하되, 총 10 단어를 초과하지 않을 것.

➡ _____
_____

08 다음 그림을 보고, 우리말에 맞게 빈칸을 채우되, 괄호 안의 어휘를 이용하시오.

Minju: Hey, Greg! Have you decided (A) _____ _____ _____? (join, club, 어느 클럽에 가입할지)

Greg: Not yet. I don't even know (B) _____ _____ _____ . (apply, 어디로 신청할지)

Minju: It is the student council office.

Greg: Let me know (C) _____ _____ _____ . (will, 네가 언제 신청할지)

Ask Dr. Money

The Green Middle School Times

Teens' Spending Habits

How smart are you <u>with</u> your money? These are the results of a survey of 100 students at Green Middle School.

We first asked students "Are you smart with your money?" <u>As</u> Graph 1 shows, 70% answered "No" while 30% answered "Yes." We <u>then</u> asked <u>the students who answered "No"</u> <u>what their biggest money worry is</u>. As Graph 2 shows, <u>60%</u> think they don't have enough allowance while 28% think they <u>have difficulty saving</u> money. Lastly, 12% said <u>they spent money on things they didn't need</u>. Our survey shows <u>that</u> the majority of students <u>think</u> they are not smart with their money. <u>Managing</u> money is not easy, and <u>becoming</u> a smart spender takes effort.

[Glossary]

habit 습관
result 결과
worry 걱정. 걱정거리
allowance 용돈
have difficulty -ing ~하는 데 어려움을 겪다
save 저축하다
majority 대다수
effort 노력

[Annotations under the reading text]
- with: ~에
- As: 접속사: ~이듯이, ~처럼
- then: 그 다음에
- the students who answered "No": asked의 간접목적어, who: 주격 관계대명사
- what their biggest money worry is: asked의 직접목적어
- 60%: 60% 뒤에는 of the students who answered "No" 생략
- have difficulty saving: ~하는데 비해 (비교, 대조) / 28% 뒤에는 of the students who answered "No" 생략 / have difficulty[trouble/a hard time/a problem] ~ing: ~하는 데 어려움을 겪다
- they spent money on things they didn't need: spend+돈+on: ~에 돈을 쓰다 / things 뒤에 목적격 관계대명사 that[which] 생략
- that: 접속사. shows의 목적어를 이끎
- think: think 뒤에 목적어 that절에서 접속사 that 생략
- Managing: 동명사 주어: '~하는 것'
- becoming: 동명사 주어: ~하는 것

확인문제

● 다음 문장이 본문의 내용과 일치하면 T, 일치하지 않으면 F를 쓰시오.

1 The Green Middle School Times first asked students "Are you smart with your money?" ☐

2 70% of the students answered "Yes" while 30% answered "No." ☐

3 60% of the students who answered "No" think they don't have enough allowance. ☐

4 28% of the students who answered "No" said they spent money on things they didn't need. ☐

5 The majority of students think they are not smart with their money. ☐

6 Managing money is not difficult. ☐

Do you have <u>any</u> money worries? Let's talk with Dr. Money.
주로 부정문이나 의문문에서 쓰이며 '약간의, 좀'이라는 의미

Q I'm Jason. I get a weekly allowance, but I never have enough. <u>By</u>
전치사 by+시간: ~쯤에는, ~까지는
Thursday, all of my money <u>is gone</u>. I don't know <u>how to solve</u> this
be gone: 사라지고 없다   how+to부정사: ~하는 방법, 어떻게 ~하는지
problem.

A Hi, I'm Dr. Money. Let's look at your spending diary. You used up
<u>most of</u> your money at the beginning of the week. Here's my tip. <u>Don't</u>
~의 대부분   부정명령문
carry around all of your weekly allowance. <u>Divide</u> the money <u>into</u>
divide A into B: A를 B로 나누다
days. Then carry only <u>the money you need</u> for each day.
money와 you 사이에 목적격 관계대명사 that 생략.

Q Hello, Dr. Money. I'm Steve. I have <u>difficulty saving</u> money. For
have difficulty[trouble/a hard time/a problem] ~ing: ~하는 데 어려움을 겪다
example, I've been saving <u>to go</u> to my favorite singer's concert for the
현재완료진행시제로 과거부터 현재까지 돈을 저   to go ~: to부정사의 부사적 용법(목적)
축해 오고 있다는 의미. 현재완료진행은 현재완료
(have+과거분사)보다 진행의 의미가 더 확실한 표현
last two months. However, I still don't have enough money. I don't
know <u>what to do</u>.
의문사+to부정사(what to do): 목적어 역할을 하고 있음. 무엇을 해야 할지

weekly 매주의
solve 해결하다
use up ~을 다 쓰다
tip 조언
carry around ~을 가지고 다니다
divide 나누다
for example 예를 들면

📎 **확인문제**

- 다음 문장이 본문의 내용과 일치하면 T, 일치하지 <u>않으면</u> F를 쓰시오.

1 Jason gets a weekly allowance, but he never has enough. ☐

2 By Tuesday, all of Jason's money is gone. ☐

3 Dr. Money advises Jason not to carry around all of his weekly allowance. ☐

4 Dr. Money advises Jason to divide the money into weeks. ☐

5 Steve has difficulty saving money. ☐

6 Steve has been saving to go to his favorite singer's concert for the last three months. ☐

A Let's see. In the last few weeks, you spent 80% of your allowance
어디 보자.

and only saved 20%. I think you've been spending too much.
현재완료진행시제는 과거부터 현재까지 어떤 행동이 지속된다는 의미.

To save money, you need to have a tighter budget. For example, you
to부정사의 부사적 용법(목적): 돈을 모으기 위해서

can follow the 50%-40%-10% rule. Save 50%, spend 40%, and donate
동사원형으로 시작하는 명령문. Save ~. spend ~. and donate의 동사가 병렬을 이룸.

the remaining 10% to charity. By following the rule, you can manage
by ~ing: ~함으로써

your money better. Then you can save money faster to buy the ticket.

Q I'm Minji. I like to buy things on sale. If something's on sale, I
on sale: 할인 중인   if: '만약 ~라면'의 뜻으로 조건을 나타내는 접속사

buy it although I don't need it. Last week, I bought two T-shirts on
although+절(주어 +동사): 비록 ~일지라도(접속사)

sale, but I already have many.
= many T-shirts

A Buying things on sale is good if you buy things you need.
동명사(주어)

In your case, the problem is that you buy things you don't even need.
in your case: 너의 경우에는   that 이하: 보어 역할을 하는 명사절   things 뒤에 목적격 관계대명사 생략

Here's some advice. Before you buy something, ask yourself, "Do I
Here is ~: ~가 여기 있다. 주어인 some advice와 동사 is가 도치됨. advice: 셀 수 없는 명사이므로, 단수 동사 is 사용. advices(×)

really need this?" Also, before you go shopping, make a shopping list.

Don't buy items that aren't on the list even if they're on sale. Then you
주격 관계대명사   even if+주어+동사: they: items that aren't on the list
                        ~라고 할지라도(접속사)

won't buy things on the spot.
즉각, 즉석에서

balance 잔액

tight 빠듯한

budget 예산

rule 법칙

donate 기부하다

remaining 남아 있는

charity 자선 단체

on sale 할인 중인

item 품목, 물건

on the spot 즉각, 즉석에서

📎 확인문제

● 다음 문장이 본문의 내용과 일치하면 T, 일치하지 않으면 F를 쓰시오.

1 To save money, Steve needs to have a tighter budget. ☐

2 The 50%-40%-10% rule means spending 50%, saving 40%, and donating the remaining 10% to charity. ☐

3 Minji likes to buy things on sale. ☐

4 If Minji needs something, she buys it though it's not on sale. ☐

5 In Minji's case, the problem is that she buys things she doesn't even need. ☐

6 Though the items aren't on the list, Minji must buy them if they're on sale. ☐

● 우리말을 참고하여 빈칸에 알맞은 말을 쓰시오.

1 _____ Dr. Money

2 **The Green Middle School** _____

3 **Teens'** _____ _____

4 _____ _____ are you with your money?

5 These are the results of _____ _____ of 100 students at Green Middle School.

6 We first asked students "Are you _____ _____ your money?"

7 _____ Graph 1 shows, 70% answered "No" _____ 30% answered "Yes."

8 We then asked the students who answered "No" what their _____ _____ _____ is.

9 _____ Graph 2 shows, 60% think they don't have _____ _____ while 28% think they _____ _____ _____ money.

10 _____, 12% said they _____ money _____ things they didn't need.

11 Our survey shows that _____ _____ of students think they are not _____ _____ their money.

12 _____ money is not easy, and _____ a smart spender takes effort.

13 Do you have any _____ _____?

14 Let's _____ _____ Dr. Money.

15 _____ Jason.

1 Dr. Money에게 물어보세요.

2 그린 중학교 타임스

3 10대들의 소비 습관

4 당신은 돈에 관해 얼마나 현명한가?

5 이것은 Green 중학교 학생 100명의 설문 조사 결과이다.

6 우리는 먼저 학생들에게 "당신은 돈에 관하여 현명한가?"라고 물었다.

7 그래프 1이 보여 주듯이, 30%가 "예"라고 대답한 반면 70%가 "아니요"라고 답했다.

8 그 다음 우리는 "아니요"라고 대답한 학생들에게 그들의 돈에 대한 가장 큰 고민이 무엇인지 물었다.

9 그래프 2가 보여주듯이 28%가 자신들이 돈을 모으는 것에 어려움이 있다고 생각하는 반면, 60%는 충분한 용돈을 받지 못한다고 생각한다.

10 마지막으로, 12%는 필요하지 않은 것에 돈을 소비했다고 말했다.

11 우리의 설문 조사는 대다수의 학생들이 자신들이 돈에 관련하여 현명하지 못하다고 생각한다는 것을 보여준다.

12 돈을 관리하는 것은 쉽지 않고 현명한 소비자가 되는 것에는 노력이 필요하다.

13 여러분은 돈과 관련된 걱정거리가 있는가?

14 Dr. Money와 이야기해 보자.

15 저는 Jason이에요.

16 I get a _____ _____, but I never have _____.

17 By Thursday, all of my money _____ _____.

18 I don't know _____ _____ _____ this problem.

19 Hi, _____ Dr. Money.

20 Let's look at your _____ _____.

21 You _____ _____ most of your money _____ _____ _____ of the week.

22 Here's _____ _____.

23 Don't _____ _____ all of your weekly allowance.

24 _____ the money _____ days.

25 Then _____ only the money you need _____ _____ _____.

26 _____, Dr. Money.

27 _____ Steve.

28 I _____ _____ _____ money.

29 For example, _____ _____ _____ to go to my favorite singer's concert _____ _____ _____ _____ _____.

30 _____, I _____ _____ have enough money.

31 I don't know _____ _____ _____.

32 _____ _____.

33 _____ _____ _____ _____ weeks, you spent 80% of your allowance and only saved 20%.

34 I think _____ _____ _____ too much.

16 저는 매주 용돈을 받지만, 절대로 충분하지 않아요.

17 목요일쯤이면 용돈이 모두 사라져요.

18 이 문제를 해결할 방법을 모르겠어요.

19 안녕하세요, Dr. Money입니다.

20 용돈 기입장을 한번 봅시다.

21 주의 초반에 용돈의 대부분을 다 썼군요.

22 이게 내 조언이에요.

23 일주일 용돈 전부를 가지고 다니지 마세요.

24 용돈을 하루 단위로 나누세요.

25 그리고 하루에 필요한 돈만 들고 다니세요.

26 안녕하세요, Dr. Money.

27 저는 Steve예요.

28 저는 돈을 모으기가 어려워요.

29 예를 들면, 저는 좋아하는 가수의 콘서트에 가려고 지난 두 달 동안 돈을 저축해 오고 있어요.

30 하지만 저는 여전히 충분한 돈을 가지고 있지 않아요.

31 어떻게 해야 할지 모르겠어요.

32 어디 봅시다.

33 지난 몇 주에 용돈의 80%를 사용하고 20%만을 저축했군요.

34 나는 Steve가 돈을 너무 많이 써 왔다고 생각해요.

35 To save money, you need to _____ _____ _____ _____.

36 For example, you can follow _____ _____ _____.

37 Save 50%, spend 40%, and _____ _____ _____ 10% to charity.

38 _____ _____ the rule, you can _____ your money _____.

39 Then you can save money _____ _____ _____ the ticket.

40 _____ Minji.

41 I like to buy things _____ _____.

42 If something's on sale, I buy it _____ I don't need it.

43 Last week, I bought two T-shirts on sale, but I _____ _____ many.

44 Buying things on sale is good if you buy _____ _____ _____.

45 _____ _____ _____, the problem is that you buy things you _____ _____ _____.

46 _____ some advice.

47 Before you buy something, _____ _____, "Do I really need this?"

48 Also, before you _____ _____, make a shopping list.

49 Don't buy items that aren't _____ _____ _____ even if they're on sale.

50 Then you won't buy things _____ _____ _____.

35	돈을 모으기 위해서, 더 빠듯한 예산을 세우는 것이 필요해요.
36	예를 들어, Steve는 50%-40%-10%의 규칙을 따를 수 있어요.
37	50%를 저축하고, 40%를 쓰고, 남아 있는 10%를 자선 단체에 기부하세요.
38	이 규칙을 따름으로써 돈을 더 잘 관리할 수 있어요.
39	그러면 그 티켓을 사기 위해 돈을 더 빨리 모을 수 있답니다.
40	저는 민지입니다.
41	저는 할인 판매하는 물건을 사는 것을 좋아해요.
42	어떤 물건이 할인 판매를 하면 저는 그것이 필요하지 않더라도 사요.
43	지난주에는 할인 판매하는 티셔츠 두 장을 샀지만 이미 많이 가지고 있었어요.
44	민지가 필요한 물건을 산다면 할인 판매하는 물건을 사는 것은 좋습니다.
45	민지의 경우에, 문제점은 필요하지 않은 물건도 산다는 거예요.
46	여기 몇 가지 조언이 있어요.
47	민지는 무언가를 사기 전에 "이것이 정말 필요한가?"라고 스스로에게 물어보세요.
48	또한 쇼핑하러 가기 전에 쇼핑 목록을 만드세요.
49	만약 물건들이 할인 판매 중이라고 해도 목록에 없는 물건들은 사지 마세요.
50	그러면 즉석에서 물건을 사지 않게 될 거예요.

● 우리말을 참고하여 본문을 영작하시오.

1 ▶ Dr. Money에게 물어보세요.

➡ _____

2 ▶ 그린 중학교 타임스

➡ _____

3 ▶ 10대들의 소비 습관

➡ _____

4 ▶ 당신은 돈에 관해 얼마나 현명한가?

➡ _____

5 ▶ 이것은 Green 중학교 학생 100명의 설문 조사 결과이다.

➡ _____

6 ▶ 우리는 먼저 학생들에게 "당신은 돈에 관하여 현명한가?"라고 물었다.

➡ _____

7 ▶ 그래프 1이 보여 주듯이, 30%가 "예"라고 대답한 반면 70%가 "아니요"라고 답했다.

➡ _____

8 ▶ 그 다음 우리는 "아니요"라고 대답한 학생들에게 그들의 돈에 대한 가장 큰 고민이 무엇인지 물었다.

➡ _____

9 ▶ 그래프 2가 보여주듯이 28%가 자신들이 돈을 모으는 것에 어려움이 있다고 생각하는 반면, 60%는 충분한 용돈을 받지 못한다고 생각한다.

➡ _____

_____

10 ▶ 마지막으로, 12%는 필요하지 않은 것에 돈을 소비했다고 말했다.

➡ _____

11 ▶ 우리의 설문 조사는 대다수의 학생들이 자신들이 돈에 관련하여 현명하지 못하다고 생각한다는 것을 보여준다.

➡ _____

12 ▶ 돈을 관리하는 것은 쉽지 않고 현명한 소비자가 되는 것에는 노력이 필요하다.

➡ _____

13 ▶ 여러분은 돈과 관련된 걱정거리가 있는가?

➡ _____

14 ▶ Dr. Money와 이야기해 보자.

➡ _____

15 ▶ 저는 Jason이에요.

➡ _____

16 저는 매주 용돈을 받지만, 절대로 충분하지 않아요.

➡ _____

17 목요일쯤이면 용돈이 모두 사라져요.

➡ _____

18 이 문제를 해결할 방법을 모르겠어요.

➡ _____

19 안녕하세요, Dr. Money입니다.

➡ _____

20 용돈 기입장을 한번 봅시다.

➡ _____

21 주의 초반에 용돈의 대부분을 다 썼군요.

➡ _____

22 이게 내 조언이에요.

➡ _____

23 일주일 용돈 전부를 가지고 다니지 마세요.

➡ _____

24 용돈을 하루 단위로 나누세요.

➡ _____

25 그리고 하루에 필요한 돈만 들고 다니세요.

➡ _____

26 안녕하세요, Dr. Money.

➡ _____

27 저는 Steve예요.

➡ _____

28 저는 돈을 모으기가 어려워요.

➡ _____

29 예를 들면, 저는 좋아하는 가수의 콘서트에 가려고 지난 두 달 동안 돈을 저축해 오고 있어요.

➡ _____

30 하지만 저는 여전히 충분한 돈을 가지고 있지 않아요.

➡ _____

31 어떻게 해야 할지 모르겠어요.

➡ _____

32 어디 봅시다.

➡ _____

33 지난 몇 주에 용돈의 80%를 사용하고 20%만을 저축했군요.
➡ _____

34 나는 Steve가 돈을 너무 많이 써 왔다고 생각해요.
➡ _____

35 돈을 모으기 위해서, 더 빠듯한 예산을 세우는 것이 필요해요.
➡ _____

36 예를 들어, Steve는 50%-40%-10%의 규칙을 따를 수 있어요.
➡ _____

37 50%를 저축하고, 40%를 쓰고, 남아 있는 10%를 자선 단체에 기부하세요.
➡ _____

38 이 규칙을 따름으로써 돈을 더 잘 관리할 수 있어요.
➡ _____

39 그러면 그 티켓을 사기 위해 돈을 더 빨리 모을 수 있답니다.
➡ _____

40 저는 민지입니다.
➡ _____

41 저는 할인 판매하는 물건을 사는 것을 좋아해요.
➡ _____

42 어떤 물건이 할인 판매를 하면 저는 그것이 필요하지 않더라도 사요.
➡ _____

43 지난주에는 할인 판매하는 티셔츠 두 장을 샀지만 이미 많이 가지고 있었어요.
➡ _____

44 민지가 필요한 물건을 산다면 할인 판매하는 물건을 사는 것은 좋습니다.
➡ _____

45 민지의 경우에, 문제점은 필요하지 않은 물건도 산다는 거예요.
➡ _____

46 여기 몇 가지 조언이 있어요.
➡ _____

47 민지는 무언가를 사기 전에 "이것이 정말 필요한가?"라고 스스로에게 물어보세요.
➡ _____

48 또한 쇼핑하러 가기 전에 쇼핑 목록을 만드세요.
➡ _____

49 만약 물건들이 할인 판매 중이라고 해도 목록에 없는 물건들은 사지 마세요.
➡ _____

50 그러면 즉석에서 물건을 사지 않게 될 거예요.
➡ _____

[01~03] 다음 글을 읽고 물음에 답하시오.

The Green Middle School Times
Teens' Spending Habits

How smart are you ___ⓐ___ your money? These are the results of a survey of 100 students at Green Middle School.

We first asked students "Are you smart ___ⓐ___ your money?" As Graph 1 shows, 70% answered "No" while 30% answered "Yes." We then asked the students who answered "No" what their biggest money worry is. As Graph 2 shows, 60% think they don't have enough allowance while 28% think they have difficulty saving money. Lastly, 12% said they spent money ___ⓑ___ things they didn't need.

01 위 글의 빈칸 ⓐ와 ⓑ에 들어갈 전치사가 바르게 짝지어진 것은?

	ⓐ	ⓑ		ⓐ	ⓑ
①	from	on	②	with	to
③	from	at	④	for	to
⑤	with	on			

02 위 글의 종류로 알맞은 것을 고르시오.

① essay   ② article

③ summary   ④ review

⑤ book report

서답형

03 How many students answered the first question in the negative? Fill in the blank with a suitable word.

_____ students did so.

[04~06] 다음 글을 읽고 물음에 답하시오.

Q Hello, Dr. Money. I'm Steve. I have difficulty saving money. ___ⓐ___, I've been saving to go to my favorite singer's concert for the last two months. However, I still don't have enough money. I don't know what to do.

A Let's see. In the last few weeks, you spent 80% of your allowance and only saved 20%. I think you've been spending too much. To save money, you need to have a tighter budget. For example, you can follow ⓑthe 50%-40%-10% rule. Save 50%, spend 40%, and donate the remaining 10% to charity. By following the rule, you can manage your money better. Then you can save money faster to buy the ticket.

04 위 글의 빈칸 ⓐ에 들어갈 알맞은 말을 고르시오.

① For example   ② In addition

③ Therefore   ④ However

⑤ That is

서답형

05 위 글의 밑줄 친 ⓑ가 의미하는 것을 우리말로 쓰시오.

➡ _____

_____

서답형

06 본문의 내용과 일치하도록 다음 빈칸 (A)와 (B)에 알맞은 단어를 쓰시오.

Dr. Money advises Steve to increase savings ratio from (A)_____% to (B)_____% of his allowance.

*savings ratio: 저축률

[07~09] 다음 글을 읽고 물음에 답하시오.

Do you have any money worries? Let's talk with Dr. Money.

Ⓠ I'm Jason. I get a weekly allowance, but I never have enough. By Thursday, all of my money is gone. I don't know how to solve this problem.

Ⓐ Hi, I'm Dr. Money. (①) Let's look at your spending diary. (②) You used up most of your money at the beginning of the week. (③) Here's my tip. (④) Divide the money into days. (⑤) Then carry only the money you need for each day.

07 위 글의 흐름으로 보아, 주어진 문장이 들어가기에 가장 적절한 곳은?

Don't carry around all of your weekly allowance.

①   ②   ③   ④   ⑤

08 위 글의 제목으로 알맞은 것을 고르시오.

① By Thursday, I'm Broke!
② Never Have Enough Allowance? Divide It into Days!
③ Let's Look at Your Spending Diary
④ How about Asking for More Allowance?
⑤ How to Save Your Allowance

09 According to the passage, which is NOT true?

① Jason gets a weekly allowance, but he thinks he never has enough.
② By Tuesday, all of Jason's money is gone.
③ Dr. Money found out Jason used up most of his money at the beginning of the week.

④ Dr. Money advised Jason not to carry around all of his weekly allowance.
⑤ Dr. Money advised Jason to divide the money into days and carry only the money he needs for each day.

10 주어진 글 다음에 이어질 글의 순서로 가장 적절한 것은?

How smart are you with your money? These are the results of a survey of 100 students at Green Middle School.

(A) We then asked the students who answered "No" what their biggest money worry is.

(B) We first asked students "Are you smart with your money?" As Graph 1 shows, 70% answered "No" while 30% answered "Yes."

(C) As Graph 2 shows, 60% think they don't have enough allowance while 28% think they have difficulty saving money. Lastly, 12% said they spent money on things they didn't need.

① (A) – (C) – (B)   ② (B) – (A) – (C)
③ (B) – (C) – (A)   ④ (C) – (A) – (B)
⑤ (C) – (B) – (A)

[11~12] 다음 글을 읽고 물음에 답하시오.

The Green Middle School Times
Teens' Spending Habits

How smart are you with your money? These are the results of a survey of 100 students at Green Middle School.

We first asked students "Are you smart with your money?" ⓐAs Graph 1 shows, 70% answered "No" while 30% answered "Yes." We then asked the students who answered

"No" what their biggest money worry is. As Graph 2 shows, 60% think they don't have enough allowance while 28% think they have difficulty saving money. Lastly, 12% said they spent money on things they didn't need.

11 위 글의 밑줄 친 ⓐAs와 문법적 쓰임 및 뜻이 같은 것을 고르시오.

① As it was getting dark, we soon turned back.
② He treats me as a child.
③ As rust eats iron, so care eats the heart.
④ As spring comes, the birds move northward.
⑤ I love you as much as I love her.

서답형

12 본문의 내용과 일치하도록 다음 빈칸에 알맞은 숫자를 영어로 쓰시오.

> The percent of the students who think they don't have enough allowance is _____ times as large as that of the students who said they spent money on things they didn't need.

[13~16] 다음 글을 읽고 물음에 답하시오.

A Let's see. In the last few weeks, you spent 80% of your allowance and only saved 20%. I think you've been spending too much. To save money, you need to have ___ⓐ___. For example, you can follow the 50%-40%-10% rule. Save 50%, spend 40%, and donate the remaining 10% to charity. By following the rule, you can manage your money better. Then you can save money faster to buy the ticket.

13 위 글의 빈칸 ⓐ에 들어갈 알맞은 말을 고르시오.

① a looser budget
② a tighter deposit
③ a looser plan
④ a tighter budget
⑤ a tighter payment

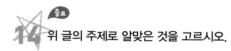 위 글의 주제로 알맞은 것을 고르시오.

① the easier way to save money
② to follow the 50%-40%-10% rule in order to save money
③ various reasons to save money
④ enough allowance to buy the ticket
⑤ the difficulty of saving money by following the 50%-40%-10% rule

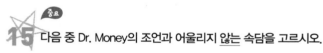 다음 중 Dr. Money의 조언과 어울리지 <u>않는</u> 속담을 고르시오.

① Every little helps.
② Little drops of water make the mighty ocean.
③ Penny-wise and pound-foolish.
④ Many a little makes a mickle.
⑤ Little brooks make great rivers.

서답형

16 본문의 내용과 일치하도록 다음 빈칸 (A)와 (B)에 알맞은 단어를 쓰시오.

> Dr. Money advises Steve to cut back on spending from (A)_____% to (B)_____% of his allowance.
>
> *cut back on: ~을 줄이다

[17~19] 다음 글을 읽고 물음에 답하시오.

Ⓠ I'm Minji. I like to buy things on sale. If something's on sale, I buy it although I don't need it. Last week, I bought two T-shirts on sale, but I already have many.

Ⓐ Buying things on sale is good if you buy things you need. In your case, the problem is that you buy things you don't even need. Here's some advice. Before you buy something, ask ⓐyourself, "Do I really need this?" Also, before you go shopping, make a shopping list. Don't buy items that aren't on the list even if ⓑthey're on sale. Then you won't buy things on the spot.

17 위 글의 밑줄 친 ⓐyourself와 문법적 쓰임이 같은 것을 모두 고르시오.

① You must love yourself.
② I heard that you yourself made it.
③ Can you imagine yourself as a fish?
④ You must do it yourself.
⑤ You must be proud of yourself.

서답형
18 위 글의 밑줄 친 ⓑthey가 가리키는 것을 본문에서 찾아 쓰시오.

➡ _____

서답형
19 다음 빈칸 (A)와 (B)에 알맞은 단어를 넣어 민지의 돈에 대한 고민과 Ⓐ의 조언을 완성하시오.

Minji's Worry: If something's (A)_____ _____, I buy it although I don't need it. Last week, I bought two T-shirts on sale, but I already have many.
The Advice: Make (B)_____ _____ _____ before you go shopping. Don't buy items that aren't on the list.

[20~22] 다음 글을 읽고 물음에 답하시오.

Do you have any money worries? Let's talk with Dr. Money.

Ⓠ I'm Jason. I get a weekly allowance, but I never have enough. By Thursday, all of my money (A)[is disappeared / is gone]. I don't know how to solve ⓐthis problem.

Ⓐ Hi, I'm Dr. Money. Let's look at your spending diary. You used up (B)[almost / most] of your money at the beginning of the week. Here's my tip. Don't carry around all of your weekly allowance. (C)[Add / Divide] the money into days. Then carry only the money you need for each day.

20 위 글의 괄호 (A)~(C)에서 문맥이나 어법상 알맞은 낱말을 골라 쓰시오.

➡ (A) _____ (B) _____ (C) _____

서답형
21 위 글의 밑줄 친 ⓐthis problem이 가리키는 것을 본문에서 찾아 쓰시오.

➡ _____

22 다음 중 위 글의 내용을 바르게 이해하지 못한 사람을 고르시오.

① 경미: Jason gets an allowance once a week.
② 성민: But he uses up the money by Thursday.
③ 규식: The problem is that though he knows what he should do, he doesn't practice it.
④ 나영: Dr. Money advises him not to carry around all of his weekly allowance.
⑤ 덕수: Dr. Money tells him to carry only the money he needs for each day.

[23~25] 다음 글을 읽고 물음에 답하시오.

The Green Middle School Times
Teens' Spending Habits

How smart are you with your money? These are the results of a survey of 100 students at Green Middle School.

We first asked students "Are you smart with your money?" As Graph 1 shows, ⓐ70% answered "No" while 30% answered "Yes." We then asked the students who answered "No" what their biggest money worry is. ⓑ As Graph 2 shows, 60% thinks they don't have enough allowance while 28% thinks they have difficulty saving money. Lastly, 12% said they spent money on things they didn't need.

서답형

23 위 글의 밑줄 친 ⓐ를 다음과 같이 바꿔 쓸 때 빈칸에 들어갈 알맞은 말을 두 단어로 쓰시오.

➡ 70% answered "in _____ _____" while 30% answered "in the affirmative."

서답형

24 위 글의 밑줄 친 ⓑ에서 어법상 틀린 부분을 찾아 고치시오.
(두 군데)

_____ ➡ _____
_____ ➡ _____

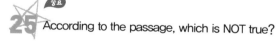

According to the passage, which is NOT true?

① The text above shows the results of a survey of 100 students at Green Middle School.

② 30 students answered they were smart with their money.

③ The biggest money worry of three-fifths of the students who answered "No" is that they don't have enough allowance.

④ More than one third of the students who answered "No" have difficulty saving money.

⑤ 12% of the students who answered "No" said they spent money on things they didn't need.

[26~28] 다음 글을 읽고 물음에 답하시오.

The Green Middle School Times
Teens' Spending Habits

How smart are you with your money? These are the ①results of a survey of 100 students at Green Middle School.

We first asked ⓐstudents "Are you smart with your money?" As Graph 1 shows, 70% answered "No" ②while 30% answered "Yes." We then asked the students who answered "No" what ⓑtheir biggest money worry is. As Graph 2 shows, ⓒ60% think they don't have enough ③allowance while 28% think they have difficulty ④saving money. ⑤ Lastly, 12% said they spent money on things they didn't need.

26 위 글의 밑줄 친 ①~⑤와 바꿔 쓸 수 있는 말로 옳지 않은 것을 고르시오.

① outcomes   ② whereas
③ pocket money   ④ rescuing
⑤ Finally

서답형

27 위 글의 밑줄 친 ⓐstudents와 ⓑtheir가 가리키는 것을 각각 본문에서 찾아 쓰시오.

➡ ⓐ _____
   ⓑ _____

서답형

28 위 글의 밑줄 친 ⓒ60%를 분수로 표현하여 읽는 법을 영어로 쓰시오.

➡ _____

[01~04] 다음 글을 읽고 물음에 답하시오.

The Green Middle School Times
Teens' Spending Habits

How smart are you with your money? These are the results of a survey of 100 students at Green Middle School.

We first asked students "Are you smart with your money?" (A)[As / Since] Graph 1 shows, 70% answered "No" while 30% answered "Yes." We then asked the students (B)[what / who] answered "No" what their biggest money worry is. As Graph 2 shows, 60% think they don't have enough allowance while 28% think they have ⓐdifficulty saving money. (C)[At last / Lastly], 12% said they spent money on things they didn't need.

01 위 글의 괄호 (A)~(C)에서 문맥이나 어법상 알맞은 낱말을 골라 쓰시오.

➡ (A) _____ (B) _____ (C) _____

02 위 글의 밑줄 친 ⓐdifficulty와 바꿔 쓸 수 있는 말을 쓰시오.

➡ _____

03 How many students think they don't have enough allowance? Fill in the blank with a suitable word.

_____ students do so.

04 위 글의 내용을 다음과 같이 정리하고자 한다. 빈칸 (A)와 (B)에 들어갈 알맞은 말을 본문의 단어를 이용하여 쓰시오.

70 students among 100 students at Green Middle School don't spend money in a (A)_____ way, and they have (B)_____ _____ like not having enough allowance, having difficulty saving money and spending money on things they don't need.

[05~07] 다음 글을 읽고 물음에 답하시오.

Do you have any money worries? Let's talk with Dr. Money.

Ⓠ I'm Jason. I get a weekly allowance, but I never have enough. By Thursday, all of my money is gone. ⓐI don't know how to solve this problem.

Ⓐ Hi, I'm Dr. Money. Let's look at your spending diary. You used up most of your money at the beginning of the week. Here's my tip. Don't carry around all of your weekly allowance. Divide the money into days. ⓑ그리고 하루에 필요한 돈만 들고 다니세요.

05 위 글의 밑줄 친 ⓐ를 다음과 같이 바꿔 쓸 때 빈칸에 들어갈 알맞은 말을 두 단어로 쓰시오.

➡ I don't know how _____ _____ solve this problem.

06 위 글의 밑줄 친 ⓑ의 우리말에 맞게 주어진 어휘를 알맞게 배열하시오.

each day / you / the money / then / only / for / carry / need

➡ _____

07 다음 빈칸 (A)와 (B)에 알맞은 단어를 넣어 Jason의 돈에 대한 고민과 Dr. Money의 조언을 완성하시오.

> Jason's Worry: I get an allowance, but I (A)_____ _____ _____. By Thursday, all of my money is gone.
>
> Dr. Money's Advice: Don't carry around all of weekly allowance. (B)_____ the money into days and take only one day's portion with you.
>
> *one day's portion: 하루치

[08~09] 다음 글을 읽고 물음에 답하시오.

> A Let's see. In the last few weeks, you spent 80% of your allowance and only saved 20%. I think you've been spending too much. ⓐ 돈을 모으기 위해서, 더 빠듯한 예산을 세우는 것이 필요해요. For example, you can follow the 50%-40%-10% rule. Save 50%, spend 40%, and donate the remaining 10% to charity. By following the rule, you can manage your money better. Then you can save money faster to buy the ticket.   <you: Steve>

08 위 글의 밑줄 친 ⓐ의 우리말에 맞게 주어진 어휘를 이용하여 10 단어로 영작하시오.

> save, have, tighter

➡ _____

또는 _____

09 Steve의 일주일 용돈이 만원인 경우, 다음 빈칸 ①~⑥에 들어갈 알맞은 숫자를 쓰시오.

	지난 몇 주의 예산	충고 내용
save	①_____ 원	②_____ 원
spend	③_____ 원	④_____ 원
donate	⑤_____ 원	⑥_____ 원

[10~11] 다음 글을 읽고 물음에 답하시오.

> A Buying things on sale is good if you buy things you need. In your case, the problem is that you buy things you don't even need. Here's some advice. Before you buy something, ask yourself, "Do I really need this?" Also, before you go shopping, make a shopping list. Don't buy items that aren't on the list even if they're on sale. Then you won't buy things on the spot.. <you: Minji>

10 What does Minji have to do? Fill in the blanks (A) and (B) with suitable words.

➡ (1) Before she buys something: She has to (A)_____ _____, "Do I really need this?"

(2) Before she goes shopping: She has to (B)_____ _____ _____ list.

11 위 글의 내용과 일치하도록 아래 문장의 괄호 (A)~(C)에서 각각 알맞은 낱말을 고르시오.

> Minji (A)[should / should not] buy an item (B)[if / even if] it is on sale (C)[if / though] it is not on her shopping list.

➡ (A) _____ (B) _____ (C) _____

After You Read C

Teens' Money Worries and Dr. Money's Advice

Jason's Worry: I get an allowance, but I never have enough. By Thursday, all
전치사 by+시간: ~쯤에는, ~까지는

of my money is gone.
be gone: 사라지고 없다

Dr. Money's Advice: Don't carry around all of weekly allowance. Divide the
divide A into B: A를 B로 나누다

money into days and carry only the money you need for each day.
money와 you 사이에 목적격 관계대명사 생략.

구문해설 · worry: 걱정거리 · allowance: 용돈 · weekly: 매주의 · divide: 나누다

십대들의 돈과 관련된 걱정거리와 **Dr. Money**의 조언

Jason의 걱정거리: 저는 매주 용돈을 받지만, 절대로 충분하지 않아요. 목요일쯤이면 용돈이 모두 사라져요.

Dr. Money의 조언: 일주일 용돈 전부를 가지고 다니지 마세요. 용돈을 하루 단위로 나누고 하루에 필요한 돈만 들고 다니세요.

Language in Use A

1. The computer I bought on sale was very cheap.
computer와 I 사이에 목적격 관계대명사 that[which] 생략

2. It is foolish to go camping during the rainy season.
가주어 →smart 진주어 during 다음에는 기간을 나타내는 명사가 온다.

3. My jeans are too tight, so I am going to exchange them for a bigger size.
부사(너무) 결과를 나타내는 절을 이끄는 접속사 exchange A for B: A를 B로 교환하다

구문해설 · on sale: 할인 중인, 판매되는 · go camping: 캠핑을 가다 · rainy season: 우기

1. 할인 중에 산 컴퓨터는 매우 값이 쌌다.

2. 우기에 캠핑을 가는 것은 어리석다.

3. 내 청바지가 너무 꽉 끼여서 나는 그것을 더 큰 사이즈로 교환할 것이다.

Think and Write

My money problem is that I buy things on the spot. One time, I bought a
접속사(명사절)-보어 역할 전치사+명사

smartphone case because it looked nice. However, I found out that I already
접속사(부사절)-이유 2형식 동사+형용사 접속사(명사절)-목적어 역할

had three cases at home. I don't know how to stop buying things on the spot.
의문사+to부정사(명사구) stop+동명사 목적어(~하는 것을 멈추다)

구문해설 · on the spot: 즉석에서, 현장에서 · find out: 알게 되다, 알아내다

나의 돈과 관련된 고민은 즉석에서 물건을 산다는 것이다. 한번은, 나는 스마트폰 케이스가 좋아 보여서 그것을 샀다. 하지만, 집에 와서는 내가 이미 케이스를 세 개 갖고 있다는 것을 발견했다. 나는 즉석에서 물건을 사는 것을 어떻게 멈출 수 있는지 모르겠다.

Words & Expressions

01 〈보기〉의 밑줄 친 어휘와 같은 의미로 쓰이지 <u>않은</u> 것을 고르시오.

┌─ 보기 ─┐

As we look deeply within, we understand our perfect <u>balance</u>.

① You can check your bank <u>balance</u> on the Internet.
② You need to try to keep a <u>balance</u> between work and play.
③ Athletes need a good sense of <u>balance</u>.
④ At that moment he lost his <u>balance</u> and fell.
⑤ The impact of the blow knocked Jack off <u>balance</u>.

02 다음 영영풀이에 해당하는 단어를 주어진 철자로 시작하여 빈칸에 쓰고, 알맞은 것을 골라 문장을 완성하시오.

• c_____: an organization that gives money or help to people who need it
• e_____: the act of giving someone something and receiving something else from them

(1) He founded the _____ in memory of his late wife.
(2) The _____ of prisoners took place this morning.

03 다음 대화의 빈칸에 〈영영풀이〉에 해당하는 단어를 쓰시오.

A: How much are these apples?
B: They're _____, so they're very cheap now.

<영영풀이> being offered at a reduced price

➡ _____

04 괄호 안에 주어진 어휘를 이용하여 빈칸에 알맞게 쓰시오.

• I'll let you be a big _____ next time. (spend)
• I receive an _____ from my parents. (allow)

05 다음 빈칸 (A)~(C)에 알맞은 말을 쓰시오. (주어진 철자로 시작하여 쓸 것.)

• I want her to eat these and fall asleep. But I'm having so much (A)d_____ selling them.
• I think it is (B)f_____ to buy such a trash.
• These shoes are much too (C)t_____, so I am going to exchange them for a bigger size.

Conversation

[06~08] 다음 대화를 읽고 물음에 답하시오.

(A) OK. Was there anything wrong with it?

(B) Yes, please. (a)I'd like to return this baseball glove.

(C) No, I just changed my mind. Can I have my money back?

(D) Hello. May I help you?

W: OK. (b)Here's your money.

06 주어진 문장 앞에 나올 대화의 순서로 알맞은 것은?

① (B) – (A) – (C) – (D)

② (C) – (B) – (A) – (D)

③ (D) – (A) – (C) – (B)

④ (D) – (B) – (A) – (C)

⑤ (D) – (B) – (C) – (A)

07 위 대화의 밑줄 친 (a)와 같은 뜻의 문장을 괄호 안에 주어진 어휘를 이용하여 쓰시오.

➡ _____

(a refund, get, like to)

08 위 대화의 밑줄 친 (b)와 같은 뜻의 문장을 3 단어로 두 개를 쓰시오.

➡ _____, _____

09 다음 중 짝지어진 대화가 <u>어색한</u> 것은?

① A: Can I help you?

B: Yes. I'd like to exchange this yellow T-shirt. It's too small for me.

② A: Can I get a refund for this hat?

B: I'm afraid you can.

③ A: Can I exchange this necktie for the gloves over there?

B: Sure. What would you like?

④ A: I'd like to get a refund for this T-shirt.

B: I'm afraid you can't return it.

⑤ A: Was there anything wrong with it?

B: No, I just changed my mind.

[10~13] 다음 대화를 읽고 물음에 답하시오.

B: _____(A)_____ I'd like to exchange this T-shirt for these pants.

W: OK. (B)티셔츠에 무슨 문제가 있나요? (there, wrong, it)

B: I don't like the color.

W: I see.

10 주어진 〈영영풀이〉를 참고하여 위 대화의 빈칸 (A)에 알맞은 말을 쓰시오.

〈영영풀이〉

This expression is used

(1) before you do or say something that might annoy somebody, or to get somebody's attention

(2) when you are leaving the room for a short time

➡ _____

11 Why does the boy want to exchange the T-shirt?

➡ _____

12 밑줄 친 (B)의 우리말을 영작하시오.

➡ _____

13 위 대화의 내용과 일치하는 것은?

① 소년은 티셔츠를 맘에 들어 하고 있다.

② 소년은 환불을 요청하고 있다.

③ 여자는 교환을 거절하고 있다.

④ 여자는 티셔츠의 문제를 이미 알고 있었다.

⑤ 소년과 여자는 상점에서 대화를 나누고 있다.

Grammar

14 다음 중 어법상 올바른 문장은?

① Sophia didn't know why to fish the small octopus.

② Robert couldn't decide when they to do next.

③ Don't ask the people where to wait for the singer.

④ I don't even know where to starting.

⑤ They learned how they should using the photocopier.

15 다음 두 문장을 현재완료진행시제를 이용하여 한 문장으로 만드시오.

- Isabelle began to study wild animals in Africa 11 years ago.
- She is still studying them now.

➡ Isabelle _____

_____ .

16 다음 주어진 문장의 밑줄 친 부분과 의미가 같은 것은?

Sir, let me know <u>when to start training</u>.

① I will let you know when you should start training

② please let me know when you started training

③ I know when I should start training

④ tell me when I should start training

⑤ you told me when I should start training

17 다음 Emily에 대한 우리말에 맞게 〈보기〉에서 적절한 단어를 선택하여 빈칸에 채우시오. (동사는 변형 가능)

Emily는 처음 배우가 된 이래로 최고의 배우가 되기 위해 노력해 오고 있다.

┤ 보기 ├

for / before / since / until / to

take / solve / try / have / be / show

Emily (A)_____ _____ _____

_____ _____ the best actress

(B)_____ she first became an actress.

18 Which of the followings are NOT grammatically correct? Choose all.

① Susan's grandfather has ever played basketball before.

② Morris has been running for an hour.

③ I have been fell in love with the ants.

④ The auditorium has been feeling too hot.

⑤ Amber has been driving for 5 years since she got the license.

19 다음 그림을 보고 괄호 안의 단어를 활용해서 어법에 맞게 빈칸에 채우시오.

(1)

➡ Junsu _____

in the flower garden for an hour since lunch time. (take, be, himself, picture)

(2)

➡ Youngsu _____ in the woods for half an hour since 3 o'clock. (watch, be, bird)

20 다음 우리말을 영작할 때 빈칸 ⓐ에 들어갈 단어로 가장 적절한 것은?

> 언제 떠날지 그녀가 알게 해주세요.
> = Let ( ) ( ) ( ) (ⓐ) ( ).

① to   ② her   ③ know
④ leave   ⑤ when

21 다음 대화의 빈칸에 들어갈 말로 알맞은 것은?

> A: _____
> B: The yellow one smells much better.

① Tell me what shape to choose.
② Do you know how to smell the perfume?
③ Don't you know where to go?
④ I wonder when to visit Rainbow town.
⑤ Can you tell me which to buy?

22 다음 밑줄 친 부분 중 어법상 어색한 것을 고르시오.

① James <u>has been taking</u> care of his sister's little kids since last week.
② Anna <u>has been making</u> the chocolate candies until now.
③ William <u>has been owning</u> the building since he was born.

④ Bentley <u>has been studying</u> the 3-D printing technology for his mom.
⑤ Lucas' relatives <u>have been living</u> in Suwon for four years.

Reading

[23~25] 다음 글을 읽고 물음에 답하시오.

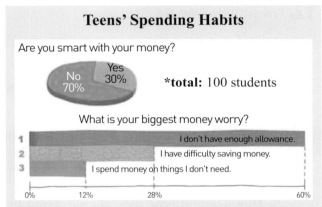

Our survey shows that the majority of students think they are not smart with their money. Managing money is not easy, and ⓐ <u>becoming</u> a smart spender takes effort.

23 위 글의 밑줄 친 ⓐbecoming과 문법적 쓰임이 같은 것을 <u>모두</u> 고르시오.

① Tom's hobby is <u>writing</u> poems.
② <u>Writing</u> poems makes your mind flexible.
③ Where is Tom <u>writing</u> poems?
④ Do you know the man <u>writing</u> poems on the bench?
⑤ Who is good at <u>writing</u> poems?

24 What percent of the students have difficulty saving money? Fill in the blank with a suitable word.

> _____ percent of the students do so.

25 위 글을 읽고 대답할 수 <u>없는</u> 질문을 고르시오.

① How many students are smart spenders?

② How many students aren't smart with their money?

③ What do the majority of students think about their spending habits?

④ On average, how much do the students get for allowance in a week?

⑤ Can you become a smart spender without any effort?

[26~28] 다음 글을 읽고 물음에 답하시오.

Do you have any money worries? Let's talk with Dr. Money.

Q I'm Jason. I get a weekly allowance, but I never have enough. ___ⓐ___ Thursday, all of my money is gone. I don't know how to solve this problem.

A Hi, I'm Dr. Money. Let's look at your spending diary. You used up most of your money ___ⓑ___ the beginning of the week. Here's my tip. Don't carry around all of your weekly allowance. ⓒ<u>용돈을 하루 단위로 나누세요.</u> Then carry only the money you need for each day.

26 위 글의 빈칸 ⓐ와 ⓑ에 들어갈 전치사가 바르게 짝지어진 것은?

ⓐ ⓑ
① On – for
③ By – at
⑤ By – for

ⓐ ⓑ
② In – at
④ On – in

27 위 글의 밑줄 친 ⓒ의 우리말에 맞게 5 단어로 영작하시오.

➡ _____

28 How often does Jason get an allowance? Fill in the blank with a suitable word.

He gets an allowance _____ a week.

[29~32] 다음 글을 읽고 물음에 답하시오.

Q I'm Minji. I like to buy things on sale. If something's on sale, I buy (A)<u>it</u> although I don't need it. Last week, I bought two T-shirts on sale, but I already have many.

A Buying things on sale is good if you buy things you need. In your case, the problem is that you buy things you don't even need. (B)<u>Here's some advice.</u> Before you buy something, ask yourself, "Do I really need this?" Also, before you go ___ⓐ___, make a shopping list. Don't buy items that aren't on the list even if they're on sale. Then you won't buy things on the spot.

29 위 글의 빈칸 ⓐ에 shop을 알맞은 형태로 쓰시오.

➡ _____

30 위 글의 밑줄 친 (A)it이 가리키는 것을 본문의 단어를 변형하여 쓰시오. (관계대명사 포함 5글자)

➡ _____

31 위 글의 밑줄 친 문장 (B)를 advice 대신 tip을 이용하여 고치시오.

➡ _____

32 What's the reason Minji is not a smart spender though she buys things on sale? Answer in English beginning with "Because". (8 words)

➡ _____

01 출제율 95%

다음 중 짝지어진 단어의 관계가 나머지와 다른 것은?

① recently – lately
② divide – combine
③ pocket money – allowance
④ result – outcome
⑤ paper money – bill

02 출제율 100%

밑줄 친 부분의 의미로 알맞지 않은 것은?

① We make the medicines that help doctors keep you healthy. (의약품)
② The machine works on its own. (작동하다)
③ It was the first case of mad cow disease in the U.S. (사례)
④ Too many coins are too heavy to carry around. (넣어 두다)
⑤ I found out the money was gone after they left. (사라지다, 없어지다)

03 출제율 90%

다음 빈칸에 공통으로 들어갈 알맞은 말을 쓰시오.

• If it fails, you can have the money _____.
• What time did you get _____ last night?

04 출제율 95%

다음 주어진 우리말에 맞게 빈칸을 채우시오. (주어진 철자로 시작할 것)

(1) 그 가방이 낡긴 했지만, 나는 디자인이 마음에 든다.
➡ A_____ the bag is old, I like the bag's design.
(2) 이 지역의 원주민 사진이 이 책에 있다.
➡ There is a picture of a n_____ of this area in this book.
(3) 난 최근에 체중이 늘었다.
➡ I've gained weight r_____.

[05~06] 다음 대화를 읽고 물음에 답하시오.

M: Hello. May I help you?
G: Yes, please. _____ (A)
M: I'm afraid you can't.
G: (B)Then, can I exchange this hat for the gloves over there?
M: Yes, you can.

05 출제율 95%

위 대화의 빈칸 (A)에 들어갈 말로 알맞은 것을 고르시오.

① Do you sell this hat here?
② I want to buy this hat.
③ Can I get this hat?
④ Can I get a refund for this hat?
⑤ Is it possible to exchange this hat?

06 출제율 90%

위 대화의 (B)Then을 if를 포함한 절로 바꿔 쓰시오. (9 words)

➡ _____

[07~08] 다음 대화를 읽고 물음에 답하시오.

G: I bought this red skirt last week. I like the skirt, but my sister says that the color doesn't look good on me. I wonder ___(A)___ I should exchange it for a different color.

B: It's up to you but I think it's fine.

07 위 대화의 빈칸 (A)에 들어갈 알맞은 말을 쓰시오.

➡ _____

08 Why does the girl think about exchanging what she bought?

➡ _____

_____

[09~10] 다음 대화를 읽고 물음에 답하시오.

W: Hello. Do you need some help?

B: Yes. (①) I'd like to return this smartphone case.

W: (②) Do you have the receipt with you?

B: Here it is. (③) I bought it three days ago. (④)

W: Oh, then it's possible. (⑤)

09 (①)~(⑤) 중 주어진 문장이 들어갈 곳은?

Let's see.

①   ②   ③   ④   ⑤

10 위 대화를 읽고 대답할 수 없는 질문을 고르시오.

① When did the boy buy the smartphone case?

② What does the boy need?

③ Why does the boy want to return the smartphone case?

④ Does the boy have the receipt with him?

⑤ Does the woman allow B to return the smartphone case?

11 What is the purpose of the boy's visiting the store? Answer by using 'to infinitive.'

➡ _____

12 다음 문장의 빈칸 (A), (B), (C)에 들어갈 말로 가장 적절한 것은?

• Miranda isn't sure ___(A)___ to stay in Rome during her business trip.

• The boy showed the foreigner ___(B)___ to get to the Big Ben.

• The little girl didn't know ___(C)___ to do with the boys, so she went out.

	(A)	(B)	(C)
①	which	how	where
②	which	when	where
③	where	how	what
④	where	when	what
⑤	when	how	how

13 다음 중 어법상 어색한 것을 고르시오.

① They have been watching her sing and dance on TV since this evening.

② What have you been trying to looking for in those caves?

③ Ken has been reading books for 45 minutes.

④ My daughters have been playing the trumpet recently.

⑤ Trump's sons have been playing poker during the summer vacation.

14 다음 중 빈칸에 들어갈 의문사의 종류가 나머지 셋과 <u>다른</u> 두 개를 고르시오.

① Billy wanted to know _____ to wear to the party.
② The little children didn't know _____ to play basketball on the court.
③ The homeless man didn't know _____ to beg for money, for he was first in that town.
④ Amy hasn't decided _____ to buy with her money.
⑤ Scarlet wanted to know _____ to meet her friends.

15 다음 각 문장에서 어법상 <u>어색한</u> 부분을 골라 고치시오.

ⓐ The oil prices have been risen steadily for 2 years.
ⓑ The coach showed me what to swim in the deep sea.
ⓒ She wanted to know which to eat noodles as she had never used chopsticks.
ⓓ They have been shouting for help since 15 minutes.
ⓔ Sarah has been having the dress since she was a very little kid.

➡ ⓐ _____ ⓑ _____
　 ⓒ _____ ⓓ _____
　 ⓔ _____

[16~18] 다음 글을 읽고 물음에 답하시오.

The Green Middle School Times
Teens' Spending Habits

How smart are you with your money? These are the results of a survey of 100 students at Green Middle School.

We first asked students "Are you smart with your money?" As Graph 1 shows, 70% answered "No" (A)<u>while</u> 30% answered "Yes." We then asked the students who answered "No" what their biggest money worry is. As Graph 2 shows, 60% think they don't have enough ___ⓐ___ while 28% think they have difficulty saving money. Lastly, 12% said they spent money on things they didn't need.

16 주어진 영영풀이를 참고하여 빈칸 ⓐ에 철자 a로 시작하는 단어를 쓰시오.

money that is given to someone, usually on a regular basis, in order to help them pay for the things that they need

➡ _____

17 위 글의 밑줄 친 (A)while과 같은 의미로 쓰인 것을 고르시오.

① While you are eating, you shouldn't speak.
② Did anyone call while I was away?
③ Strike while the iron is hot.
④ While there is life, there is hope.
⑤ I've read fifty pages, while he's read only twenty.

18 다음 문장에서 위 글의 내용과 <u>다른</u> 부분을 찾아서 고치시오.

More than ten students said they spent money on things they didn't need.

_____ ➡ _____

[19~21] 다음 글을 읽고 물음에 답하시오.

Q Hello, Dr. Money. I'm Steve. I have difficulty saving money. For example, ⓐ <u>I've been saving</u> to go to my favorite singer's concert for the last two months. However, I still don't have enough money. I don't know what to do.

A Let's see. In the last few weeks, you spent 80% of your allowance and only saved 20%. (①) I think you've been spending too much. (②) For example, you can follow the 50%-40%-10% rule. (③) Save 50%, spend 40%, and donate the remaining 10% to charity. (④) By following the rule, you can manage your money better. (⑤) Then you can save money faster to buy the ticket.

19 위 글의 흐름으로 보아, 주어진 문장이 들어가기에 가장 적절한 곳은?

> To save money, you need to have a tighter budget.

①   ②   ③   ④   ⑤

20 위 글의 밑줄 친 ⓐ와 현재완료의 용법이 같은 것을 <u>모두</u> 고르시오.

① I <u>have been</u> to England before.
② They <u>have watched</u> TV since this morning.
③ I <u>have lost</u> my cell phone.
④ <u>Have</u> you <u>finished</u> your lunch yet?
⑤ How long <u>has</u> she <u>played</u> it?

21 Which question CANNOT be answered after reading the passage?

① Why has Steve been saving for the last two months?
② Does Steve have enough money to go to his favorite singer's concert?
③ On what did Steve spend 80% of his allowance?
④ What does Steve need to do to save money?
⑤ What advice does Dr. Money give to Steve?

[22~23] 다음 글을 읽고 물음에 답하시오.

My money problem is that I buy things on the spot. One time, I bought a smartphone case because it looked nice. However, I found out that I already had three cases at home. ⓐ <u>I don't know how to stop to buy things on the spot.</u>

22 위 글의 밑줄 친 ⓐ에서 어법상 <u>틀린</u> 부분을 찾아 고치시오.

_____ ➡ _____

23 위 글의 내용과 일치하도록 다음 빈칸에 알맞은 단어를 고르시오.

> The writer wants to get some advice on the problem of his or her _____ habit.

① saving   ② spending
③ earning   ④ speaking
⑤ donating

[01~03] 다음 대화를 읽고 물음에 답하시오.

> M: Hello. May I help you?
> G: Yes, please. I'd like to get a refund for this cap.
> M: Do you have the receipt?
> G: No, I don't. I ___(A)___ it as a gift.
> M: If you don't have the receipt, then, it's not possible to get a refund.
> G: I see. Then, can I exchange it for something else?
> M: Yes, you can. What would you like to get?
> G: I want to get this blue bag.
> M: Let me see .... The price is the same, so you can just take it.
> G: Thank you.

01 다음 영영풀이에 해당하는 말을 빈칸 (A)에 과거형으로 쓰시오.

> to get something after someone gives it to you or sends it to you

➡ _____

02 What does the girl take instead of the cap?

➡ _____

03 How come the girl is able to get the blue bag? Use the word, 'because' and 'that.' (15 words)

➡ _____

04 다음 우리말과 같은 뜻이 되도록 주어진 단어들을 사용하여 제시된 글자 수에 맞게 영작하시오. (단어 변형 불가하며 숫자는 영어로만 쓰시오.)

(1) Brian이 9시 이후로 무엇을 보고 있는 중이니? (been, o'clock, watching, what, since, 총 8 단어)

➡ _____
_____

(2) 그녀는 인천의 한 중학교에서 프랑스어를 5년간 가르쳐 왔다. (been, teaching, for, French, Incheon, middle, in, 총 14 단어)

➡ _____
_____

05 다음 〈보기〉와 같이 두 문장이 같은 의미가 되도록 빈칸에 알맞은 말을 쓰시오.

> ┤ 보기 ├
> I wonder when to turn right.
> → I wonder when I should turn right.

(1) Ted is wondering what to do next.
  → Ted is wondering _____
  _____.

(2) Ms. Rose doesn't know how to get to the subway station.
  → Ms. Rose doesn't know _____
  _____.

(3) Ann told Mike where to park his luxury car.
  → Ann told Mike _____
  _____.

(4) The baby girl wanted to know how to move the toy.
  → The baby girl wanted to know _____
  _____.

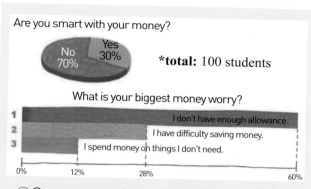

ⓐOur survey shows that the minority of students think they are not smart with their money. ⓑManaging money is not easy, and becoming a smart spender takes effort.

06 위 글의 밑줄 친 ⓐ에서 흐름상 어색한 부분을 찾아 고치시오.

_____ ➡ _____

07 위 글의 밑줄 친 ⓑ를 to부정사를 사용하여 고칠 때, 빈칸에 들어갈 알맞은 말을 쓰시오.

➡ _____ is not easy to manage money

08 What percent of the students spend money on things they don't need? Fill in the blank with a suitable word.

_____ percent of the students do so.

[09~11] 다음 글을 읽고 물음에 답하시오.

Ｑ Hello, Dr. Money. I'm Steve. I have difficulty saving money. For example, I've been saving to go to my favorite singer's concert for the last two months. However, ⓐ 저는 여전히 충분한 돈을 가지고 있지 않아요. I don't know what to do.

Ａ Let's see. In the last few weeks, you spent 80% of your allowance and only saved 20%. ⓑI think you've been saving too much. To save money, you need to have a tighter budget. For example, you can follow the 50%-40%-10% rule. Save 50%, spend 40%, and donate the remaining 10% to charity. By following the rule, you can manage your money better. Then you can save money faster to buy the ticket.

09 위 글의 밑줄 친 ⓐ의 우리말에 맞게 한 단어를 보충하여, 주어진 어휘를 알맞게 배열하시오.

enough / have / I / money / don't

➡ _____

10 위 글의 밑줄 친 ⓑ에서 흐름상 어색한 부분을 찾아 고치시오. (위 글에 나오는 동사를 변형하여 쓸 것.)

_____ ➡ _____

11 다음 빈칸 (A)와 (B)에 알맞은 단어를 넣어 Steve의 돈에 대한 고민과 Dr. Money의 조언을 완성하시오.

Steve's Worry: I have difficulty (A)_____ _____ to go to my favorite singer's concert. I need to save more money.
Dr. Money's Advice: You need to have a tighter budget. Follow the (B)_____ rule. Save 50%, spend 40%, and donate the remaining 10% to charity.

01 주어진 표현을 이용하여 〈보기〉와 같이 다음 대화의 빈칸에 알맞은 말을 쓰시오.

> possible, get a refund for / OK, get a refund for

A: _____ this skirt?
B: Sure. Was there anything wrong with it?

┌─ 보기 ─┐

A: Can I get a refund for this bag?
B: OK. Was there anything wrong with it?

02 다음 정보를 읽고, 주인공 Esther 또는 Alex를 주어로 하는 현재완료진행형 문장을 두 개 이상 쓰시오. (인칭과 시제 등에 유의하여 활용할 것.)

- Alex started to teach English to the middle school students 15 years ago.
- Alex began to teach his students how to solve the cube puzzle 5 years ago.
- Esther, one of Alex's students, first learned to solve the cube puzzle last year when she entered the middle school.
- He is still teaching the middle school students English and the way of solving the cube puzzle until now.
- Esther is still learning to solve the cube puzzle.
- Esther is still learning English from Alex.

03 다음 내용을 바탕으로 자신의 소비 습관의 문제점에 관한 조언을 구하는 글을 쓰시오.

My Spending Habits
- my money problem: I buy things on the spot.
- episode showing my problem: I once bought a smartphone case because it looked nice. However, I found out that I already had three cases at home.

My (A)_____ is that I buy things (B)_____. I once bought a smartphone case because it looked (C)_____. However, I found out that I already (D)_____ at home. I don't know how to stop buying things on the spot.

단원별 모의고사

01 다음 짝지어진 단어의 관계가 같도록 빈칸에 알맞은 말을 쓰시오. (주어진 철자로 시작할 것)

> lastly – finally : result – o_____

[02~03] 주어진 영어 설명에 알맞은 어휘를 빈칸에 쓰시오.

02

> Listen to the _____ of your father and mother.

> <영어 설명> an opinion you give someone about what they should do

➡ _____

03

> She saved up all her _____ and bought a laptop computer.

> <영어 설명> money given by parents to a child regularly that the child can spend

➡ _____

04 다음 빈칸에 알맞은 말로 짝지어진 것을 고르시오.

> • Ice cream is on _____ for half price.
> • Jack drank the _____ juice.

① refund – waiting
② refund – remaining
③ sale – waiting
④ sale – remaining
⑤ return – staying

[05~06] 다음 영영풀이를 참고하여 빈칸에 알맞은 말을 쓰시오.

05

> the state or situation of having a problem

> I had _____ in communicating in English.

06

> in the exact place where something is happening

> He took a look at the car and decided to buy it _____.

[07~08] 다음 대화를 읽고 물음에 답하시오.

M: Hello. ⓐMay I help you?
G: Yes, please. Can I get ⓑa refund for this hat?
M: _____ (A) _____
G: Then, can I ⓒchange this hat ⓓfor the gloves over there?
M: Yes, you ⓔcan.

07 위 대화의 빈칸 (A)에 들어갈 말로 알맞은 것을 고르시오.

① Yes, you can.
② Why not?
③ Do you want to return the hat?
④ We can give customers some discount.
⑤ I'm afraid you can't.

08 위 대화의 밑줄 친 ⓐ~ⓔ 중 어색한 것은?

① ⓐ   ② ⓑ   ③ ⓒ   ④ ⓓ   ⑤ ⓔ

[09~11] 다음 대화를 읽고 물음에 답하시오.

M: Hello. May I help you?

G: Yes, please. I'd like to get a refund for this cap. (①)

M: Do you have the receipt?

G: No, I don't. I received it ___(A)___ a gift.

M: If you don't have the receipt, then, it's not possible to get a refund. (②)

G: I see. Then, can I exchange it for something else? (③)

M: Yes, you can. (④)

G: I want to get this blue bag.

M: Let me see .... (B)가격이 같으니까 그것을 가져 가셔도 돼요. (just, the price, same, take, so) (⑤)

G: Thank you.

09 (①)~(⑤) 중 주어진 문장이 들어갈 곳은?

> What would you like to get?

①   ②   ③   ④   ⑤

10 위 대화의 빈칸 (A)에 알맞은 말을 1 단어로 쓰시오.

➡ _____

11 위 대화의 밑줄 친 우리말 (B)에 맞게 주어진 어휘를 이용하여 11 단어로 쓰시오.

➡ _____

12 다음 그림을 보고 괄호 안의 단어를 활용해서 우리말에 맞게 빈칸을 채우시오.

(1) 원님이 농부에게 그 초대형 당근을 어떻게 처리할지 물어보고 있다.

➡ The governor is asking the farmer _____ _____ _____ the super big carrot. (handle)

(2) 5분 전부터 나의 개가 내 성적표를 물어 뜯고 있는 중이다.

➡ My dog _____ _____ _____ my report card since 5 minutes ago. (bite)

(3) 그 강아지는 어느 발을 내밀지 고민 중이다.

➡ The puppy is wondering _____ _____. (put out)

13 다음 밑줄 친 부분 중 어법상 어색한 것을 고르시오.

① Timothy wants to know where to buy his new coat.

② The couple decided when to leave for Hawaii.

③ The old pilot almost forgot how to fly.

④ Could you please tell her what to use the monitoring system?

⑤ The girl asked Charlie how to open the box.

14 다음 세 문장을 주어진 〈조건〉에 맞게 한 문장으로 쓰시오.

┌─ 조건 ─┐
- 현재완료진행시제를 사용할 것.
- 분사가 명사의 뒤에서 수식할 것.
- for를 반드시 사용할 것.
- 10 단어를 넘지 않을 것.

(1) • John started to watch the flims last Saturday.
   • Bong directed the films.
   • It's Tuesday today and John is still watching them.
   = John _____
   _____ days.

(2) • Daisy started working at a store last week.
   • Butler owns the store.
   • Daisy is still working there.
   = Daisy _____
   _____ a week.

15 우리말과 일치하도록 괄호 안의 단어를 바르게 배열하시오.

(1) Wilson은 오늘 아침부터 복사기를 어떻게 수리하는지 배우고 있다.
   (photocopier, to, Wilson, fix, has, since, how, been, morning, learning, the, this)
   ➡ _____
   _____

(2) Susan의 친구들이 3시간 동안 저 무거운 가방들을 옮겨 주고 있다.
   (three, bags, friends, hours, carrying, been, heavy, for, Susan's, those, have)
   ➡ _____
   _____

16 다음 중 밑줄 친 부분의 쓰임이 〈보기〉와 다른 것은?

┌─ 보기 ─┐
The people have lived in this city of New-Town since early 1990s.
└────────┘

① Thomas' uncle has kept the machine working since he first operated it.
② Dave has finished checking all the rooms in his building.
③ Sean has stayed in Paris since he went there to study painting 2 years ago.
④ The girls have known each other since they're born at the same hospital.
⑤ It has been quite chilly these days.

17 다음 우리말을 아래의 어휘들을 배열하여 영작하되 현재완료진행시제로 쓰시오.

┌────────┐
Jack은 지난달 이후로 백화점에서 일하고 있다.
(working / Jack / last month / the department store / has / since / been / at).
└────────┘

➡ _____
_____

[18~19] 다음 글을 읽고 물음에 답하시오.

A Buying things on sale is good if you buy things you need. (①) Here's some advice. (②) Before you buy something, ask yourself, "Do I really need this?" (③) Also, before you go shopping, make a shopping list. (④) ⓐDon't buy items that isn't on the list even if they're on sale. (⑤) Then you won't buy things on the spot.

18 위 글의 흐름으로 보아, 주어진 문장이 들어가기에 가장 적절한 곳은?

> In your case, the problem is that you buy things you don't even need.

①   ②   ③   ④   ⑤

19 위 글의 밑줄 친 ⓐ에서 어법상 틀린 부분을 찾아 고치시오.

_____ ➡ _____

[20~22] 다음 글을 읽고 물음에 답하시오.

The Green Middle School Times
Teens' Spending Habits

How smart are you with your money? These are the results of a survey of 100 students at Green Middle School.

We first asked students "Are you smart with your money?" As Graph 1 shows, 70% answered "No" while 30% answered "Yes." We then asked the students who answered "No" ⓐ그들의 돈에 대한 가장 큰 고민이 무엇인지. As Graph 2 shows, 60% think they don't have enough allowance while 28% think they have difficulty saving money. Lastly, 12% said they spent money on things they didn't need.

20 위 글의 밑줄 친 ⓐ의 우리말에 맞게 주어진 어휘를 알맞게 배열하시오.

> money / their / is / biggest / what / worry

➡ _____

21 According to the survey, are the majority of students smart spenders? Answer in English in a full sentence. (3 words)

➡ _____

22 본문의 내용과 일치하도록 다음 빈칸에 들어갈 알맞은 분수를 고르시오.

> The percent of the students who spent money on things they didn't need is _____ _____ of the percent of the students who think they don't have enough allowance.

① one third   ② two-thirds
③ one fourth   ④ three-fourths
⑤ one fifth

[23~25] 다음 글을 읽고 물음에 답하시오.

Q Hello, Dr. Money. I'm Steve. I have difficulty ①saving money. For example, I've been ②saving to go to my favorite singer's concert for the last two months.   ⓐ , I still don't have enough money. I don't know what to do.

A Let's see. In the last few weeks, you spent 80% of your allowance and only saved 20%. I think you've been ③spending too much. To save money, you need to have a tighter budget. For example, you can follow the 50%-40%-10% rule. Save 50%, spend 40%, and donate the ④remained 10% to charity. By ⑤following the rule, you can manage your money better. Then you can save money faster to buy the ticket.

23 위 글의 빈칸 @에 들어갈 알맞은 말을 고르시오.

① In addition   ② However

③ Thus   ④ For example

⑤ Similarly

24 위 글의 밑줄 친 ①~⑤ 중 어법상 틀린 것을 찾아 고치시오.

_____ ➡ _____

25 According to the passage, which is NOT true?

① It is not easy for Steve to save money to go to his favorite singer's concert.

② In the last few weeks, Steve spent four-fifths of his allowance.

③ In the last few weeks, Steve only saved one fifth of his allowance.

④ To save money, Steve needs to follow the 50%-40%-10% rule.

⑤ The 50%-40%-10% rule means spending 50%, saving 40%, and donating the remaining 10% to charity.

[26~28] 다음 글을 읽고 물음에 답하시오.

Q I'm Minji. I like to buy things on sale. If something's on sale, I buy it (A)[although / in spite of] I don't need it. Last week, I bought two T-shirts on sale, but I already have many.

A Buying things on sale is good if you buy things you need. In your case, the problem is that you buy things you don't even need. Here's some (B)[advice / advices]. Before you buy something, ask yourself, "Do I really need this?" Also, before you go shopping, make a shopping list. Don't buy items that aren't on the list (C)[as if / even if] they're on sale. Then you won't buy things @즉석에서.

26 위 글의 괄호 (A)~(C)에서 문맥이나 어법상 알맞은 낱말을 골라 쓰시오.

➡ (A) _____ (B) _____ (C) _____

27 위 글의 밑줄 친 @의 우리말에 맞게 3 단어로 영작하시오.

➡ _____

28 다음 중 민지에 대한 설명이 옳지 않은 것을 고르시오.

① Minji likes to buy things on sale.

② Minji buys something if it's on sale though she doesn't need it.

③ Minji is a smart spender as she always buys things on sale.

④ Minji should ask herself, "Do I really need this?" before she buys something.

⑤ Minji should make a shopping list before she goes shopping.

MEMO

The Team Behind the Team

🎙️ 의사소통 기능

- 빈도 묻고 말하기
  A: How often do you exercise?
  B: I exercise once a week.
- 제안이나 권유하기
  I suggest you exercise more often.

🗣️ 언어 형식

- 현재분사
  Pacers usually have flags or balloons **showing** their finish time.
- as ~ as
  They are **as** important **as** the players.

Words & Expressions

Key Words

- □ **achieve**[ətʃíːv] 동 달성하다, 성취하다
- □ **activity**[æktívəti] 명 활동
- □ **allow**[əláu] 동 허용하다
- □ **already**[ɔːlrédi] 부 이미
- □ **assistant**[əsístənt] 명 보조자
- □ **attention**[əténʃən] 명 주의, 주목
- □ **breathe**[briːð] 동 숨쉬다
- □ **carry**[kǽri] 동 운반하다
- □ **check**[tʃek] 동 점검하다
- □ **cheer**[tʃiər] 동 응원하다
- □ **cheerleader**[tʃíərliːdər] 명 응원단
- □ **choose**[tʃuːz] 동 선택하다
- □ **crew**[kruː] 명 팀, 조
- □ **direction**[dirékʃən] 명 방향
- □ **especially**[ispéʃəli] 부 특히
- □ **expensive**[ikspénsiv] 형 값비싼
- □ **experienced**[ikspíəriənst] 형 경험 있는
- □ **flag**[flæg] 명 깃발
- □ **full**[ful] 형 가득 찬
- □ **harmony**[háːrməni] 명 조화, 화합
- □ **hidden**[hídn] 형 숨겨진
- □ **hire**[haiər] 동 고용하다
- □ **hurt**[həːrt] 동 다치다
- □ **invisible**[invízəbl] 형 (눈에) 보이지 않는, 볼 수 없는
- □ **join**[dʒɔin] 동 가입하다

- □ **lead**[liːd] 동 이끌다
- □ **limit**[límit] 명 한계
- □ **main**[mein] 형 주된
- □ **manage**[mǽnidʒ] 동 관리하다
- □ **pacer**[péisər] 명 페이서, 보조를 맞춰 걷는 사람
- □ **particular**[pərtíkjulər] 형 특정한
- □ **perfect**[pə́ːrfikt] 형 완벽한
- □ **pit**[pit] 명 (자동차 경주의) 피트
- □ **pole**[poul] 명 막대기
- □ **promote**[prəmóut] 동 홍보하다
- □ **recommendation**[rèkəməndéiʃən] 명 추천
- □ **register**[rédʒistər] 동 등록하다
- □ **several**[sévərəl] 형 몇몇의
- □ **Sherpa**[ʃə́ːrpə] 명 셸파
- □ **shoot**[ʃuːt] 동 쏘다
- □ **suggest**[səgdʒést] 동 제안하다
- □ **suit**[suːt] 명 정장, 옷 한 벌
- □ **support**[səpɔ́ːrt] 동 돕다, 지원하다
- □ **tapper**[tǽpər] 명 두드리는 사람
- □ **target**[táːrgit] 명 목표
- □ **therefore**[ðέərfɔ̀ːr] 부 그러므로
- □ **tribe**[traib] 명 부족, 종족
- □ **trophy**[tróufi] 명 트로피
- □ **wear**[wɛər] 동 입다, 신다, 쓰다
- □ **windy**[wíndi] 형 바람이 심한

Key Expressions

- □ **be good at** ~을 잘하다
- □ **be good for** ~에 좋다
- □ **be over** 끝나다
- □ **depending on** ~에 따라
- □ **do stretching** 스트레칭을 하다
- □ **get attention** 주목을 받다
- □ **give a speech** 연설하다
- □ **guide runner** 가이드 러너(시각 장애인의 눈 역할을 해주는 선수)
- □ **have difficulty -ing** ~에 어려움을 겪다
- □ **How about ~?** ~은 어때?
- □ **in many ways** 여러 가지 면에서
- □ **in short** 간단히 말해서
- □ **keep track of** ~을 파악하다

- □ **look for** ~을 찾다
- □ **most of all** 무엇보다도
- □ **not ~ at all** 결코 ~ 아닌
- □ **on one's own** 혼자서
- □ **once a week** 일주일에 한 번
- □ **play an important role** 중요한 역할을 하다
- □ **put up** (텐트 등을) 치다, 세우다
- □ **sign up for** 등록하다, 신청하다
- □ **stay on the track** 트랙에 머무르다
- □ **take bowling lessons** 볼링 수업을 받다
- □ **take care of** ~을 돌보다
- □ **wear out** (낡아서) 떨어지다, 헤지다
- □ **would like to** ~하고 싶다

Word Power

※ 서로 비슷한 뜻을 가진 어휘

- □ achieve 달성하다 : accomplish 성취하다
- □ cheer 응원하다 : encourage 용기를 불어 넣다
- □ hire 고용하다 : employ 고용하다
- □ register 등록하다 : enroll 등록하다

- □ allow 허용하다 : permit 허가하다
- □ main 주된 : major 주된
- □ suggest 제안하다 : propose 제안하다
- □ tribe 부족 : clan 부족

※ 서로 반대의 뜻을 가진 어휘

- □ allow 허용하다 ↔ forbid 금지하다
- □ experienced 경험 있는 ↔ inexperienced 경험 없는
- □ hire 고용하다 ↔ fire 해고하다

- □ expensive 값비싼 ↔ cheap 값싼
- □ full 가득 찬 ↔ empty 비어 있는
- □ visible 눈에 보이는 ↔ invisible 보이지 않는

※ 동사 – 명사

- □ achieve 달성하다 – achievement 성취
- □ allow 허용하다 – allowance 허용, 용돈
- □ promote 홍보하다 – promotion 홍보

- □ act 행동하다 – activity 활동, action 활동, 행동
- □ breathe 숨쉬다 – breath 호흡
- □ suggest 제안하다 – suggestion 제안

※ in+형용사, im+형용사

- □ impatient 초조해 하는
- □ impolite 무례한
- □ incomplete 불완전한
- □ independent 독립적인
- □ inexperienced 경험이 없는

- □ imperfect 불완전한
- □ impossible 불가능한
- □ indirect 간접적인
- □ ineffective 효과가 없는
- □ informal 격식을 차리지 않는

English Dictionary

- □ **achieve** 달성하다, 성취하다
  → to succeed in doing or getting something you want
  원하는 것을 하거나 얻는 것에 성공하다

- □ **breathe** 숨쉬다
  → to take air into your body and let it out again
  공기를 체내로 빨아들이고 다시 내보내다

- □ **crew** 팀, 조
  → a group of people with a particular skill who work together 함께 일하는 특정한 기술을 가진 한 무리의 사람들

- □ **hire** 고용하다
  → to pay someone to work for you
  당신을 위해 일을 하도록 누군가에게 돈을 지불하다

- □ **invisible** (눈에) 보이지 않는, 볼 수 없는
  → not able to be seen 볼 수 없는

- □ **pit** (자동차 경주의) 피트
  → the area beside a race track where cars are repaired or get more gas during a race 경주를 하는 동안 차들이 수리되거나 기름을 넣는 경주 트랙 옆에 있는 구역

- □ **register** 등록하다
  → to put someone's or something's name on an official list 공식적인 명단에 이름을 올리다

- □ **support** 돕다, 지원하다
  → to say that you agree with a person, group, or idea 어떤 사람, 그룹 또는 생각에 동의한다고 말하다

- □ **tribe** 부족, 종족
  → a group of people who have their own language and ways of living
  자신들의 언어와 생활 방식을 가지고 있는 사람들의 집단

- □ **trophy** 트로피
  → a metal cup or other objects that someone gets for winning a game or race
  경기 또는 경주에서 이겨서 얻는 금속 컵 또는 다른 물체들

- □ **wear out** (낡아서) 떨어지다, 헤지다
  → to use something a lot so that it no longer works, or can no longer be used 어떤 것을 많이 사용하여 더 이상 작동하지 않거나 더 이상 사용될 수 없다

01 다음 짝지어진 단어의 관계가 같도록 빈칸에 알맞은 말은?

> impolite – rude : achieve – _____

① accomplish   ② register
③ join   ④ suggest
⑤ accompany

서답형
02 주어진 영어 설명에 맞게 문장의 빈칸에 알맞은 말을 쓰시오.

> Many stars are _____ to the eye.

> <영어 설명> not able to be seen

➡ _____

03 밑줄 친 부분의 의미로 알맞지 <u>않은</u> 것은?

① It <u>is</u> probably <u>good for</u> you to get some criticism now and then. (~에 좋다)
② It's hard to <u>keep track of</u> the children's comings and goings. (~을 쫓다)
③ <u>In short</u>, there is a lot of disagreement about the best way to punish children. (간단히 말해서)
④ When you do something unusual, you <u>get attention</u> and artists want attention. (주목을 받다)
⑤ Does the rent vary <u>depending on</u> the model of car? (~에 따라)

04 다음 빈칸에 들어갈 가장 알맞은 말을 고르시오.

> How many students _____ for the English class?

① supported   ② wore
③ kept   ④ registered
⑤ achieved

중요
05 다음 <보기>의 단어를 사용하여 자연스러운 문장을 만들 수 없는 것은?

> ┤ 보기 ├
> give   tribe   cheer   target

① I can't understand why they wanted him to _____ a speech.
② I always _____ for my home team.
③ There is a _____ to my patience.
④ Who is the _____ market?
⑤ They began as a _____ in the 12th century.

06 다음 빈칸에 알맞은 말이 바르게 짝지어진 것을 고르시오.

> • Many students _____ the plans to change school uniforms.
> • The band has gone on tour to _____ their new album.

① depend – promote
② depend – need
③ register – take
④ support – need
⑤ support – promote

01 다음 영영풀이에 알맞은 어휘를 〈보기〉에서 찾아 쓰시오.

> ┌ 보기 ┐
> hire   register   achieve   support

(1) to say that you agree with a person, group, or idea

(2) to succeed in doing or getting something you want

(3) to pay someone to work for you

(4) to put someone's or something's name on an official list

➡ (1) _____ (2) _____ (3) _____
  (4) _____

02 다음 짝지어진 두 단어의 관계가 같도록 빈칸에 알맞은 말을 쓰시오.

(1) possible : impossible
  = dependent : _____

(2) achieve : achievement
  = breathe : _____

03 다음 우리말에 맞도록 빈칸에 알맞은 말을 쓰시오. (철자가 주어진 경우 그 철자로 시작할 것.)

(1) 물건이란 오래 쓰면 닳기 마련이다.
  → It's normal for things to _____ out with long use.

(2) 미나는 그 영화를 몇 번 봤다.
  → Mina has seen the movie s_____ times.

(3) 나는 목표를 이루기 위해 최선을 다해야 한다.
  → I should try my best to a_____ my goal.

(4) 그는 삼촌의 추천으로 그 소년을 고용했다.
  → He hired the boy on the r_____ of his uncle.

04 우리말에 맞게 한 단어를 추가하여 주어진 단어를 알맞게 배열하시오.

(1) 나는 우리의 위치를 파악하면서 지도를 따라 갔다. (I, position, map, our, followed, keeping, the, of)
  ➡ _____
  _____

(2) 내 성격은 사람에 따라 바뀐다. (personality, person, changes, depending, the, my)
  ➡ _____
  _____

(3) 그 집은 몇 그루의 나무 뒤로 시야에서 가려져 있었다. (the house, trees, sight, some, hidden, behind, from)
  ➡ _____
  _____

(4) 그는 그 문제를 혼자서 해결했다. (he, his, the, problem, fix, managed, on, to)
  ➡ _____
  _____

Conversation

1 빈도 묻고 말하기

> **A** How often do you exercise? 너는 얼마나 자주 운동을 하니?
> **B** I exercise once a week. 나는 일주일에 한 번 운동을 해.

■ 어떤 일이나 현상이 반복될 때, 상대방에게 어떤 활동을 하는 횟수, 즉 빈도를 물어 볼 때는 often(자주)을 사용하여 'How often do you ~?(얼마나 자주 ~하니?)'라고 표현한다. 숫자가 포함된 구체적인 횟수를 물어볼 때는 'How many times do you ~?(몇 번 ~하니?)'라고 좀 더 구체적으로 물어볼 수 있다.

■ 대략적인 빈도를 말할 때는 always, usually, often, sometimes, never 등과 같은 빈도부사를 사용하고, 구체적인 빈도를 나타낼 때는 '횟수+a day/week/month/year'로 특정 기간 동안의 횟수를 표현한다. 횟수를 나타내는 표현은 once(한 번), twice(두 번), 그리고 세 번 이상부터는 'three times'처럼 '기수+times'로 나타낸다. 자주하는 것을 강조해서 'every day/week/month/year(매 ~마다)'라고 하기도 한다. 빈도부사는 주로 조동사나 be동사 뒤에, 그리고 일반동사 앞에 쓰고, 구체적인 횟수를 나타내는 말은 대부분 문장의 끝 부분에 쓴다.

빈도 묻기

- How often do you ~? 얼마나 자주 ~하니?
- How many times do you ~? 몇 번 ~하니?

빈도 말하기

- always(항상), usually(보통), often(자주), sometimes(가끔), never(결코 ~ 아닌)
- (주어+동사+) ~ times a day/week/month/year. 하루/일주일/한 달/일 년에 ~번 …한다.

핵심 Check

1. 다음 대화의 빈칸 (A)에 들어가기에 적절한 것은?

B: _____(A)_____ do you play basketball?

G: I play once a week, but I want to play more often.

B: I suggest you join my basketball club. We play three times a week.

G: That sounds good! It'll be fun to play with you.

① How much
② How often
③ How many
④ What time
⑤ How often times

② 제안이나 권유하기

• **I suggest you exercise more often.** 나는 네가 더 자주 운동해야 한다고 제안해.

■ 상대방에게 어떤 일이나 행동을 제안하거나 권유할 때는 동사 'suggest(제안하다)'를 사용하여 'I suggest (that)+주어+(should+)동사원형 ~'의 구문으로 나타낸다. 이때 that과 should는 생략하여 말할 수 있다.

■ 'suggest'를 이용한 표현은 'suggest + that ~ (should) 절' 이외에도 'suggest+-ing', 'suggest+wh-절', 'suggest+wh- to do' 등으로 나타내기도 한다. 한편 'suggest'는 '제안하다'는 뜻 이외에도 '암시하다, 시사하다, 말하다' 등의 의미를 가지는데 제안하는 의미 이외의 경우에는 that절에 should를 사용하지 않는다.

■ 제안, 권유를 나타내는 유사한 표현으로 'Let's ~.(~하자)', 'had better ~(~하는 편이 낫다)', 'Why don't you/we ~?(~하는 것이 어때?)', 'May I suggest that ~?(~하는 것이 어떠세요?)' 등이 있다.

■ 'How about'과 'What about'은 'How/What about 명사/~ing?(~는 어때?)'의 형태로 쓰며 상대에게 제안, 권유하는 의미와 함께 상대의 의견을 물어보는 의미로도 사용한다.

■ 상대방의 제안이나 조언에 답할 때 'That's a good/great idea!', 'I'll give it a try.' 또는 'OK, I'll ~'이라고 답할 수 있다.

제안이나 권유

• I suggest (that) 주어+(should)+동사원형 ~	~하라고 제안한다.
• suggest+-ing/wh-절/wh- to do	~을 제안하다
• Let's ~	(같이) ~하자.
• had better ~	~하는 편이 낫다
• Why don't you/we ~?	~하는 것이 어때?
• May I suggest that ~?	~하는 것이 어떠세요?
• How[What] about ~ing?	~하는 것이 어떠니?

핵심 Check

2. 다음 대화의 밑줄 친 우리말을 주어진 어휘를 이용하여 영작하시오.

A: Minsu, how often do you exercise?

B: I exercise once a week.

A: 나는 네가 더 자주 운동하기를 제안해. (suggest, exercise, often)

B: OK. I'll try.

➡ _____

 Listen and Talk A 1

B: ❶How often do you play basketball?

G: I play ❷once a week, but I want to play more often.

B: ❸I suggest you join my basketball club. We play three times a week.

G: That sounds good! ❹It'll be fun to play with you.

B: 얼마나 자주 농구를 하니?
G: 일주일에 한 번 해. 그런데 더 자주 하고 싶어.
B: 네가 우리 농구 동아리에 들어오기를 제안해. 우리는 일주일에 세 번 농구를 해.
G: 좋은 생각이야! 같이 하면 재미있을 거야.

❶ '얼마나 자주 ~하니?'라는 의미로 상대방에게 어떤 활동을 하는 횟수나 빈도를 물어 볼 때 쓰는 표현이다.
❷ 'once a week'은 '일주일에 한 번'이라는 의미로 횟수를 나타내는 표현이다.
❸ suggest 다음에 that이 생략되어 있으며 join 앞에는 should가 생략되어 있다.
❹ It은 가주어이고 'to play with you'가 진주어이다.

Check(√) True or False

(1) The boy wants to know how often the girl plays basketball.

T ☐ F ☐

(2) The girl won't join the boy's club.

T ☐ F ☐

 Listen and Talk C

W: Hello. Welcome to Sports World. May I help you?

B: Yes, I came to register for a swimming class.

W: Is this your first time ❶taking swimming lessons?

B: Yes, it is. I don't know ❷how to swim at all.

W: I see. How often do you want to take classes?

B: I want to take classes twice a week. I'd like to take classes on weekdays and not on weekends.

W: Then, ❸I suggest that you take the Beginner 2 class. This class meets on Tuesdays and Thursdays.

B: ❹That sounds good. I'd like to sign up for that class. How big is the class?

W: The class has a limit of 10 people.

B: ❺That's perfect.

W: 안녕하세요. Sports World에 오신 것을 환영합니다. 무엇을 도와드릴까요?
B: 네, 수영 수업을 등록하려고 왔어요.
W: 수영 수업을 받는 것이 이번이 처음인가요?
B: 네. 저는 수영하는 법을 전혀 알지 못해요.
W: 알겠어요. 얼마나 자주 수업을 받고 싶으신가요?
B: 일주일에 두 번 수업을 듣길 원해요. 주말이 아니라 주중에 수업을 듣고 싶어요.
W: 그럼, 초급 2반을 들을 것을 권합니다. 이 수업은 화요일과 목요일에 있어요.
B: 좋아요. 그 수업에 등록할게요. 그 수업은 몇 명이 듣나요?
W: 그 수업은 제한 인원이 열 명입니다.
B: 좋아요.

❶ taking은 앞에 나온 time을 수식하는 현재분사이다.
❷ know의 목적어로 '의문사+to부정사'가 쓰이고 있다. 'not ~ at all'은 '전혀 ~ 아니다'라는 뜻이다.
❸ 상대방에게 어떤 일이나 행동을 제안하거나 권유할 때 쓰는 표현이다.
❹ That은 'This class meets on Tuesdays and Thursdays.'를 가리킨다.
❺ That은 'The class has a limit of 10 people.'을 가리킨다.

Check(√) True or False

(3) The boy wants to take swimming lessons.

T ☐ F ☐

(4) The Beginner 2 class has a limit of 10 people.

T ☐ F ☐

Listen and Talk A 2

B: I don't swim often. How about you, Kate? How often do you swim?
G: I swim four times a week.
B: ❶ That often? Anyway, ❷it'll be fun swimming together today.
G: Yes, but before we swim, I suggest we do stretching exercises.
B: ❸That's a good idea.

❶ That은 지시부사로 쓰여 '그렇게, 그 정도로'의 의미이다.
❷ it은 가주어이며 진주어는 'swimming together today'이다.
❸ 상대방의 제안이나 조언에 답하는 표현이다.

Listen and Talk A 3

B: Suji, how often do you take bowling lessons?
G: Twice a week. I'm just a beginner. I heard you're very good.
B: Well, I love bowling. Hmm. Your bowling ball ❶looks heavy for you. I suggest you use a lighter ball.
G: OK. I'll look for a lighter ❷one, then.

❶ 'look+형용사'로 '~하게 보이다'라는 의미이다.
❷ one은 'bowling ball'을 대신하는 부정대명사이다.

Listen and Talk A 4

B: Mina, how often do you come here ❶to run?
G: Every day.
B: Can I run with you today?
G: Sure, but I suggest you wear running shoes. Your shoes ❷aren't good for running.

❶ to부정사의 목적을 나타내는 부사적 용법이다.
❷ be good for: ~에 좋다

Listen and Talk B

A: Minsu, how often do you exercise?
B: I exercise once ❶a week.
A: I suggest you exercise more often.
B: ❷OK. I'll try.

❶ a는 'per(~마다)'의 의미이다.
❷ 상대방의 제안이나 조언에 답하는 표현이다.

Talk and Play

A: Jiho, ❶how often do you exercise?
B: I exercise ❷three times a week.
A: That's good.

❶ 'how many times do you exercise a week?'이라고 좀 더 구체적으로 물어볼 수도 있다.
❷ 3번 이상의 경우 '기수+times'로 나타낸다. 요즘에는 twice 대신에 'two times'라고 하기도 한다.

Review 1

B: Mina, how often do you swim?
G: I swim every day.
B: Can I ❶go swimming with you this afternoon?
G: Sure, but ❷I suggest you bring a swimming cap. Without a swimming cap, you ❸aren't allowed in the pool.

❶ 'go -ing'는 '~하러 가다'라는 의미이며 주로 오락을 나타낼 때 쓰인다. (go studying: X)
❷ 'you'd better bring a swimming cap.'으로 바꿔 쓸 수 있다.
❸ '허락되는' 것이므로 수동태로 써야 한다.

Review 2

B: Somi, ❶is your piano practice over?
G: Yes, it is.
B: How often do you practice?
G: I practice twice a week.

❶ 'be over'는 '끝나다'라는 의미이다.

Review 3

W: Hello. May I help you?
B: Yes, I came to register for a soccer class.
W: I see. How often do you want to ❶take classes?
B: I want to take classes twice a week. I'd like to take classes ❷on weekends.
W: Then, I suggest that you take the Beginner 1 class. This class meets on Saturdays and Sundays.
B: ❸That sounds good.

❶ take classes: 수업을 듣다
❷ on weekends: 주말에
❸ That은 'This class meets on Saturdays and Sundays.'를 가리킨다.

● 다음 우리말과 일치하도록 빈칸에 알맞은 말을 쓰시오.

Listen and Talk A 1

B: How _____ do you play basketball?

G: I play _____ a week, but I want to play _____ often.

B: I _____ you join my basketball club. We play _____ _____ a week.

G: That sounds _____! It'll be fun _____ _____ with you.

Listen and Talk A 2

B: I don't swim often. How _____ you, Kate? _____ _____ do you swim?

G: I swim _____ _____ a week.

B: _____ often? Anyway, _____'ll be fun _____ together today.

G: Yes, but before we swim, I _____ we _____ _____ exercises.

B: That's a good idea.

Listen and Talk A 3

B: Suji, _____ _____ do you _____ bowling lessons?

G: _____ a week. I'm just a _____. I heard you're very good.

B: Well, I love bowling. Hmm. Your bowling ball looks _____ for you. I _____ you _____ a lighter ball.

G: OK. I'll look _____ a lighter _____, then.

Listen and Talk A 4

B: Mina, _____ _____ do you come here _____ _____?

G: Every day.

B: Can I run with you today?

G: Sure, but I _____ you _____ running shoes. Your shoes aren't _____ _____ running.

Listen and Talk B

A: Minsu, _____ _____ do you exercise?

B: I exercise once _____ week.

A: I _____ you exercise more often.

B: OK. I'll _____.

해석

B: 얼마나 자주 농구를 하니?

G: 일주일에 한 번 해. 그런데 더 자주 하고 싶어.

B: 네가 우리 농구 동아리에 들어오기를 제안해. 우리는 일주일에 세 번 농구를 해.

G: 좋은 생각이야! 같이 하면 재미있을 거야.

B: 난 수영을 자주 하지 않아. 넌 어떠니, Kate? 얼마나 자주 수영을 하러 가니?

G: 일주일에 네 번 수영을 해.

B: 그렇게 자주? 어쨌든 오늘 같이 수영을 하면 재미있을 거야.

G: 응, 그런데 우리가 수영하기 전에 스트레칭을 하는 것을 제안해.

B: 좋은 생각이다.

B: 수지야, 너는 얼마나 자주 볼링 수업을 받니?

G: 일주일에 두 번 받아. 나는 초보야. 난 네가 볼링을 잘한다고 들었어.

B: 음, 난 볼링을 좋아해. 흠. 네 볼링공이 무거워 보인다. 더 가벼운 공을 쓰는 것을 제안해.

G: 알겠어. 그럼 더 가벼운 공을 찾아봐야겠다.

B: 미나야, 넌 달리기를 하러 이곳에 얼마나 자주 오니?

G: 매일 와.

B: 오늘 너와 함께 달리기를 해도 될까?

G: 물론이야, 하지만 네가 운동화를 신는 것을 제안해. 네 신발은 달리기에 적합하지 않아.

A: 민수야, 너는 얼마나 자주 운동을 하니?

B: 나는 일주일에 한 번 운동을 해.

A: 더 자주 운동하기를 제안해.

B: 알겠어. 시도해 볼게.

Listen and Talk C

W: Hello. Welcome to Sports World. May I help you?

B: Yes, I came _____ _____ _____ a swimming class.

W: Is this your first time _____ swimming lessons?

B: Yes, it is. I don't know _____ _____ _____ _____ _____.

W: I see. _____ _____ do you want to _____ classes?

B: I want to _____ classes _____ _____ _____. I'd like to _____ classes _____ weekdays and not _____ weekends.

W: Then, I suggest _____ you _____ the Beginner 2 class. This class meets _____ Tuesdays and Thursdays.

B: That _____ _____. I'd like to _____ _____ _____ that class. How big is the class?

W: The class has _____ _____ _____ 10 people.

B: That's perfect.

Talk and Play

A: Jiho, _____ _____ do you exercise?

B: I exercise _____ _____ _____ _____.

A: That's good.

Review 1

B: Mina, _____ _____ do you swim?

G: I swim every day.

B: Can I _____ _____ with you this afternoon?

G: Sure, but I _____ you _____ a swimming cap. _____ a swimming cap, you _____ _____ in the pool.

Review 2

B: Somi, is your piano practice _____?

G: Yes, it is.

B: _____ _____ do you practice?

G: I practice _____ _____ _____.

Review 3

W: Hello. May I help you?

B: Yes, I came to _____ _____ a soccer class.

W: I see. _____ _____ do you want to _____ classes?

B: I want to _____ classes _____ _____ _____. I'd like to _____ classes _____ weekends.

W: Then, I _____ that you _____ the Beginner 1 class. This class meets _____ Saturdays and Sundays.

B: That sounds _____.

해석

W: 안녕하세요. Sports World에 오신 것을 환영합니다. 무엇을 도와드릴까요?

B: 네, 수영 수업을 등록하려고 왔어요.

W: 수영 수업을 받는 것이 이번이 처음인가요?

B: 네. 저는 수영하는 법을 전혀 알지 못해요.

W: 알겠어요. 얼마나 자주 수업을 받고 싶으신가요?

B: 일주일에 두 번 수업을 듣길 원해요. 주말이 아니라 주중에 수업을 듣고 싶어요.

W: 그럼, 초급 2반을 들을 것을 권합니다. 이 수업은 화요일과 목요일에 있어요.

B: 좋아요. 그 수업으로 등록할게요. 그 수업은 몇 명이 듣나요?

W: 그 수업은 제한 인원이 열 명입니다.

B: 좋아요.

A: 지호야, 너는 얼마나 자주 운동을 하니?

B: 나는 일주일에 세 번 운동을 해.

A: 좋다.

B: 미나야, 너는 얼마나 자주 수영을 하니?

G: 나는 매일 수영을 해.

B: 오늘 오후에 너와 수영하러 가도 될까?

G: 물론이지, 하지만 수영 모자를 챙기는 것을 제안해. 수영 모자 없이 수영장에 들어가는 것은 허락되지 않아.

B: 소미야, 피아노 연습은 끝났니?

G: 응, 그래.

B: 얼마나 자주 연습을 하니?

G: 나는 일주일에 두 번 연습을 해.

W: 안녕하세요. 무엇을 도와드릴까요?

B: 네, 축구 수업을 등록하러 왔어요.

W: 알겠습니다. 얼마나 자주 수업을 수강하기를 원하나요?

B: 일주일에 두 번 수강하고 싶어요. 주말에 수업을 수강하는 게 좋아요.

W: 그럼, 초급 1반을 수강하기를 제안드려요. 이 수업은 토요일과 일요일에 있어요.

B: 좋아요.

Conversation 시험대비 기본평가

01 다음 빈칸 (A)에 알맞은 문장은?

> B: _____(A)_____
> G: I play once a week, but I want to play more often.

① I would like to play basketball.
② Would you like to play basketball?
③ How often do you play basketball?
④ Do you play basketball?
⑤ Can you play basketball?

02 주어진 어휘를 이용하여 밑줄 친 우리말을 영작하시오.

> B: I don't swim often. How about you, Kate? How often do you swim?
> G: I swim four times a week.
> B: That often? Anyway, it'll be fun swimming together today.
> G: Yes, but before we swim, 스트레칭을 하는 것을 제안해. (suggest, stretching exercises) (6 words)
> B: That's a good idea.

➡ _____

[03~04] 다음 대화를 읽고 물음에 답하시오.

> B: Suji, how often do you take bowling lessons?
> G: (A)일주일에 두 번. I'm just a beginner. I heard you're very good.
> B: Well, I love bowling. Hmm. Your bowling ball looks heavy for you. I __(a)__ you use a lighter ball.
> G: OK. I'll look for a lighter one, then.

03 다음 영영풀이를 참고하여 대화의 빈칸 (a)에 알맞은 말은?

> to make a proposal

① register ② support ③ suggest ④ guess ⑤ pursue

04 밑줄 친 (A)의 우리말을 3 단어로 쓰시오.

➡ _____

01 다음 중 짝지어진 대화가 <u>어색한</u> 것은?

① A: How often do you exercise?
   B: I exercised a lot.
② A: How did you win the race?
   B: I kept track of the time very well.
③ A: I have breakfast every day.
   B: That's good.
④ A: Somi, is your piano practice over?
   B: Yes, it is.
⑤ A: I think I have a cold.
   B: I suggest you go see a doctor.

[02~05] 다음 대화를 읽고 물음에 답하시오.

W: Hello. Welcome to Sports World. May I help you?
B: Yes, I came to register for a swimming class.
W: Is this your first time taking swimming lessons?
B: Yes, it is. (a)저는 수영하는 법을 전혀 알지 못해요.
W: I see. How often do you want to take classes?
B: I want to take classes twice a week. I'd like to take classes ___(A)___ weekdays and not ___(A)___ weekends.
W: Then, _____(B)_____ the Beginner 2 class. This class meets on Tuesdays and Thursdays.
B: That sounds good. I'd like to sign up for that class. How big is the class?
W: The class has a limit of 10 people.
B: That's perfect.

02 빈칸 (A)에 공통으로 들어갈 말을 고르시오.

① about   ② on   ③ for
④ at   ⑤ in

03 위 대화의 빈칸 (B)에 들어갈 알맞은 말을 주어진 어휘를 배열하여 쓰시오.

> I, you, that, take, suggest

➡ _____

04 밑줄 친 (a)의 우리말에 맞게 주어진 어휘를 이용하여 영작하시오. (how, all)

➡ _____

05 위 대화의 내용과 일치하지 <u>않는</u> 것은?

① The boy visited Sports World.
② The boy wants to register for a swimming class.
③ The boy wants to take classes twice a week.
④ The Beginner 2 class meets on Tuesdays and Thursdays.
⑤ The boy already signed up for the Beginner 2 class.

06 다음 대화가 자연스럽게 연결되도록 (A)~(D)를 순서대로 가장 적절하게 배열한 것은?

> (A) I suggest you play computer games less often.
> (B) Seonmi, how often do you play computer games?
> (C) I play computer games every day.
> (D) OK. I'll try.

① (B) – (A) – (C) – (D)
② (B) – (C) – (A) – (D)
③ (B) – (C) – (D) – (A)
④ (C) – (B) – (D) – (A)
⑤ (C) – (D) – (B) – (A)

[07~08] 다음 대화를 읽고 물음에 답하시오.

> A: Hojun, how (a)[often / much] do you read a book?
> B: I read a book twice (b)[a / the] week.
> A: I suggest you (c)[read / will read] more books.
> B: _____ (A) _____

07 위 대화의 빈칸 (A)에 들어갈 말로 알맞은 것을 모두 고르시오.

① Will you try?
② OK. I'll try.
③ Excuse me, but will you read more?
④ I'll give it a try.
⑤ Enjoy your reading.

08 위 대화의 괄호 (a)~(c)에서 알맞은 것을 골라 바르게 짝지은 것은?

	(a)	(b)	(c)
①	often	a	read
②	often	the	read
③	often	a	will read
④	much	the	will read
⑤	much	a	will read

[09~10] 다음 대화를 읽고 물음에 답하시오.

> B: Somi, is your piano practice __(A)__ ?
> G: Yes, it is.
> B: How often do you practice?
> G: _____ (B) _____

09 '피아노 연습이 끝났는지' 묻는 질문이 되도록 위 대화의 빈칸 (A)에 알맞은 말을 고르시오.

① up   ② down   ③ for
④ over   ⑤ on

10 위 대화의 빈칸 (B)에 들어갈 말로 가장 적절한 것은?

① I play a lot.
② I practice very much.
③ I practice twice a week.
④ I practice playing the piano.
⑤ I practice playing computer games.

11 다음 대화의 밑줄 친 부분의 의도로 가장 적절한 것은?

> A: Hajun, <u>how often do you eat late at night?</u>
> B: I eat late at night five times a week.
> A: I suggest that you eat late at night less.

① 궁금증 표현하기   ② 제안하기
③ 설명 요청하기   ④ 반복 요청하기
⑤ 빈도 묻기

[12~13] 다음 대화를 읽고 물음에 답하시오.

> W: Hello. (①) May I help you?
> B: Yes, I came to register for a soccer class.
> W: I see. (②) How often do you want to take classes?
> B: (③) I want to take classes twice a week. (④) I'd like to take classes on weekends.
> W: (⑤) This class meets on Saturdays and Sundays.
> B: That sounds good.

12 위 대화의 (①)~(⑤) 중 주어진 문장이 들어갈 곳은?

> Then, I suggest that you take the Beginner 1 class.

①   ②   ③   ④   ⑤

서답형
13 How often will the boy take the soccer class?

➡ _____

[01~03] 다음 대화를 읽고 물음에 답하시오.

W: Hello. Welcome to Sports World. May I help you?

B: Yes, I came to register for a swimming class.

W: Is this your first time taking swimming lessons?

B: Yes, it is. I don't know how to swim at all.

W: I see. How often do you want to take classes?

B: I want to take classes twice a week. (a)주말이 아니라 주중에 수업을 듣고 싶어요.

(A) The class has a limit of 10 people.

(B) That's perfect.

(C) That sounds good. I'd like to sign up for that class. How big is the class?

(D) Then, I suggest that you take the Beginner 2 class. This class meets on Tuesdays and Thursdays.

01 위 대화의 (A)~(D)를 알맞은 순서로 배열하시오.

➡ _____

02 괄호 안에 주어진 어휘를 이용하여 밑줄 친 (a)를 11 단어로 쓰시오.

➡ _____

_____ (like, take classes, weekdays, not)

03 How many people can the Beginner 2 class have? Use the words "up to."

➡ _____

[04~05] 다음 글을 읽고 물음에 답하시오.

Do you like riding a bike? Then, I suggest you join our club, Fun Wheels. We ride bikes once a week, on Saturdays. We ride along the river or in parks. (a)함께 자전거를 타는 것은 즐거워. (fun, bikes, to)

04 What does the writer suggest?

➡ _____

05 괄호 안에 주어진 어휘를 이용하여 밑줄 친 우리말 (a)에 맞게 6 단어로 쓰시오.

➡ _____

[06~07] 다음 대화를 읽고 물음에 답하시오.

B: Mina, how often do you swim?

G: I swim every day.

B: Can I go swimming with you this afternoon?

G: ____(A)____, but (a)수영 모자를 챙기는 것을 제안해. (suggest, bring, a swimming cap) Without a swimming cap, you aren't allowed in the pool.

06 위 대화의 빈칸 (A)에 알맞은 말을 (1) 1 단어로, (2) 2 단어로 쓰시오.

➡ (1) _____ (2) _____

07 괄호 안에 주어진 어휘를 이용하여 밑줄 친 우리말 (a)에 맞게 7 단어로 쓰시오.

➡ _____

교과서

Grammar

1 분사

> • Pacers usually have flags or balloons **showing** their finish time.
> 페이서들은 보통 자신들의 완주 시간을 나타내는 깃발이나 풍선을 가지고 있다.
>
> • The girl **waiting** at the bus stop is my sister.
> 버스 정류장에서 기다리고 있는 소녀는 내 여동생이다.

■ 현재분사는 '동사원형+-ing' 형태로 형용사처럼 명사를 앞 또는 뒤에서 꾸며준다. 일반적으로는 명사 앞에서, 다른 어구와 함께 구(phrase)를 이룰 때는 명사 뒤에서 꾸민다.

  • The **singing** bird is very big. 노래를 하고 있는 새는 매우 크다.

  • The bird **singing in the tree** is very big. 나무에서 노래를 하고 있는 새는 매우 크다.

■ 현재분사(-ing)는 능동/진행, 과거분사(p.p.)는 수동/완료의 의미를 갖는다.

  • Jack is **sleeping** on the floor. Jack은 바닥에서 자고 있다.

  • My hobby is to collect the **fallen** leaves. 내 취미는 낙엽을 모으는 것이다.

■ 명사를 뒤에서 꾸미는 분사구는 '주격 관계대명사+be동사'가 생략된 것으로 볼 수 있다.

  • The men (**who are**) **climbing** the mountain are Africans. 그 산을 등반하는 사람들은 아프리카인들이다.

  • Tom watched the movie (**which was**) **made** by the director.
  Tom은 그 감독에 의해 만들어진 영화를 보았다.

■ 분사는 명사를 꾸며주는 역할 외에도, 주어나 목적어를 보충 설명하는 서술 용법이 있다. 이 경우, 주격 보어 또는 목적격 보어가 된다.

  • The idol star was standing **surrounded** by her fans. 그 아이돌 스타는 그녀의 팬들에게 둘러싸인 채 서 있었다.

  • She kept them **raising their hands**. 그녀는 그들이 계속해서 손을 들고 있도록 했다.

  • Matilda felt her shoulder **pushed** by someone. Matilda는 누군가에 의해 그녀의 어깨가 밀리는 것을 느꼈다.

■ 분사와 동명사의 구분은 수식받는 명사의 능동성이나 용도 여부를 통해 판단한다.

  • Look at a **singing** bird. 노래를 부르는 새를 보아라. (능동-현재분사)

  • This is a **singing** room. 이것은 노래방이다. (용도-동명사)

핵심 Check

1. 다음 괄호 안에서 알맞은 단어를 고르시오.

  (1) The woman (wearing / wore) glasses is my teacher.

  (2) The actor had his arms (breaking / broken) in the accident.

② as 형용사/부사 as

> • They are **as important as** the players. 그들은 선수들만큼이나 중요하다.
> • Jason can run **as fast as** Mike. Jason은 Mike만큼 빠르게 달릴 수 있다.

■ 'as 형용사/부사 as …' 구문은 '…만큼 어떠한[어떻게]'라는 뜻이다.
  • I am **as hungry as** you. 나는 너만큼 배가 고프다.
  • Canada is **as large as** the USA. 캐나다는 미국만큼 크기가 크다.

■ 'as ~ as' 사이에는 형용사/부사의 '원급'만 들어갈 수 있다.
  • Peter was **as ~~happier~~ as** his brother. (×) Peter는 그의 형만큼 행복했다. (→ happy)
  • Jim walks **as ~~fastest~~ as** his friends. (×) Jim은 그의 친구들만큼 빨리 걷는다. (→ fast)

■ 'as ~ as'의 부정은 not을 앞에 쓰며, 앞의 as 대신 so를 쓸 수 있다.
  'not as[so] 형용사/부사 as …' 구문은 '비교급' 의미가 된다.
  • Sujin is **not so[as] tall as** Eric. Sujin은 Eric만큼 키가 크지는 않다. (Eric이 Sujin보다 크다.)
    = Sujin is **less tall than** Eric. = Eric is **taller than** Sujin.
  • Turtles are **not as[so] slow as** snails. 거북이들은 달팽이만큼 느리지는 않다.
    = Snails are **slower than** turtles.

■ 원칙적으로 'as 형용사/부사 as …'에서 대명사의 격을 구분해서 써야 한다.
  • Susan loves him **as much as** I. Susan은 나만큼 그를 사랑해. (내가 그를 사랑하는 것만큼)
  • Susan loves him **as much as** me. Susan은 나만큼 그를 사랑해. (Susan이 나를 사랑하는 것만큼)

  cf. 그러나, 의미의 혼동이 없을 경우 격을 구분하지 않고 사용하기도 한다.
    • Simpson is **as lazy as** I. (○) (as lazy as I am)
    • Simpson is **as lazy as** me. (○) 관용적으로 사용

■ 'as ~ as' 사이에 들어가는 말이 명사를 수식하면 형용사, 동사를 수식하면 부사를 쓴다.
  • Minju drives **as [~~good~~ / well] as** Sein (does). Minju는 Sein만큼이나 운전을 잘한다.
  • The cake that Mary baked for me was as [~~softly~~ / **soft**] as the sponge.
    Mary가 내게 구워 준 케이크는 스폰지처럼 부드러웠다.

핵심 Check

2. 다음 우리말과 같은 뜻이 되도록 주어진 단어를 알맞은 순서로 배열하시오.
  (1) 오늘은 어제만큼이나 바람이 분다. (as, is, today, yesterday, windy, as)
    ➡ _____

  (2) 그 램프는 의자만큼 크지 않다. (as, the stool, is, the lamp, tall, so, not)
    ➡ _____

01 다음 as ～ as 문장에서 어법상 어색한 부분을 바르게 고쳐 쓰시오.

(1) The clock is as more expensive as the furniture.

_____ ➡ _____

(2) They arrived at the airport as earliest as we did.

_____ ➡ _____

(3) Frank is not as honest than Jerome.

_____ ➡ _____

(4) The villagers were as diligent as them in other towns.

_____ ➡ _____

02 다음 중 어법상 바르지 않은 것은?

① The man using the photocopier is Saunders.
② The kids singing downstairs are my students.
③ The people watching the fight were shocked.
④ The girl digging the hole in the garden is my daughter.
⑤ The room crowding with insects is already reserved.

03 다음 대화의 밑줄 친 부분 중에서 어법상 잘못된 곳을 고르시오.

A: ①Is Australia ②bigger ③than Brazil?
B: No. It is not so ④bigger ⑤as Brazil.

04 다음 우리말에 맞게 주어진 어구를 바르게 배열하시오. (필요하면 어형을 바꿀 것.)

(1) 길 건너편에서 손을 흔들고 있는 소녀는 Sarah이다. (is, the street, the girl, Sarah, wave, across)

➡ _____

(2) 우리나라를 향해 접근 중인 폭풍은 강한 위력을 갖고 있다. (our country, a strong force, the storm, has, approach)

➡ _____

01 다음 우리말을 바르게 영작한 것은?

> 호박은 오이만큼 맛있지 않다.

① A pumpkin is not also yummy but as a cucumber.
② A pumpkin is no less yummy as a cucumber.
③ A pumpkin is very not yummy as a cucumber.
④ A pumpkin is not so yummy as a cucumber.
⑤ A pumpkin is as not yummy as a cucumber.

서답형

02 다음 문장에서 어법상 틀린 부분을 찾아 바르게 고쳐 쓰시오.

> I saw her pictures taking in London.

➡ _____

03 다음 표의 내용과 일치하지 <u>않는</u> 것은?

	Sam	John
Age	6	6
Weight	22kg	23kg
Height	135cm	129cm

① Sam is as old as John.
② John is not so tall as Sam.
③ John is not as heavy as Sam.
④ Sam is not as short as John.
⑤ John is not so light as Sam.

04 다음 괄호 안의 단어의 알맞은 형태가 순서대로 바르게 짝 지어진 것은?

> • The audience (attend) the lecture can be given the free coupons.
> • The time (spend) playing computer games by the kids is too much.
> • The concert was (excite).

① attending – spending – exciting
② attending – spent – excited
③ attending – spent – exciting
④ attended – spending – excited
⑤ attended – spent – exciting

05 다음 중 어법상 옳은 것은?

① Those rocks are as harder as steel.
② The walking stick is as long as the snake.
③ The mouse is as faster as the cat.
④ Jinhee is as tallest as her mother.
⑤ The boxer is as heavier as the other.

중요

06 다음 중 밑줄 친 부분의 쓰임이 <u>다른</u> 하나는?

① There is a <u>singing</u> elephant in Bangkok.
② The officer <u>standing</u> next to the police car is Corbie.
③ The <u>sleeping</u> baby is Jane's son.
④ The kids forgot <u>opening</u> the door.
⑤ The girl <u>looking</u> at him was happy.

07 다음 우리말을 영어로 옳게 옮긴 것은?

> 내 배낭은 수진이의 배낭만큼 크다.

① My backpack is big as Sujin's backpack.
② Sujin's backpack is so big as mine.
③ My backpack is as big as Sujin.
④ My backpack is as big as Sujin's.
⑤ My backpack is big enough as Sujin.

08 다음 중 짝지어진 두 문장의 의미가 서로 <u>다른</u> 것은?

① My team played better than his.
　→ His team didn't play as well as mine.
② Susan is slimmer than Yujin.
　→ Yujin isn't as slim as Susan.
③ Julie arrived earlier than Thomas.
　→ Thomas didn't arrive as early as Julie.
④ I've lived here longer than Peter.
　→ Peter haven't lived here as long as I.
⑤ Ron picked more berries than Sean.
　→ Sean picked as many berries as Ron.

09 다음 중 밑줄 친 부분의 쓰임이 <u>어색한</u> 것을 <u>모두</u> 고르면?

① People thought the movie was <u>touched</u>.
② The story by the comedian is so <u>boring</u> that everyone wants to get out.
③ The football game was the most <u>excited</u> in my life.
④ How many <u>developing</u> countries are there in the world?
⑤ The thief tried to climb over the wall <u>covered</u> with snow.

서답형
10 다음 각 문장에서 어법상 <u>어색한</u> 부분을 하나씩 찾아서 알맞게 고치시오.

(1) Have you met the girl sung the song in the hall?
　_____ ➡ _____
(2) Bentley found the seashells using by the people in ancient times.
　_____ ➡ _____
(3) There were a lot of players ran in the playground.
　_____ ➡ _____

11 다음 중 어법상 <u>어색한</u> 것을 <u>모두</u> 고르면?

① The girl pointing at me was Jenny.
② The people I meeting here were so good.
③ The pictures got stolen by the thief were found in a different country.
④ The boy in a wide pool swims fast is Domus.
⑤ The girls walking their dogs talked to the strangers.

12 다음 문장의 빈칸에 들어갈 말로 가장 알맞은 것은?

Five baby penguins eat as _____ as two adults.

① most
② more
③ better
④ good
⑤ much

서답형
13 다음 예시와 같이 두 문장을 한 문장으로 연결할 때, 빈칸에 알맞은 말을 넣으시오.

• The old lady is watching the film.
• She is my grandma.
→ The old lady watching the film is my grandma.

(1) • The table is very old.
　• It was made by my ancestors.
　→ The table _____ _____ very old.
(2) • There were some flies.
　• They were buzzing around the jam.
　→ There _____ _____ _____ the jam.

14 Translate the following Korean into English as directed below.

> 검은 선글라스를 끼고 있는 남자들이 버스를 탔다.

<Directions>
- Use the words: sunglasses, on, wear, get, men, black (Change the form if necessary.)
- Complete it with 9 words in total.

➡ The _____
the bus.

15 다음 중 밑줄 친 부분의 쓰임이 같은 것끼리 짝지어진 것은?

ⓐ Participants are expected to be in the <u>waiting</u> room.
ⓑ There were no more trains <u>leaving</u> after 11 p.m.
ⓒ The girls <u>dancing</u> in the middle of the square are my granddaughters.
ⓓ My aunt <u>living</u> in Paris spent most of her money collecting the luxury bags.
ⓔ Choose an appropriate <u>sleeping</u> bag for your camping.

① ⓐ, ⓑ   ② ⓐ, ⓒ
③ ⓐ, ⓑ, ⓔ   ④ ⓑ, ⓒ, ⓓ
⑤ ⓓ, ⓔ

16 다음 문장의 밑줄 친 부분이 어색한 것은?

① Shane decided to get up as <u>early</u> as possible.
② It would be good for your health to drink as <u>many</u> water as possible.
③ The medical staff examined the patient as <u>quickly</u> as possible.

④ After the car accident, Sarah walks as <u>often</u> as possible.
⑤ Remember to call your mom as <u>soon</u> as possible.

17 다음 중 어법상 어색한 문장들의 개수는 모두 몇 개인지 고르시오.

┤ 보기 ├
ⓐ The clocks producing in Switzerland are among the best ones in the world.
ⓑ The basketball player calling the Black Mamba was Kobe Bryant.
ⓒ The baby ducks walked zigzag made the noisy sounds.
ⓓ The song composed by the singer became popular.
ⓔ There are many tourists taken photos in the forbidden areas.

① 1개   ② 2개   ③ 3개   ④ 4개   ⑤ 5개

18 다음 중 주어진 문장과 가장 가까운 뜻을 가진 문장을 고르시오.

> Alicia is the strongest student in her class.

① Alicia is stronger than most of the students in her class.
② No other student in her class is as strong as Alicia.
③ No one in her class is the strongest for Alicia.
④ Alicia is as strong as any other student in her class.
⑤ Alicia isn't as strong as any other student in her class.

01 다음 표를 보고 괄호 안에 주어진 단어를 이용하여, 표의 내용과 일치하도록 영작하시오. (단어 변형 불가능)

	Dave	Sean	Key
Age	16	15	16
Weight	65kg	67kg	62kg
Height	175cm	175cm	178cm

(1) Dave _____ .
(old, as, Key)

(2) Sean _____ .
(old, so, Key)

(3) Sean _____ .
(tall, as, Dave)

(4) Dave _____ .
(tall, so, not)

(5) No one _____ .
(heavy, so)

(6) No one _____ . (tall, so)

02 다음 그림을 보고, 우리말에 맞게 괄호 안의 어휘를 이용하여 빈칸을 채우시오.

Unlike his friends (A)_____(hold) their arms high, Yunho was standing at the court (B)_____(look) at them.
(팔을 높이 들고 있는 그의 친구들과는 달리, Yunho는 코트에서 그들을 바라보며 서 있었다.)

03 다음 우리말을 괄호 안에 주어진 단어를 이용하여 영작하시오. (어형 변화 가능)

(1) Minju는 그녀의 선생님만큼 영어를 자유롭게 말할 수 있다. (speak, free, can)
→ Minju _____
_____ .

(2) Sein은 그 가수처럼 노래를 잘 불렀다. (sing, well)
→ Sein _____ .

(3) 내 남동생은 엄마만큼 자주 설거지를 한다. (do, often, my mom)
→ My brother _____
_____ .

(4) 그 영화는 원작 소설만큼 재미있지는 않았다. (novel, so, interest, original)
→ The movie _____
_____ .

04 다음 괄호 안의 단어들을 바르게 배열하여 문장을 완성하시오. (단, 동사를 어법상 알맞은 형태로 변형할 것.)

(1) Daisy was watching _____
_____ . (the, in, garden, flowers, plant, my)

(2) The _____
are waiting for their teacher. (the, stand, girls, office, near, post)

(3) The book _____ .
(by, write, is, Mark Twain, excite)

(4) Who are the _____
_____ ? (the, dance, music, gentlemen, disco, to)

05 다음 그림을 보고, 우리말에 맞게 괄호 안의 어휘를 이용하여 빈칸을 채우시오.

(1)

- 석봉은 엄마가 떡을 자른 것만큼 반듯하게 글씨를 쓰지 못했다.

Seokbong ＿＿＿＿＿＿＿＿＿＿＿

＿＿＿＿＿＿＿＿＿ the rice cake.

(could, cut, neatly, as, write, as, not)

(2)

- 그는 생각한 것만큼 살이 빠지지 않아서 실망했다.

He was disappointed because he ＿＿＿＿

＿＿＿＿＿＿＿＿＿＿＿＿＿＿＿＿＿.

(lose, weight, not, thought, much, as, as)

06 다음 〈보기〉에 주어진 동사를 한 번씩만 사용하여 어법에 맞게 바꿔 빈칸을 완성하시오.

┌─ 보기 ┐

appear　make　write　cover　know

Parasite is the film (A)＿＿＿＿ by director Bong, who is well (B)＿＿＿＿ for the movie *Host*. Its poster shows the black band (C)＿＿＿＿ the eyes of the characters, (D)＿＿＿＿ the movie more mysterious. There are many stairs (E)＿＿＿＿ in the movie, which symbolizes the status of the characters.

07 다음 각각의 두 문장을 분사를 활용하여, 괄호 안의 조건에 맞게 한 문장으로 고치시오.

(1) I met a lady. She was wearing a colorful skirt. (명사를 뒤에서 수식)

→ I met ＿＿＿＿＿＿＿＿＿＿＿＿＿.

(2) Those are the books. The books were copied illegally. (명사를 앞에서 수식)

→ Those ＿＿＿＿＿＿＿＿＿＿＿＿＿.

(3) My kids saw an airplane. The airplane is flying between the clouds. (명사를 뒤에서 수식)

→ My kids saw ＿＿＿＿＿＿＿＿＿

＿＿＿＿＿＿＿＿＿＿.

(4) The violin is so expensive. It is made by the master craftsman. (명사를 뒤에서 수식)

→ The violin ＿＿＿＿＿＿＿＿＿＿

＿＿＿＿＿＿＿＿＿.

(5) Be careful not to wake up the baby. She is sleeping. (명사를 앞에서 수식)

→ Be ＿＿＿＿＿＿＿＿＿＿＿＿＿

＿＿＿＿＿＿＿＿＿.

08 다음 그림을 보고, 괄호 안의 단어를 적절한 분사로 활용하여 빈칸에 알맞게 채우시오.

➡ Minho found his father ＿＿＿＿(sleep) in the sofa, ＿＿＿＿(wear) his suit as soon as he came home from work.

Reading

Hidden People in Sports

In sports, only the players get a trophy or medal, but they don't win on their own. There are people who help the players. These people are often hidden and don't get attention. However, they are as important as the players. Here are some examples.

Pacers in a Marathon

Pacers run with other runners and lead them in a marathon. Pacers are experienced runners, and their job is to help other runners manage their race better. There can be several pacers in a race. Each pacer runs at different speeds and finishes the race in different times. Pacers usually have flags or balloons showing their finish time.

Runners can choose a pacer depending on their target finish time. For example, if a runner wants to finish the race in four hours, the runner will follow the four-hour pacer. Since the pacer keeps track of the time, the runner can achieve his or her goal of finishing the marathon in a particular time more easily. In short, pacers run but they don't run to win. They run for others.

hidden 숨겨진, 숨은

trophy 트로피

on one's own 혼자서, 혼자 힘으로(=alone, by oneself)

attention 주목, 관심

experienced 경험이 풍부한, 능숙한

several 몇몇의

depending on ~에 따라

target 목표, 목표로 하는 대상

keep track of (계속해서) ~을 파악하다, ~에 주의를 기울이다

achieve 달성하다, 성취하다

particular 특정한

in short 요컨대, 요약하면

확인문제

● 다음 문장이 본문의 내용과 일치하면 T, 일치하지 <u>않으면</u> F를 쓰시오.

1 Pacers are experienced runners and help other runners to manage their race better. ☐

2 Each pacer runs at the same speed. ☐

3 Runners can choose a pacer depending on their target finish time. ☐

4 Runners keep track of the time. ☐

5 The runner can achieve his or her goal of finishing the marathon in a particular time more easily by following a pacer. ☐

6 Pacers run to win. ☐

Pit Crews in Car Racing

You may only see the car and the driver during most car races, but there is a team behind the driver. This team is called a pit crew. A pit is a place on the side of the race track, and drivers stop there several times during a race. The main job of the pit crew is to check the car and change the tires. Changing the tires is especially important because the tires wear out easily in a high speed race.

A pit stop can be as short as 2 seconds, and there are as many as 20 members on a crew. Therefore, the pit crew has to work in perfect harmony. The driver may get all the attention, but as people say, "Races are won in the pits."

Sherpas in Mountain Climbing

The word *Sherpa* comes from the Sherpa tribe, which lives in the eastern part of Nepal. Sherpas have good climbing skills and know their way around the mountains well. They also have little difficulty breathing high up in the mountains. Therefore, mountain climbers started to hire Sherpas to help them climb Mount Everest.

Sherpas lead mountain climbers to the top of the mountain. They support climbers in many ways. For example, they put up tents and carry climbers' bags. Sherpas are often called the invisible people of Mount Everest because people often see a picture of only the climbers at the top of the mountain.

pit 피트(자동차 경주 도중에 급유, 타이어 교체나 수리를 하는 곳)

crew (같은 일에 종사하는) 팀, 조

especially 특히

wear out (낡아서) 떨어지다, 못 쓰게 되다, 닳아 버리다

second 초

therefore 그러므로

harmony 조화, 화합

tribe 종족, 부족

eastern 동쪽의, 동쪽에 위치한

skill 기량, 기술

breathe 숨을 쉬다

hire 고용하다

support 지원하다, 지지하다

put up (텐트, 벽 등을) 치다, 세우다

invisible 보이지 않는, 볼 수 없는

확인문제

● 다음 문장이 본문의 내용과 일치하면 T, 일치하지 않으면 F를 쓰시오.

1 A pit is a place on the side of the race track, where drivers stop several times during a race. ☐

2 The main job of the pit crew is to check the condition of the driver. ☐

3 The pit crew has to work in perfect harmony. ☐

4 The Sherpa tribe lives in the northern part of Nepal. ☐

5 Sherpas have little trouble breathing high up in the mountains. ☐

6 Sherpas are often called the visible people of Mount Everest. ☐

● 우리말을 참고하여 빈칸에 알맞은 말을 쓰시오.

1 _____ People in Sports

2 In sports, only the players get a trophy or medal, but they don't win _____ _____ _____.

3 There are people _____ help the players.

4 These people are often _____ and don't _____ _____.

5 However, they are _____ _____ _____ the players.

6 _____ _____ some examples.

7 _____ in a Marathon

8 Pacers _____ _____ other runners and _____ them in a marathon.

9 Pacers are _____ runners, and their job is to help other runners _____ _____ _____ _____ _____.

10 _____ _____ _____ several pacers in a race.

11 Each pacer runs _____ _____ _____ and finishes the race _____ _____ _____.

12 Pacers usually have flags or balloons _____ their finish time.

13 Runners can choose a pacer _____ _____ their target finish time.

14 For example, if a runner wants to finish the race _____ _____, the runner will follow the _____-hour pacer.

15 Since the pacer _____ _____ _____ the time, the runner can achieve his or her goal of finishing the marathon in a particular time more _____.

16 In short, pacers run but they don't run _____ _____.

17 They run _____ _____.

18 Pit Crews in _____ _____

19 You may only see the car and the driver _____ most car races, but there is a team _____ _____ _____ _____.

1	스포츠 속 숨은 조력자들
2	스포츠에서 선수들만 트로피나 메달을 받지만, 그들은 혼자 힘으로 이긴 것이 아니다.
3	그 선수들을 돕는 사람들이 있다.
4	이 사람들은 종종 숨겨져 있고 주목을 받지 못한다.
5	하지만 그들은 선수들만큼 중요하다.
6	여기 몇 가지 예가 있다.
7	마라톤의 페이서들
8	페이서들은 마라톤에서 다른 선수들과 함께 달리며 그들을 이끈다.
9	페이서들은 경험이 많은 선수들이며 그들의 역할은 다른 선수들이 경기를 더 잘 운영하도록 돕는 것이다.
10	한 경기에는 여러 명의 페이서들이 있을 수 있다.
11	각각의 페이서는 다른 속도로 달리고 다른 시간대에 경기를 마친다.
12	페이서들은 주로 자신들의 완주 시간을 나타내는 깃발이나 풍선들을 가지고 있다.
13	선수들은 자신들의 목표 완주 시간에 따라 페이서를 선택할 수 있다.
14	예를 들어, 한 선수가 4시간 안에 경기를 마치고 싶다면, 그 선수는 4시간 페이서를 따라갈 것이다.
15	페이서가 시간을 계속해서 파악하기 때문에, 선수는 특정 시간에 마라톤을 완주하려는 자신의 목표를 더 쉽게 달성할 수 있다.
16	요컨대, 페이서들은 달리지만 우승을 하기 위해 달리는 것은 아니다.
17	그들은 다른 선수들을 위해 달린다.
18	자동차 경주의 피트 크루
19	여러분은 대부분의 자동차 경주에서 자동차와 레이서만 보겠지만 그 레이서 뒤에는 팀이 있다.

20 This team _____ _____ a pit crew.

21 A pit is a place _____ _____ _____ _____ _____, and drivers stop there several times during a race.

22 The main job of the pit crew is _____ _____ the car and change the tires.

23 _____ the tires _____ especially important because the tires _____ _____ easily in a high speed race.

24 A pit stop can be _____ _____ _____ 2 seconds, and there are _____ _____ _____ 20 members on a crew.

25 Therefore, the pit crew has to work _____ _____ _____.

26 The driver may _____ _____ _____ _____ _____, but as people say, "Races are won _____ _____ _____."

27 Sherpas in Mountain Climbing

28 The word *Sherpa* _____ _____ the Sherpa tribe, which lives in the eastern part of Nepal.

29 Sherpas have _____ _____ _____ and know their way around the mountains well.

30 They also _____ _____ _____ _____ high up in the mountains.

31 Therefore, mountain climbers started to hire Sherpas _____ _____ _____ _____ Mount Everest.

32 Sherpas _____ mountain climbers _____ the top of the mountain.

33 They support climbers _____ _____ _____.

34 For example, they _____ _____ tents and carry climbers' bags.

35 Sherpas are often called the _____ people of Mount Everest because people often see a picture of only the climbers _____ _____ _____ the mountain.

---

20 이 팀은 피트 크루라고 불린다.

21 피트는 경주 트랙의 한쪽에 있는 공간으로 레이서들은 경주 도중에 그곳에서 여러 번 정지한다.

22 피트 크루가 하는 주요 역할은 자동차를 점검하고 타이어를 교체하는 것이다.

23 빠른 속도의 경주에서는 타이어가 쉽게 마모되기 때문에 타이어를 교체하는 것이 특히 중요하다.

24 피트에서의 정지는 짧게는 2초 정도이고 한 팀에는 많게는 20명에 이르는 구성원이 있다.

25 그러므로 피트 크루는 완벽한 조화를 이루며 일해야 한다.

26 레이서만 주목을 받을지 모르지만 사람들이 말하는 것처럼, "경주의 우승은 피트에서 이루어진다."

27 등반에서의 셰르파

28 'Sherpa'라는 단어는 셰르파족에서 유래되었는데, 셰르파족은 네팔의 동쪽 지역에 산다.

29 셰르파는 훌륭한 등반 기량을 갖고 있으며 산 지리를 잘 안다.

30 그들은 또한 산의 높은 곳에서 호흡하는 데 어려움이 거의 없다.

31 그래서 등산가들은 자신들이 에베레스트산을 등반하는 것을 돕는 셰르파를 고용하기 시작했다.

32 셰르파는 등산가들을 산 정상까지 이끈다.

33 그들은 여러 방면에서 등산가들을 지원한다.

34 예를 들면, 그들은 텐트를 치고 등산가들의 가방을 운반한다.

35 셰르파는 종종 에베레스트산의 보이지 않는 사람들로 불리는데, 왜냐하면 사람들이 산 정상에서 등산가들만 찍힌 사진을 자주 보기 때문이다.

● 우리말을 참고하여 본문을 영작하시오.

1 스포츠 속 숨은 조력자들
➡ _____

2 스포츠에서 선수들만 트로피나 메달을 받지만, 그들은 혼자 힘으로 이긴 것이 아니다.
➡ _____

3 그 선수들을 돕는 사람들이 있다.
➡ _____

4 이 사람들은 종종 숨겨져 있고 주목을 받지 못한다.
➡ _____

5 하지만 그들은 선수들만큼 중요하다.
➡ _____

6 여기 몇 가지 예가 있다.
➡ _____

7 마라톤의 페이서들
➡ _____

8 페이서들은 마라톤에서 다른 선수들과 함께 달리며 그들을 이끈다.
➡ _____

9 페이서들은 경험이 많은 선수들이며 그들의 역할은 다른 선수들이 경기를 더 잘 운영하도록 돕는 것이다.
➡ _____

10 한 경기에는 여러 명의 페이서들이 있을 수 있다.
➡ _____

11 각각의 페이서는 다른 속도로 달리고 다른 시간대에 경기를 마친다.
➡ _____

12 페이서들은 주로 자신들의 완주 시간을 나타내는 깃발이나 풍선들을 가지고 있다.
➡ _____

13 선수들은 자신들의 목표 완주 시간에 따라 페이서를 선택할 수 있다.
➡ _____

14 예를 들어, 한 선수가 4시간 안에 경기를 마치고 싶다면, 그 선수는 4시간 페이서를 따라갈 것이다.
➡ _____

15 페이서가 시간을 계속해서 파악하기 때문에, 선수는 특정 시간에 마라톤을 완주하려는 자신의 목표를 더 쉽게 달성할 수 있다.
➡ _____
_____

16 요컨대, 페이서들은 달리지만 우승을 하기 위해 달리는 것은 아니다.
➡ _____

17 그들은 다른 선수들을 위해 달린다.
➡ _____

18 자동차 경주의 피트 크루

➡ _____

19 여러분은 대부분의 자동차 경주에서 자동차와 레이서만 보겠지만 그 레이서 뒤에는 팀이 있다.

➡ _____

20 이 팀은 피트 크루라고 불린다.

➡ _____

21 피트는 경주 트랙의 한쪽에 있는 공간으로 레이서들은 경주 도중에 그곳에서 여러 번 정지한다.

➡ _____

22 피트 크루가 하는 주요 역할은 자동차를 점검하고 타이어를 교체하는 것이다.

➡ _____

23 빠른 속도의 경주에서는 타이어가 쉽게 마모되기 때문에 타이어를 교체하는 것이 특히 중요하다.

➡ _____

24 피트에서의 정지는 짧게는 2초 정도이고 한 팀에는 많게는 20명에 이르는 구성원이 있다.

➡ _____

25 그러므로 피트 크루는 완벽한 조화를 이루며 일해야 한다.

➡ _____

26 레이서만 주목을 받을지 모르지만 사람들이 말하는 것처럼, "경주의 우승은 피트에서 이루어진다."

➡ _____

27 등반에서의 셰르파

➡ _____

28 'Sherpa'라는 단어는 셰르파족에서 유래되었는데, 셰르파족은 네팔의 동쪽 지역에 산다.

➡ _____

29 셰르파는 훌륭한 등반 기량을 갖고 있으며 산 지리를 잘 안다.

➡ _____

30 그들은 또한 산의 높은 곳에서 호흡하는 데 어려움이 거의 없다.

➡ _____

31 그래서 등산가들은 자신들이 에베레스트산을 등반하는 것을 돕는 셰르파를 고용하기 시작했다.

➡ _____

32 셰르파는 등산가들을 산 정상까지 이끈다.

➡ _____

33 그들은 여러 방면에서 등산가들을 지원한다.

➡ _____

34 예를 들면, 그들은 텐트를 치고 등산가들의 가방을 운반한다.

➡ _____

35 셰르파는 종종 에베레스트산의 보이지 않는 사람들로 불리는데, 왜냐하면 사람들이 산 정상에서 등산가들만 찍힌 사진을 자주 보기 때문이다.

➡ _____

_____

[01~03] 다음 글을 읽고 물음에 답하시오.

Pacers in a Marathon

Pacers run with other runners and lead them in a marathon. Pacers are experienced runners, and their job is (A)to help other runners manage their race better. There can be several pacers in a race. Each pacer runs ____ⓐ____ different speeds and finishes the race ____ⓑ____ different times. Pacers usually have flags or balloons showing their finish time.

01 위 글의 빈칸 ⓐ와 ⓑ에 들어갈 전치사가 바르게 짝지어진 것은?

|ⓐ|ⓑ||ⓐ|ⓑ|
① at – in
② on – for
③ on – from
④ for – in
⑤ at – for

02 위 글의 밑줄 친 (A)to help와 to부정사의 용법이 같은 것을 모두 고르시오.

① He was happy to help other runners.
② It's good to help other runners.
③ I decided to help other runners.
④ It's time to help other runners.
⑤ She is too weak to help other runners.

03 According to the passage, which is NOT true?

① Pacers follow other runners in a marathon.
② Pacers help other runners manage their race better.
③ The speed of each pacer is different.
④ In a race, there can be several pacers.
⑤ Pacers' flags or balloons show their finish time.

[04~06] 다음 글을 읽고 물음에 답하시오.

In sports, only the players get a trophy or medal, but they don't win (A)on their own. There are people who help the players. These people are often hidden and don't get attention. ____ⓐ____, they are as important as the players. Here are some examples.

04 위 글의 빈칸 ⓐ에 들어갈 알맞은 말을 고르시오.

① That is
② However
③ Similarly
④ As a result
⑤ In addition

05 위 글의 밑줄 친 (A)on their own과 바꿔 쓸 수 있는 말을 모두 고르시오.

① lonely
② beside themselves
③ alone
④ on behalf of them
⑤ by themselves

06 위 글의 뒤에 올 내용으로 가장 알맞은 것을 고르시오.

① the players who get a trophy or medal
② how to achieve one's goal
③ players who work in perfect harmony
④ hidden people in sports
⑤ the noticeable people in sports

[07~10] 다음 글을 읽고 물음에 답하시오.

Pit Crews in Car Racing

You may only see the car and the driver during most car races, but there is a team behind the driver. This team is called a pit crew. A pit is a place on the side of the race track, and drivers stop there several times during a race. The main job of the pit crew is to check the car and change the tires. (A) Changing the tires is especially important because the tires wear out easily in a high speed race.

(B)피트에서의 정지는 짧게는 2초 정도이고 한 팀에는 많게는 20명에 이르는 구성원이 있다. Therefore, the pit crew has to work in perfect harmony. The driver may get all the attention, but as people say, "Races are won in the ___ⓐ___."

07 위 글의 빈칸 ⓐ에 들어갈 알맞은 말을 고르시오.

① tracks   ② pits
③ fields   ④ stadiums
⑤ cheering sections

서답형

08 Why do drivers stop at a pit several times during a race? Fill in the blanks (A) and (B) with suitable words.

> They stop there to (A)_____ the car and (B)_____ the tires.

 아래 〈보기〉에서 위 글의 밑줄 친 (A)Changing과 문법적 쓰임이 같은 것의 개수를 고르시오.

> ┌─── 보기 ───┐
> ① He is changing the tires.
> ② She gave up changing the tires.
> ③ I saw my dad changing the tires.
> ④ Changing the tires, he sang a song.
> ⑤ He is good at changing the tires.

① 1개 ② 2개 ③ 3개 ④ 4개 ⑤ 5개

서답형

10 위 글의 밑줄 친 (B)의 우리말에 맞게 주어진 어휘를 이용하여 영작하시오.

> as short as, as many as

➡ _____

_____

[11~13] 다음 글을 읽고 물음에 답하시오.

(①) Each pacer runs at different speeds and finishes the race in different times. (②) Pacers usually have flags or balloons showing their finish time. (③) For example, if a runner wants to finish the race in four hours, the runner will follow the four-hour pacer. (④) Since the pacer keeps track of the time, the runner can achieve his or her goal of finishing the marathon in a particular time more easily. (⑤) ___ⓐ___, pacers run but they don't run to win. They run for others.

11 위 글의 빈칸 ⓐ에 들어갈 알맞은 말을 고르시오.

① For example   ② Additionally
③ However   ④ In short
⑤ On the other hand

 위 글의 흐름으로 보아, 주어진 문장이 들어가기에 가장 적절한 곳은?

> Runners can choose a pacer depending on their target finish time.

①   ②   ③   ④   ⑤

13 위 글의 주제로 알맞은 것을 고르시오.

① the speed of each pacer
② the flags or balloons showing pacers' finish time
③ runners' target finish time
④ the pacer's secret of keeping track of the time
⑤ the role of pacers in a marathon

[14~16] 다음 글을 읽고 물음에 답하시오.

Sherpas in Mountain Climbing

The word *Sherpa* comes from the Sherpa tribe, which lives in the eastern part of Nepal. Sherpas have good climbing skills and know their way around the mountains well. They also have little ⓐdifficulty breathing high up in the mountains. Therefore, mountain climbers started to hire Sherpas to help them climb Mount Everest.

Sherpas lead mountain climbers to the top of the mountain. They support climbers in many ways. For example, they put ____ⓑ____ tents and carry climbers' bags. Sherpas are often called the invisible people of Mount Everest because people often see a picture of only the climbers at the top of the mountain.

14 위 글의 밑줄 친 ⓐdifficulty와 바꿔 쓸 수 있는 말을 고르시오.

① trouble   ② question
③ difference   ④ solution
⑤ conflict

15 위 글의 빈칸 ⓑ에 들어갈 알맞은 말을 고르시오.

① in   ② up   ③ on
④ for   ⑤ with

16 Why are Sherpas often called the invisible people of Mount Everest? Fill in the blank with a suitable word.

> Because it is a picture of only the (A)_____ at the top of the mountain that people often see.

[17~19] 다음 글을 읽고 물음에 답하시오.

(A)In sports, only the players get a trophy or medal, but they win on their own. There are people who help the players. These people are often ____ⓐ____ and don't get attention. However, (B)they are as important as the players. Here are some examples.

17 위 글의 빈칸 ⓐ에 hide를 알맞은 형태로 쓰시오.

➡ _____

18 위 글의 밑줄 친 (A)에서 흐름상 어색한 부분을 찾아 고치시오.

_____ ➡ _____

19 위 글의 밑줄 친 (B)they가 가리키는 것을 본문에서 찾아 쓰시오.

➡ _____

[20~22] 다음 글을 읽고 물음에 답하시오.

Pit Crews in Car Racing

You may only see the car and the driver during most car races, but there is a team behind the driver. This team is called a pit crew. A pit is a place on the side of the race track, and drivers stop there several times during a race. (A)The main job of the pit crew is to check the car and change the tires. Changing the tires is especially important because the tires wear out easily in a high speed race.

(B)A pit stop can be as shorter as 2 seconds, and there are as much as 20 members on a crew. Therefore, the pit crew has to work ____ⓐ____ . The driver may get all the attention, but as people say, "Races are won in the pits."

20 위 글의 빈칸 ⓐ에 들어갈 알맞은 말을 고르시오.

① without stopping
② one after another
③ in perfect harmony
④ from time to time
⑤ little by little

서답형

21 위 글의 밑줄 친 (A)를 다음과 같이 바꿔 쓸 때 빈칸 (a)와 (b)에 들어갈 알맞은 단어를 쓰시오.

The main job of the pit crew is (a)_____ the car and (b)_____ the tires.

서답형

22 위 글의 밑줄 친 (B)에서 어법상 틀린 부분을 찾아 고치시오. (두 군데)

_____ ➡ _____, _____ ➡ _____

[23~25] 다음 글을 읽고 물음에 답하시오.

Sherpas in Mountain Climbing

The word *Sherpa* comes from the Sherpa tribe, which lives in the (A)[east / eastern] part of Nepal. Sherpas have good climbing skills and know their way around the mountains well. They also have (B)[little / much] difficulty breathing high up in the

mountains. Therefore, ⓐ등산가들은 자신들이 에베레스트산을 등반하는 것을 돕는 셰르파를 고용하기 시작했다.

Sherpas lead mountain climbers to the top of the mountain. They support climbers in many ways. For example, they put up tents and carry climbers' bags. Sherpas are often called the (C)[visible / invisible] people of Mount Everest because people often see a picture of only the climbers at the top of the mountain.

서답형

23 위 글의 괄호 (A)~(C)에서 문맥이나 어법상 알맞은 낱말을 골라 쓰시오.

➡ (A) _____ (B) _____ (C) _____

서답형

24 위 글의 밑줄 친 ⓐ의 우리말에 맞게 주어진 어휘를 알맞게 배열하시오.

climb / started / to help / Sherpas / them / Mount Everest / mountain climbers / to hire

➡ _____

25 위 글을 읽고 대답할 수 없는 것을 고르시오.

① Is the word *Sherpa* named after the place?
② Where does the Sherpa tribe live?
③ What skill do Sherpas have?
④ How do Sherpas have little difficulty breathing high up in the mountains?
⑤ Do people often see the picture of Sherpas at the top of Mount Everest?

[01~02] 다음 글을 읽고 물음에 답하시오.

In sports, only the players get a trophy or medal, but they don't win on their own. There are people who help the players. These people are often hidden and don't get attention. However, (A)they are ⓐ important ⓑ the players. Here are some examples.

01 위 글의 빈칸 ⓐ와 ⓑ에 공통으로 들어갈 알맞은 말을 쓰시오.

➡ _____

02 다음 빈칸 (a)와 (b)에 알맞은 단어를 넣어 (A)they에 대한 소개를 완성하시오.

They help the players win in sports, but they are often (a)_____ without getting (b)_____.

[03~06] 다음 글을 읽고 물음에 답하시오.

Pacers in a Marathon
Pacers run with other runners and lead them in a marathon. Pacers are experienced runners, and their job is to help other runners manage their race better. There can be several pacers in a race. Each pacer runs at different speeds and finishes the race in different times. ⓐPacers usually have flags or balloons showing their finish time.
Runners can choose a pacer depending on their target finish time. For example, if a runner wants to finish the race in four hours, the runner will follow the four-hour pacer. Since the pacer keeps track of the time, the runner can achieve his or her goal of finishing

the marathon in a particular time more easily. In short, ⓑ페이서들은 달리지만 우승을 하기 위해 달리는 것은 아니다. They run for others.

03 다음 문장에서 위 글의 내용과 다른 부분을 찾아서 고치시오.

The speed of each pacer is the same.

➡ _____ ➡ _____

04 위 글의 밑줄 친 ⓐ를 다음과 같이 바꿔 쓸 때 빈칸에 들어갈 알맞은 말을 두 단어로 쓰시오.

➡ Pacers usually have flags or balloons _____ _____ their finish time.

05 위 글의 밑줄 친 ⓑ의 우리말에 맞게 주어진 어휘를 이용하여 8 단어로 영작하시오.

to win

➡ _____

06 본문의 내용과 일치하도록 다음 빈칸 (A)와 (B)에 알맞은 단어를 쓰시오.

Runners can achieve their goal of finishing the marathon in (A)_____ _____ _____ more easily by choosing a pacer depending on their target finish time because the pacer (B)_____ _____ _____ the time.

[07~09] 다음 글을 읽고 물음에 답하시오.

Pit Crews in Car Racing
You may only see the car and the driver (A)[during / while] most car races, but there is a

team behind the driver. This team is called a pit crew. A pit is a place on the side of the race track, and drivers stop there several times during a race. The main job of the pit crew is to check the car and (B)[change / changing] the tires. Changing the tires is especially important because the tires wear out easily in a high speed race.

A pit stop can be as (C)[short / shortly] as 2 seconds, and there are as many as 20 members on a crew. Therefore, the pit crew has to work in perfect harmony. The driver may get all the attention, but as people say, "ⓐRaces are won in the pits."

07 위 글의 괄호 (A)~(C)에서 문맥이나 어법상 알맞은 낱말을 골라 쓰시오.

➡ (A) _____ (B) _____ (C) _____

08 다음 문장에서 위 글의 내용과 <u>다른</u> 부분을 찾아서 고치시오.

> Drivers stop at a pit several times after a race.

_____ ➡ _____

09 다음 빈칸 (A)와 (B)에 공통으로 들어갈 두 단어를 넣어 위 글의 밑줄 친 ⓐ가 의미하는 것을 완성하시오.

> When drivers stop at a pit to check the car and change the tires, the (A)_____ _____ has to work in perfect harmony in a very short time, and so the skillful work of the (B)_____ _____ plays a very important role in winning the race.

[10~13] 다음 글을 읽고 물음에 답하시오.

Sherpas in Mountain Climbing

The word *Sherpa* comes from the Sherpa tribe, (A)which lives in the eastern part of Nepal. Sherpas have good climbing skills and know their way around the mountains well. They also have little difficulty ___ⓐ___ high up in the mountains. Therefore, mountain climbers started to hire Sherpas to help them climb Mount Everest.

Sherpas lead mountain climbers to the top of the mountain. They support climbers in many ways. For example, they put up tents and carry climbers' bags. (B)Sherpas are often called the invisible people of Mount Everest because people often see a picture of only the sherpas at the top of the mountain.

10 위 글의 빈칸 ⓐ에 breathe를 알맞은 형태로 쓰시오.

➡ _____

11 위 글의 밑줄 친 (A)which를 두 단어로 쓰시오.

➡ _____

12 위 글의 밑줄 친 (B)에서 흐름상 <u>어색한</u> 부분을 찾아 고치시오.

_____ ➡ _____

13 다음 빈칸 (A)와 (B)에 알맞은 단어를 넣어 Sherpas에 대한 소개를 완성하시오.

> The Sherpa tribe lives in the eastern part of Nepal, and Sherpas (A)_____ mountain climbers to the top of the mountain because they have (B)_____ _____ _____ and know their way around the mountains well.

Reading **155**

해석

After You Read B

Host: Is there anything interesting about your job?
-thing으로 끝나는 부정대명사는 형용사가 뒤에서 수식한다.

Pacer: Pacers have flags or balloons showing their finish time.
능동이나 진행의 의미를 나타내는 '동사원형+-ing' 형태의 현재분사로, 앞의 명사 수식

Pit Crew: A pit stop can be as short as 2 seconds. So the pit crew has to work
as+형용사/부사+as: ~만큼 ...한/하게
in perfect harmony.

Sherpa: Sherpas like me have little difficulty breathing high up in the
have difficulty -ing: '~하는 데 어려움이 있다'
mountains.

구문해설
- **pit**: 피트(자동차 경주 도중에 급유, 타이어 교체나 수리를 하는 곳)
- **crew**: (같은 일에 종사하는) 팀, 조 • **harmony**: 조화, 화합 • **breathe**: 숨을 쉬다

사회자: 여러분의 직업에 관해 어떤 흥미로운 것이 있나요?

페이서: 페이서는 자신들의 완주 시간을 나타내는 깃발이나 풍선들을 가지고 있어요.

피트 크루: 피트에서의 정지는 짧게는 2초 정도입니다. 그래서 피트 크루는 완벽한 조화를 이루며 일해야 해요.

셰르파: 저와 같은 셰르파는 산의 높은 곳에서 호흡하는 데 어려움이 거의 없어요.

Think and Write

Cheerleaders in Football Games

Although people usually don't think that cheerleaders are a part of a football
'양보'의 부사절을 이끄는 접속사: ~할지라도
team, they play an important role in a football game. By cheering at a game,
by V-ing: ~함으로써(방법, 수단)
they create team spirit. They also encourage their team and fans. To do their
to부정사의 부사적 용법 '목적'
job well, cheerleaders need to be fit and strong. They also need to be good
to부정사의 명사적 용법 'need의 목적어'
at jumping and dancing. Most of all, they need to work as hard as players.
전치사+동명사   병렬(and)+동명사   ~만큼 ...한(as 원급 as)

구문해설
- **usually**: 보통, 대개 • **play a role in ~**: ~에서 역할을 하다 • **cheering**: 응원
- **team spirit**: 공동체 정신 • **fit**: 건강한 • **be good at**: ~를 잘하다
- **most of all**: 무엇보다도

미식축구 경기에서의 치어리더

사람들이 보통 치어리더는 미식축구팀의 일원이라고 생각하지 않을지라도 그들은 축구 경기에서 중요한 역할을 한다. 경기에서 응원을 함으로써 그들은 공동체 정신을 만들어낸다. 그들은 또한 팀과 팬들을 격려한다. 자신의 역할을 잘하기 위해, 치어리더들은 몸을 건강하게 관리하고 강해야 한다. 그들은 또한 점프하는 것과 춤추는 것을 잘해야 한다. 무엇보다도, 그들은 선수들만큼이나 열심히 일해야 한다.

Around the World

1. In swimming, a tapper uses a long pole to help a blind swimmer swim.
to부정사의 부사적 용법(목적) help의 목적격보어로 동사원형(= to swim)

2. In a race, a guide runner runs with a blind runner and helps him or her
runs와 병렬 관계
stay on the track.
help의 목적격보어로 동사원형(= to stay)

3. In blind football, a shooting assistant tells his or her team players
which direction to shoot.
'의문사+to부정사'로 tells의 직접목적어(which는 direction을 수식하는 의문형용사임)

구문해설
- **tapper**: 두드리는 사람 • **guide runner**: 가이드 러너(시각장애인의 눈 역할을 해주는 선수)
- **assistant**: 보조자 • **direction**: 방향

1. 수영에서, **tapper**는 시각 장애인 수영 선수가 수영하는 것을 돕기 위해 장대를 사용한다.

2. 달리기에서, **guide runner**는 시각 장애인 선수와 함께 달리며 그들이 트랙에서 벗어나지 않도록 돕는다.

3. 시각 장애인 축구에서, **shooting assistant**는 자신의 팀 선수들에게 슛하는 방향을 말해 준다.

01 〈보기〉의 밑줄 친 join과 같은 의미로 쓰인 것을 고르시오.

┌─ 보기 ┤

For reasons of his own, he refused to join the club.

① What do you think of that new gym that you joined?

② He joined one section of pipe to the next.

③ Are you free on Thursday to join us for dinner?

④ In 1189, Richard joined forces with Philip II of France against his father.

⑤ It was glued tightly so the join could not be seen.

02 다음 영영풀이에 해당하는 단어를 주어진 철자로 시작하여 빈칸에 쓰고, 알맞은 것을 골라 문장을 완성하시오.

• c_____ : a group of people with a particular skill who work together

• p_____ : special, or more than usual

• d_____ : the way something or someone moves or faces

(1) Is there a _____ type of book he enjoys?

(2) The film _____ entered the sea to shoot the scene.

(3) I lost all sense of _____ .

03 다음 문장의 빈칸에 〈영영풀이〉에 해당하는 단어를 쓰시오.

It's normal for things to _____ _____ with long use.

〈영영풀이〉 to use something a lot so that it no longer works, or can no longer be used

➡ _____

04 다음 빈칸 (A)~(C)에 알맞은 말을 쓰시오. (주어진 철자로 시작하여 쓸 것.)

• They lived in (A)h_____ with each other.

• Teenagers often have (B)d_____ expressing themselves.

• Tourism is expected to play an important (C)r_____ in the development of the nation's economy.

05 다음 괄호 안에 주어진 어휘를 이용하여 빈칸에 알맞게 쓰시오.

(1) Good will is an _____ asset. (visible)

(2) She was _____ and needed a guiding hand. (experience)

(3) As time went on, he grew more and more _____ . (patient)

Conversation

[06~07] 다음 대화를 읽고 물음에 답하시오.

(A) (a)That often? Anyway, it'll be fun swimming together today.

(B) I swim four times a week.

(C) Yes, but before we swim, I suggest we do stretching exercises.

(D) I don't swim often. How about you, Kate? How often do you swim?

That's a good idea.

06 주어진 문장 앞에 나올 대화의 순서로 알맞은 것은?

① (B) – (A) – (C) – (D)
② (C) – (B) – (A) – (D)
③ (D) – (A) – (C) – (B)
④ (D) – (B) – (A) – (C)
⑤ (D) – (B) – (C) – (A)

07 위 대화의 밑줄 친 (a)That과 같은 용법으로 쓰인 것은?

① Look at that man over there.

② She was so tired that she couldn't think straight.

③ Are you sure she's that young?

④ He is the greatest novelist that has ever lived.

⑤ There was no hope that she would recover her health.

08 다음 중 짝지어진 대화가 어색한 것은?

① A: I clean my room once a week.
   B: I suggest that you clean your room more often.

② A: How much do you eat fast food?
   B: I eat fast food three times a week.

③ A: I have breakfast every day.
   B: That's good.

④ A: This class meets on Saturdays and Sundays.
   B: That sounds good.

⑤ A: May I help you?
   B: Yes, I came to register for a swimming class.

[09~10] 다음 대화를 읽고 물음에 답하시오.

W: Hello. Welcome to Sports World. May I help you?

B: Yes, I came to register for a swimming class.

W: Is this your first time taking swimming lessons?

B: Yes, it is. I don't know how to swim at all.

W: I see. How often do you want to take classes?

B: I want to take classes twice a week. I'd like to take classes on weekdays and not on weekends.

W: Then, I suggest that you take the Beginner 2 class. This class meets on Tuesdays and Thursdays.

B: That sounds good. I'd like to (a)sign up for that class. How big is the class?

W: The class has a ___(A)___ of 10 people.

B: That's perfect.

09 주어진 〈영영풀이〉를 참고하여 위 대화의 빈칸 (A)에 알맞은 말을 쓰시오.

〈영영풀이〉

the largest or smallest amount of something such as time or money that is allowed because of a rule, law, etc.

➡ _____

10 밑줄 친 (a)sign up과 같은 뜻의 어휘를 대화에서 찾아 쓰시오.

➡ _____

Grammar

11 다음 중 어법상 올바른 문장은?

① The movie directing by Bong won the four Oscars this year.

② He showed me the car which invented by the scientist.

③ She has a pet dog naming "Bow".

④ These are the books printed in the city of Paju last year.

⑤ Some politicians inviting to the meeting didn't come.

[12~13] 다음 빈칸 (A)~(C)에 들어갈 말이 바르게 짝지어진 것은?

12

• Vicky received a letter __(A)__ in French.
• The man __(B)__ the guitar in the band looked happy.
• The boy __(C)__ his bicycle is Charlie.

	(A)	(B)	(C)
①	written	playing	fixing
②	writing	playing	fixing
③	writing	played	fixed
④	written	playing	fixed
⑤	written	played	fixing

13

• Mina runs as __(A)__ as her brother.
• The volleyball players jump as __(B)__ as deer.
• The steak is as __(C)__ as a pizza.

	(A)	(B)	(C)
①	fast	high	big
②	fast	highly	big
③	faster	high	bigger
④	faster	higher	bigger
⑤	fastest	higher	biggest

14 다음 우리말을 영어로 옮긴 문장들 중 어법상 어색한 것을 고르시오.

① Peter는 TV를 켜 둔 채로 잠이 들었다.
   → Peter fell asleep with the TV on.

② Amy는 다리를 꼰 채로 책을 읽었다.
   → Amy read a book with her legs crossing.

③ 선생님은 팔짱을 낀 채로 학생들이 그림 그리는 모습을 쳐다보았다.
   → The teacher saw his students drawing pictures with his arms folded.

④ 그 가수는 눈을 감은 채로 피아노를 연주하며 부드럽게 노래를 불렀다.
   → The singer sang softly while playing the piano with her eyes closed.

⑤ Bill의 친구들은 옷이 땀으로 젖은 채로 교실로 뛰어 들어왔다.
   → Bill's friends ran into the classroom with their clothes wet with sweat.

15 다음 두 문장을 분사를 이용하여 한 문장으로 만들 때, 빈칸에 적절한 단어를 써 넣으시오.

• The card is for Mike.
• Susan wrote the card.

➡ The card _____ _____ _____ _____ _____ Mike.

16 다음 밑줄 친 부분의 쓰임이 나머지와 다른 것은?

① The actor was <u>playing</u> an evil character in the movie.

② The family <u>eating</u> fast food every day have difficulty running.

③ The students <u>studying</u> together for the final exam will get good grades.

④ The dogs <u>protecting</u> their puppies were not moving at all.

⑤ My uncle was busy <u>finishing</u> his project through the summer.

17 다음 중 어법상 어색한 것을 고르시오.

① Mary's nose is as long as Kevin's.

② The toy train his mom bought for David wasn't so strong as the toy doll.

③ Sally is as tall and slim as the tree near the playground.

④ The light is much faster than any other thing in the world.

⑤ The books written by Shakespeare are not so more valuable as his plays.

18 다음 중 밑줄 친 단어의 바로 앞에 '주격 관계대명사+be동사'가 생략되어 있다고 볼 수 없는 것을 모두 고르면?

① Don't feed the animals <u>approaching</u> the visitors in the zoo.

② There weren't any brave mice to wake up the <u>sleeping</u> cat.

③ What is the language <u>spoken</u> in Ivory Coast?

④ The toys <u>made</u> in China are quite dangerous to play with.

⑤ Bob was so <u>interested</u> in the ancient architecture that he majored in history.

⑥ The trucks <u>parked</u> in the parking lot should be moved away.

⑦ The professor's lecture was <u>boring</u> rather than interesting.

[19~20] 다음 글을 읽고 물음에 답하시오.

Runners can choose a pacer depending on their target finish time. For example, if a runner wants to finish the race in four hours, the runner will follow the four-hour pacer. Since the pacer keeps track of the time, the runner can achieve his or her goal ⓐ<u>of</u> finishing the marathon in a particular time more easily. In short, pacers run but they don't run to win. ⓑ<u>They run for themselves.</u>

19 위 글의 밑줄 친 ⓐ<u>of</u>와 문법적 쓰임이 같은 것을 고르시오.

① He lives in the north <u>of</u> Seoul.

② Look at the plate made <u>of</u> wood.

③ There is no possibility <u>of</u> my winning the game.

④ His poem expresses his love <u>of</u> nature.

⑤ He is a man <u>of</u> ability.

20 위 글의 밑줄 친 ⓑ에서 흐름상 어색한 부분을 찾아 고치시오.

➡ _____ 또는 _____

[21~23] 다음 글을 읽고 물음에 답하시오.

Pit Crews in Car Racing

You may only see the car and the driver during most car races, but there is a team behind the driver. This team is called a pit crew. A pit is a place on the side of the race track, and drivers stop there several times during a race. The main job of the pit crew is to check the car and change the tires.

Changing the tires is especially important because the tires wear out easily in a high speed race.

A pit stop can be as short as 2 seconds, and there are as many as 20 members on a crew. _____ⓐ_____, the pit crew has to work in perfect harmony. The driver may get all the attention, but ⓑas people say, "Races are won in the pits."

21 위 글의 빈칸 ⓐ에 들어갈 알맞은 말을 고르시오.

① However　　② Nonetheless
③ That is　　④ Alternatively
⑤ Therefore

22 위 글의 밑줄 친 ⓑas와 같은 의미로 쓰인 것을 고르시오.

① As we go up higher, the air grows colder.
② As rust eats iron, so care eats the heart.
③ This box can be used as a table.
④ As it was getting dark, we soon turned back.
⑤ This is twice as large as that.

23 According to the passage, which is NOT true?

① A pit crew is a team behind the driver.
② A place on the side of the race track is called a pit.
③ The main job of the pit crew is checking the car and changing the tires.
④ A pit stop can be as short as 2 minutes, and there are as many as 20 members on a crew.
⑤ The pit crew has to work perfectly harmoniously.

[24~25] 다음 글을 읽고 물음에 답하시오.

Sherpas in Mountain Climbing

The word *Sherpa* comes from the Sherpa tribe, which lives in the eastern part of Nepal. Sherpas have good climbing skills and know ①their way around the mountains well. ②They also have little difficulty breathing high up in the mountains. Therefore, mountain climbers started to hire Sherpas to help ③them climb Mount Everest.

Sherpas lead mountain climbers to the top of the mountain. ④They support climbers in many ways. For example, ⑤they put up tents and carry climbers' bags. Sherpas are often called the invisible people of Mount Everest because people often see a picture of only the climbers at the top of the mountain.

24 밑줄 친 ①~⑤ 중에서 가리키는 대상이 나머지 넷과 다른 것은?

①　　②　　③　　④　　⑤

25 위 글의 주제로 알맞은 것을 고르시오.

① the origin of the word *Sherpa*
② the role of Sherpas in mountain climbing
③ the reason Sherpas have good climbing skills
④ the visible people of Mount Everest
⑤ the climbers at the top of the mountain

출제율 95%

01 다음 중 짝지어진 단어의 관계가 나머지와 <u>다른</u> 것은?

① perfect – imperfect
② allow – permit
③ complete – incomplete
④ hire – fire
⑤ full – empty

출제율 100%

02 밑줄 친 부분의 의미로 알맞지 <u>않은</u> 것은?

① In a race, a guide runner runs with a blind runner and helps him or her <u>stay on the track</u>. (트랙에 머무르다)
② How do I <u>sign up for</u> your milage program? (~에 등록하다)
③ It's <u>not at all</u> easy to deal with customers. (결코 ~ 아닌)
④ It was what she wanted <u>most of all</u>. (대부분)
⑤ She'd rather die than <u>give a speech</u>. (연설하다)

출제율 95%

03 다음 주어진 우리말에 맞게 빈칸을 채우시오. (주어진 철자로 시작할 것)

(1) Tom은 사서로 고용되었다.
　➡ Tom was h_____ as a librarian.
(2) 그것이 끝나자 우리는 모두 안도의 한숨을 내쉬었다.
　➡ We all breathed a sigh of relief when it was o_____.
(3) 우리는 그의 연설에 집중해야 한다.
　➡ We have to pay a_____ to his speech.

출제율 90%

04 다음 빈칸에 공통으로 들어갈 알맞은 말을 쓰시오.

> • He's able to take care _____ himself.
> • Bank statements help you keep track _____ where your money is going.

[05~06] 다음 대화를 읽고 물음에 답하시오.

W: Hello. May I help you?
B: Yes, I came to register for a soccer class.
W: I see. How often do you want to take classes?
B: I want to take classes twice a week. I'd like to take classes on weekends.
W: Then, I suggest that you take the Beginner 1 class. This class meets on Saturdays and Sundays.
B: (A)That sounds good.

출제율 100%

05 위 대화를 읽고 대답할 수 <u>없는</u> 질문을 고르시오.

① When did the boy make a visit to the place?
② How often does the boy want to take a soccer class?
③ When does the boy want to take a soccer class?
④ When does the Beginner 1 class meet?
⑤ What class does the woman suggest that the boy take?

출제율 90%

06 위 대화의 밑줄 친 (A)That이 가리키는 것을 25자 내외의 우리말로 쓰시오.

➡ _____

[07~09] 다음 대화를 읽고 물음에 답하시오.

> B: Suji, how often do you take bowling lessons?
> G: Twice a week. (①) I'm just a beginner. (②) I heard you're very good.
> B: Well, I love bowling. (③) Hmm. Your bowling ball looks heavy for you. (④)
> G: OK. (⑤) I'll look for a lighter (a)one, then.

출제율 100%

07 (①)~(⑤) 중 주어진 문장이 들어갈 곳은?

> I suggest you use a lighter ball.

①   ②   ③   ④   ⑤

출제율 90%

08 Why does the boy suggest that Suji use a lighter ball? Answer in English with a full sentence.

➡ _____

출제율 95%

09 위 대화의 밑줄 친 (a)one이 가리키는 것을 찾아 쓰시오.

➡ _____

출제율 100%

10 다음 그림을 보고, 괄호 안의 단어를 적절한 분사로 바꿔 빈칸을 채우시오.

➡ Jeffrey was _____(embarrass) with the _____(break) bicycle as he didn't know how to fix it.

출제율 100%

11 다음 밑줄 친 부분 중 어법상 어색한 것을 고르시오.

① My friend's husband is <u>as busy as a</u> honeybee.

② The comedian could speak Japanese <u>as fluently as</u> a native.

③ The Spanish language spoken in most of Latin America is not <u>as hardly as</u> Korean.

④ All the students in class H act <u>as nicely as</u> the nobles.

⑤ The dress that my daughter wore tonight looked <u>as lovely as</u> the queen's.

출제율 100%

12 다음 중 밑줄 친 부분의 성격이 나머지 넷과 다른 것은?

① Volunteers are picking up the trashes <u>fallen</u> on the beach.

② Do you know the girl <u>smiling</u> at me?

③ A lot of visitors come to see Monet's pictures <u>displayed</u> in the museum.

④ She couldn't help <u>being</u> scared of the news that the war broke out.

⑤ I received a huge box <u>filled</u> with the lego bricks from my uncle.

출제율 95%

13 다음 표에 대해 설명하는 각 문장들 중 옳지 않은 것은?

	Mary	Paul	Jim	Steve	Yuna
Age	16	14	16	16	15

① Mary is as old as Steve.

② Paul is not as old as Yuna.

③ Jim isn't as old as Paul.

④ Steve is not older than Mary.

⑤ Yuna isn't as old as Steve.

[14~16] 다음 글을 읽고 물음에 답하시오.

Pacers in a Marathon

Pacers run with other runners and lead them in a marathon. ⓐPacers are experiencing runners, and their job is to help other runners manage their race better. There can be several pacers in a race. Each pacer runs at different speeds and finishes the race in different times. Pacers usually have flags or balloons showing their finish time.

Runners can choose a pacer depending on their target finish time. For example, if a runner wants to finish the race in four hours, the runner will follow the four-hour pacer. Since the pacer keeps track of the time, the runner can achieve his or her goal of finishing the marathon in a particular time more easily. ⓑIn short, pacers run but they don't run to win. They run for others.

14 위 글의 밑줄 친 ⓐ에서 어법상 틀린 부분을 찾아 고치시오.

➡ _____

15 위 글의 밑줄 친 ⓑIn short와 바꿔 쓸 수 없는 말을 고르시오. (2개)

① In brief
② In addition
③ To put it shortly
④ In a word
⑤ In other words

16 위 글을 읽고 알 수 없는 것을 고르시오.

① What do pacers do?
② At first, how do pacers decide their running speed?
③ What do pacers usually have?

④ How can runners choose a pacer?
⑤ How can the runner achieve his or her goal of finishing the marathon in a particular time more easily?

[17~19] 다음 글을 읽고 물음에 답하시오.

Pit Crews in Car Racing

You may only see the car and the driver during most car races, but there is a team behind the driver. This team is called a pit crew. A pit is a place on the side of the race track, and drivers stop there several times during a race. The main job of the pit crew is to check the car and change the tires. Changing the tires is especially important because the tires wear out easily in a high speed race.

A pit stop can be as short as 2 seconds, and there are as many as 20 members ___ⓐ___ a crew. Therefore, the pit crew has to work ___ⓑ___ perfect harmony. The driver may get all the attention, but as people say, "Races are won in the pits."

17 위 글의 빈칸 ⓐ와 ⓑ에 들어갈 전치사가 바르게 짝지어진 것은?

ⓐ	ⓑ		ⓐ	ⓑ
① on	to		② at	with
③ in	to		④ on	in
⑤ at	in			

18 다음 중 위 글의 pit crew에 대한 설명을 바르게 하지 <u>못한</u> 사람을 고르시오.

① 수희: 우리는 그들을 대부분의 자동차 경주에서 흔히 볼 수 있어.
② 혜민: 그들은 경주 트랙의 한쪽에 있는 공간인 피트에서 일해.

③ 영재: 그들은 주로 자동차를 점검하고 타이어를 교체해.

④ 진규: 한 팀에 많게는 20명에 이르는 구성원이 있어.

⑤ 민성: 그들은 완벽한 조화를 이루며 일해야 해.

출제율 100%

19 위 글의 제목으로 알맞은 것을 고르시오.

① What Do You Need to Be a Pit Crew?

② Where Is a Pit?

③ What Does a Pit Crew Mainly Do?

④ Why Do Drivers Stop at a Pit during a Race?

⑤ How Many Members Are There in a Pit Crew?

[20~21] 다음 글을 읽고 물음에 답하시오.

Sherpas in Mountain Climbing

The word *Sherpa* comes from the Sherpa tribe, which lives in the eastern part of Nepal. (①) They also have little difficulty breathing high up in the mountains. (②) Therefore, mountain climbers started to hire Sherpas to help them climb Mount Everest. (③)

Sherpas lead mountain climbers to the top of the mountain. (④) They support climbers in many ways. (⑤) For example, they put up tents and carry climbers' bags. Sherpas are often called the invisible people of Mount Everest because people often see a picture of only the climbers at the top of the mountain.

출제율 90%

20 주어진 영영풀이에 해당하는 단어를 본문에서 찾아 쓰시오.

a group of people of the same race, language, and customs

➡ _____

출제율 95%

21 위 글의 흐름으로 보아, 주어진 문장이 들어가기에 가장 적절한 곳은?

Sherpas have good climbing skills and know their way around the mountains well.

①   ②   ③   ④   ⑤

[22~24] 다음 글을 읽고 물음에 답하시오.

1. In swimming, a tapper uses a long pole to help a blind swimmer swim.

2. In a race, a guide runner runs with a blind runner and helps ⓐhim or her stay on the track.

3. In blind football, a shooting assistant tells ⓑhis or her team players ⓒwhich direction to shoot.

출제율 95%

22 위 글의 밑줄 친 ⓐhim or her와 ⓑhis or her가 가리키는 것을 각각 본문에서 찾아 쓰시오.

➡ ⓐ _____ ⓑ _____

출제율 90%

23 위 글의 밑줄 친 ⓒ를 다음과 같이 바꿔 쓸 때 빈칸에 들어갈 알맞은 말을 두 단어로 쓰시오.

➡ which direction _____ _____ shoot

출제율 95%

24 본문의 내용을 참조하여 다음 빈칸 (A)~(C)에 알맞은 단어를 쓰시오.

(A) _____ _____ , (B) _____ _____ _____ , and (C) _____ _____ are the assistants in the Paralympic Games.

[01~03] 다음 대화를 읽고 물음에 답하시오.

W: Hello. Welcome to Sports World. May I help you?

B: Yes, I came to register for a swimming class.

W: Is this your first time taking swimming lessons?

B: Yes, it is. I don't know how to swim at all.

W: I see. How often do you want to take classes?

B: I want to take classes twice a week. I'd like to take classes on weekdays and not on weekends.

W: Then, I suggest that you take the Beginner 2 class. This class meets on Tuesdays and Thursdays.

B: That sounds good. I'd like to sign up for that class. How big is the class?

W: The class has a limit of 10 people.

B: That's perfect.

01 How come the woman suggests the boy take the Beginner 2 class? Use the word, 'because'. (11 words)

➡ _____

_____

02 How often does the boy want to take the swimming lessons?

➡ _____

03 On which days will the boy take the swimming classes?

➡ _____

_____

04 다음 우리말과 같은 뜻이 되도록 주어진 단어들을 알맞게 배열하시오.

(1) 인도의 인구 성장률은 중국의 그것만큼 빠르다. (as, China, rate, population, as, is, of, fast, growth, that, India's)

➡ _____

(2) 중국 정부는 일본 정치 지도자들만큼이나 부끄러움을 모른다. (the Japanese, as, is, the Chinese, political, unashamed, government, as, leaders)

➡ _____

_____

05 다음 중 밑줄 친 부분을 어법에 맞게 고치고, 고친 단어의 종류, 즉 품사가 다른 하나를 찾아 그 이유를 설명하시오.

ⓐ Suji burned her finger with boil water.

ⓑ I read aloud some poems write by Yun Dongju.

ⓒ The train leave for New York is cancelled because of the disease.

ⓓ Sandra drew a beautiful mountain cover with snow.

ⓔ The baby cry on the bed was certainly feeling hungry.

ⓕ You need to buy a sleep bag for camping with us.

ⓖ Please listen to the fantastic music compose by Ludwig Beethoven.

➡ ⓐ _____ ⓑ _____ ⓒ _____

ⓓ _____ ⓔ _____ ⓕ _____

ⓖ _____

이유: _____

Pacers in a Marathon

Each (A)[pacer runs / pacers run] at different speeds and finishes the race in different times. Pacers usually have flags or balloons showing their finish time.

Runners can choose a pacer depending on their target finish time. For example, if a runner wants to finish the race in (B)[four hours / four-hour], the runner will follow the (C)[four hours / four-hour] pacer. Since the pacer keeps track of the time, ⓐ선수는 특정 시간에 마라톤을 완주하려는 자신의 목표를 더 쉽게 달성할 수 있다. In short, pacers run but they don't run to win. They run for others.

06 위 글의 괄호 (A)~(C)에서 어법상 알맞은 낱말을 골라 쓰시오.

➡ (A) _____ (B) _____

(C) _____

07 위 글의 밑줄 친 ⓐ의 우리말에 맞게 한 단어를 보충하여, 주어진 어휘를 알맞게 배열하시오.

> finishing the marathon / more easily / the runner / his or her goal / in a particular time / can achieve

➡ _____

_____

08 What is a pacer's role in a marathon? Answer in English with a full sentence. (10 words)

➡ _____

_____

Pit Crews in Car Racing

You may only see the car and the driver during most car races, but there is a team behind the driver. This team ___ⓐ___ a pit crew. A pit is a place on the side of the race track, and drivers stop there several times during a race. The main job of the pit crew is to check the car and change the tires. ⓑ Changing the tires are especially important because the tires wear out easily in a high speed race.

A pit stop can be as short as 2 seconds, and there are as many as 20 members on a crew. Therefore, the pit crew has to work in perfect harmony. The driver may get all the attention, but as people say, "Races are won in the pits."

09 위 글의 빈칸 ⓐ에 call을 알맞은 형태로 쓰시오.

➡ _____

10 위 글의 밑줄 친 ⓑ에서 어법상 틀린 부분을 찾아 고치시오.

_____ ➡ _____

11 다음 빈칸 (A)와 (B)에 알맞은 단어를 넣어 'pit'에 대한 소개를 완성하시오.

> A pit is a place on (A)_____ _____ of the race track where drivers stop several times during (B)_____ _____ to check the car and change the tires.

창의사고력 서술형 문제

01 주어진 표현을 이용하여 〈보기〉와 같이 다음 대화의 빈칸에 알맞은 말을 쓰시오.

> A: How _____?   B: I _____.

보기

> A: How often do you have breakfast?   B: I have breakfast every day.

> have breakfast / play computer games / eat late at night / take swimming classes
> every day / three times a week / five times a week / twice a week

02 다음 학생들의 체력 측정 기록표를 보고, as ~ as를 사용하여, 내용에 맞게 자유롭게 영작하시오.

	Sein	Minju	Seohyun	Bona	Ahrin
100m record (seconds)	18	19	21	18	20
standing jump (cm)	44	36	34	36	42
ball throwing (m)	19	21	27	16	27

(1) _____

(2) _____

03 다음 내용을 바탕으로 스포츠 분야의 숨은 조력자인 치어리더에 관한 설명문을 쓰시오.

> **Who:** cheerleaders in football games
>
> **What they do:**
> • cheer at a game
> • create team spirit
>
> **What they need to be or do:**
> • be fit and strong
> • be good at jumping and dancing
> • encourage their team and fans

> **Cheerleaders in Football Games**
>
> Although people usually don't think that cheerleaders are a part of a football team, they play an important role in a football game. By (A)_____ at a game, they create (B)_____. They also encourage (C)_____. To do their job well, cheerleaders need to be (D)_____. They also need to be good at (E)_____.

단원별 모의고사

01 다음 짝지어진 단어의 관계가 같도록 빈칸에 알맞은 말을 쓰시오. (주어진 철자로 시작할 것)

> suggest – propose : employ – _____

[02~03] 주어진 영어 설명에 알맞은 어휘를 빈칸에 쓰시오.

02
> I can hardly _____ in this cave.

> <영어 설명> to take air into your body and let it out again

➡ _____

03
> We can learn the culture of the Masai _____ in this class.

> <영어 설명> a group of people who have their own language and ways of living

➡ _____

04 다음 빈칸에 알맞은 말로 짝지어진 것을 고르시오.

> • We do not _____ smoking in the hall.
> • I _____ that we go out to eat.

① register – promote
② register – suggest
③ allow – promote
④ allow – suggest
⑤ permit – manage

05 다음 우리말을 주어진 어휘를 이용하여 영작하시오.

(1) 내 부츠가 닳기 시작한다. (boots, wear, beginning)
➡ _____

(2) 교통 체증이 있어서 우리는 지하철을 타야 한다. (heavy traffic, there, therefore, should, take)
➡ _____

(3) 특별히 생각해 둔 식당이 있나요? (have, particular, in mind)
➡ _____

[06~07] 다음 대화를 읽고 물음에 답하시오.

> B: Mina, how ⓐoften do you swim?
> G: I swim every day.
> B: Can I go ⓑto swim with you this afternoon?
> G: Sure, but (a)수영 모자를 챙기는 것을 제안해.(bring, a swimming cap) ⓒWithout a ⓓswimming cap, you ⓔaren't allowed in the pool.

06 위 대화의 밑줄 친 우리말 (a)에 맞게 주어진 어휘를 이용하여 영작하시오. (7 words)
➡ _____

07 밑줄 친 ⓐ~ⓔ 중 어색한 것은?
① ⓐ   ② ⓑ   ③ ⓒ   ④ ⓓ   ⑤ ⓔ

[08~09] 다음 대화를 읽고 물음에 답하시오.

> B: Mina, how often do you come here to run?
> G: Every day.
> B: Can I run with you today?
> G: Sure, but _____(A)_____. (wear, running, should, shoes) Your shoes aren't good for running.

08 위 대화의 빈칸 (A)에 알맞은 말을 주어진 어휘를 이용하여 8 단어로 쓰시오.

➡ _____

09 Why does Mina come here every day?

➡ _____

[10~12] 다음 대화를 읽고 물음에 답하시오.

W: Hello. Welcome to Sports World. May I help you?
B: Yes, I came to register for a swimming class.
W: Is this your first time taking swimming lessons?
B: Yes, it is. I don't know _____(A)_____ at all.
W: I see. How often do you want to take classes?
B: I want to take classes twice a week. I'd like to take classes on weekdays and not on weekends.
W: Then, I suggest that you take the Beginner 2 class. This class meets on Tuesdays and Thursdays.
B: That sounds good. I'd like to sign up for that class. How big is the class?
W: The class has a ___(B)___ of 10 people.
B: That's perfect.

10 위 대화의 빈칸 (A)에 'how I should swim'과 같은 뜻의 말을 3 단어로 쓰시오.

➡ _____

11 위 대화의 빈칸 (B)에 알맞은 것을 고르시오.

① limit   ② harmony
③ circumstance   ④ boundary
⑤ member

12 위 대화의 내용과 일치하지 <u>않는</u> 것은?

① 소년은 수영 수업을 등록하려고 왔다.
② 소년은 수영 수업을 받는 것이 이번이 처음이다.
③ 소년은 수영하는 법을 전혀 알지 못한다.
④ 소년은 주말에 수업을 듣고 싶어 한다.
⑤ 초급 2반의 제한 인원은 열 명이다.

13 다음 그림을 보고, 괄호 안에 주어진 단어를 활용하여 글자 수 조건에 맞게 영작하시오.

• Reporter: Is there anything interesting about your job?
• Pacer: (A) Pacers _____ _____. (페이서들은 자신들의 출발 시간을 나타내는 깃발이나 풍선을 가지고 있어요.) (flags, show, start, balloons, or, 8 단어)
• Pit Crew: (B) The pit crew has to work in perfect harmony _____ _____. (피트에서의 정지는 짧게는 2분 정도이기 때문에, 피트 크루는 완벽한 조화를 이루며 일해야 합니다.) (can, short, as, since, a pit stop, 11 단어)

14 다음 밑줄 친 부분 중 어법상 어색한 것을 고르시오.

① Susan was <u>interested</u> in Egypt.
② I know the great baseball player <u>called</u> Lion King.
③ My mom likes to listen to the sound of rain <u>falling</u> onto the roof.
④ I bought much stationery <u>included</u> paper, pencils, erasers, and so on.
⑤ There were <u>broken</u> pieces of the glass.

15 다음 우리말과 일치하도록 괄호 안의 단어를 바르게 배열하시오.

(1) 내 필통은 Mina의 것만큼 가볍다. (case, light, as, pencil, is, Mina's, as, my).

➡ _____

(2) Isabelle은 John만큼 키가 크지만, 그녀의 몸무게는 그만큼 되지 않는다. (John, Isabelle, as, is, isn't, as, so, tall, heavy, but, he, she, as).

➡ _____

16 다음 문장의 빈칸을 괄호 안의 단어를 사용하여 어법에 맞게 쓸 때, 〈보기〉의 빈칸에 들어갈 말과 쓰임이 다른 것을 모두 고르면?

┌─ 보기 ┐
My grandfather has a scar _____ (make) at the war field on his forehead.
└─────┘

① Look at the statue _____ (place) in front of the building.
② Mom cleared the pieces of the dishes _____ (break) by my mistake.
③ Joshua wants to buy some ice boxes _____ (design) to keep beer bottles cold.
④ The CEO of the company cancelled the meeting _____ (schedule) tomorrow.
⑤ A lot of volunteers gathered to help the elderly _____ (live) alone.

17 다음 우리말을 괄호 안에 주어진 단어를 알맞게 배열하여 영작하시오. (동사는 어법에 맞게 형태 변화 가능)

┌─────────────────────────┐
엄마는 '백주부'라고 불리는 남자만큼 맛있는 요리를 만드신다.
(as, make, call, as, dishes, a man, mom, delicious, 'Housewife Baek')
└─────────────────────────┘

➡ _____

18 다음 중 밑줄 친 단어의 쓰임이 어법상 어색한 것은?

① Who is that girl <u>wearing</u> a colorful evening dress?
② Jane can recite the whole poem <u>written</u> by Yoon Dongju.
③ You can see laundries <u>hanging</u> on the washing lines on sunny days.
④ My father has collected many old coins <u>making</u> in ancient days.
⑤ Please remember the legendary singer <u>called</u> 'Mawang, the Devil King'.

[19~20] 다음 글을 읽고 물음에 답하시오.

Pacers in a Marathon

Runners can choose a pacer depending on their target finish time. For example, if a runner wants to finish the race in four hours, the runner will follow the four-hour pacer. Since the pacer ⓐ _____ the time, the runner can achieve his or her goal of finishing the marathon in a particular time more easily. In short, pacers run but they don't run ⓑto win. They run for others.

19 위 글의 빈칸 ⓐ에 들어갈 알맞은 말을 고르시오.

① catches up with
② puts up with
③ comes up with
④ keeps track of
⑤ makes up for

20 아래 〈보기〉에서 위 글의 밑줄 친 ⓑto win과 to부정사의 용법이 다른 것의 개수를 고르시오.

┌─── 보기 ───┐
① My dream is to win a marathon.
② She practiced hard every day to win a marathon.
③ The best way to win a marathon is to practice running every day.
④ I really want to win a marathon.
⑤ She is strong enough to win a marathon.
└────────────┘

① 1개   ② 2개   ③ 3개   ④ 4개   ⑤ 5개

[21~23] 다음 글을 읽고 물음에 답하시오.

Pit Crews in Car Racing

You may only see the car and the driver during most car races, but there is a team behind the driver. (①) This team is called a pit crew. (②) A pit is a place on the side of the race track, and drivers stop there several times during a race. (③) Changing the tires is especially important because the tires wear out easily in a high speed race. (④)

A pit stop can be as short as 2 seconds, and there are as many as 20 members on a crew. (⑤) Therefore, the pit crew has to work in perfect harmony. ⓐThe driver may get all the attention, but as people say, "Races win in the pits."

21 위 글의 흐름으로 보아, 주어진 문장이 들어가기에 가장 적절한 곳은?

┌────────────────────────────────────┐
The main job of the pit crew is to check the car and change the tires.
└────────────────────────────────────┘

①   ②   ③   ④   ⑤

22 위 글의 밑줄 친 ⓐ에서 어법상 틀린 부분을 찾아 고치시오.

_____ ➡ _____

23 본문의 내용과 일치하도록 다음 빈칸 (A)와 (B)에 알맞은 단어를 쓰시오.

┌────────────────────────────────────┐
During most car races, the driver may get all (A)_____ _____, but a team called a (B)_____ _____ plays an important role helping the driver win the race behind the driver.
└────────────────────────────────────┘

[24~26] 다음 글을 읽고 물음에 답하시오.

Sherpas in Mountain Climbing

The word *Sherpa* comes from the Sherpa tribe, which lives in the eastern part of Nepal. Sherpas have good climbing skills and know their way around the mountains well. They also have little difficulty breathing high up in the mountains. ___ⓐ___, mountain climbers started to hire Sherpas to help them climb Mount Everest.

Sherpas lead mountain climbers to the top of the mountain. They support climbers in many ways. ___ⓑ___, they put up tents and carry climbers' bags. Sherpas are often called the invisible people of Mount Everest ⓒ왜냐하면 사람들이 산 정상에서 등산가들만 찍힌 사진을 자주 보기 때문이다.

24 위 글의 빈칸 ⓐ와 ⓑ에 들어갈 알맞은 말을 고르시오.

① Therefore – For example
② In other words – By contrast
③ In addition – Thus
④ Whereas – Moreover
⑤ For example – Likewise

25 위 글의 밑줄 친 ⓒ의 우리말에 맞게 주어진 어휘를 이용하여 16 단어로 영작하시오.

because, often, of, at the top of

➡ _____

_____

26 According to the passage, which is NOT true?

① The word *Sherpa* is named after the Sherpa tribe.

② The Sherpa tribe lives in the eastern part of Nepal.

③ Sherpas know their way around the mountains well.

④ It's not easy for Sherpas to breathe high up in the mountains.

⑤ Sherpas put up tents and carry climbers' bags.

[27~29] 다음 글을 읽고 물음에 답하시오.

Cheerleaders in Football Games

(A)[Although / As] people usually don't think that cheerleaders are a part of a football team, they play an important role in a football game. By cheering at a game, they create team spirit. They also encourage their team and fans. To do their job well, cheerleaders need to be fit and strong. They also need to be good (B)[at / for] jumping and dancing. ⓐMost of all, they need to work as (C)[hard / hardly] as the players.

27 위 글의 괄호 (A)~(C)에서 문맥상 알맞은 낱말을 골라 쓰시오.

➡ (A) _____ (B) _____ (C) _____

28 위 글의 밑줄 친 ⓐMost of all과 바꿔 쓸 수 있는 말을 모두 고르시오.

① At first ② First of all

③ After all ④ Above all

⑤ More than anything else

29 다음 중 '미식축구 경기에서의 치어리더'에 대한 설명으로 옳지 않은 것을 고르시오.

① 공동체 정신을 만들어낸다.

② 팀과 팬들을 격려한다.

③ 몸을 건강하게 관리하고 강해야 한다.

④ 점프하는 것과 노래 부르는 것을 잘해야 한다.

⑤ 선수들만큼이나 열심히 일해야 한다.

MEMO

INSIGHT
on the textbook
교과서 파헤치기

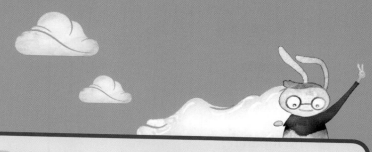

※ 다음 영어를 우리말로 쓰시오.

01 cause _____

02 present _____

03 decide _____

04 contact _____

05 explorer _____

06 factory _____

07 slave _____

08 flood _____

09 anger _____

10 century _____

11 civilization _____

12 suggest _____

13 advanced _____

14 shortly _____

15 originally _____

16 meaning _____

17 universe _____

18 trader _____

19 design _____

20 experience _____

21 justice _____

22 expression _____

23 law _____

24 myth _____

25 include _____

26 nervous _____

27 origin _____

28 storm _____

29 judge _____

30 originate _____

31 produce _____

32 tool _____

33 borrow _____

34 slice _____

35 pass through _____

36 come from ~ _____

37 be made into ~ _____

38 pick up _____

39 rain cats and dogs _____

40 keep in touch _____

41 make a long face _____

42 call ~ after … _____

43 see eye to eye _____

※ 다음 우리말을 영어로 쓰시오.

01 진보한, 발전된 _____

02 초래하다; 원인 _____

03 경험하다 _____

04 화나게 하다 _____

05 스페인의 _____

06 빌리다 _____

07 표현 _____

08 공장 _____

09 접촉 _____

10 홍수 _____

11 세기, 100년 _____

12 곧, 즉시 _____

13 문명 _____

14 포함하다 _____

15 탐험가 _____

16 창조하다 _____

17 상인, 거래자 _____

18 폭풍 _____

19 정의 _____

20 법 _____

21 생산하다 _____

22 언어 _____

23 얇게 썬 조각; 한 조각 _____

24 제안하다 _____

25 재판관, 판사; 재판하다 _____

26 불안한 _____

27 의미 _____

28 기원, 유래 _____

29 현재의 _____

30 노예 _____

31 우주, 은하계 _____

32 유래하다 _____

33 원래, 본래 _____

34 신화 _____

35 ~에서 오다, 유래하다 _____

36 놀리다 _____

37 우울한 얼굴을 하다 _____

38 거쳐 지나가다 _____

39 행운을 빌다 _____

40 몸이 안 좋은 _____

41 연락하다 _____

42 전혀 ~가 아니다 _____

43 ~로 만들어지다 _____

※ 다음 영영풀이에 알맞은 단어를 <보기>에서 골라 쓴 후, 우리말 뜻을 쓰시오.

1 _____ : in a short time; soon: _____

2 _____ : to make someone angry: _____

3 _____ : happening or existing now: _____

4 _____ : a period of a hundred years: _____

5 _____ : a society that is well organized and developed: _____

6 _____ : a lot of water that covers land that is usually dry: _____

7 _____ : in the beginning, before other things happened: _____

8 _____ : someone who buys and sells goods: _____

9 _____ : all of space, including all the stars and planets: _____

10 _____ : to tell someone you think he or she should do something: _____

11 _____ : communication between people, countries either by talking or writing:
_____

12 _____ : something you say, write, or do that shows what you think or feel:
_____

13 _____ : the action of pressing and rubbing someone's body to help him or her
relax: _____

14 _____ : someone who is owned by another person and works for them for no
money: _____

15 _____ : a system of rules that a society or government develops in order to deal
with crime and etc.: _____

16 _____ : to use something that belongs to someone else and that you must give
back to them later: _____

 보기

law	expression	flood	present
massage	anger	century	shortly
trader	universe	slave	contact
borrow	suggest	civilization	originally

※ 다음 우리말과 일치하도록 빈칸에 알맞은 말을 쓰시오.

Listen and Talk A 1

G: Look. It's raining _____ _____ _____.

B: Raining _____ _____ _____? What does _____ _____?

G: It _____ "It's _____ _____ _____."

B: Oh. _____ _____. I have an umbrella _____ _____ _____.

G: 봐. 고양이와 개처럼 비가 내려.
B: 고양이와 개처럼 비가 내린다고? 그게 무슨 뜻이니?
G: 그것은 "비가 아주 많이 내린다."라는 뜻이야.
B: 오, 걱정 마. 내 배낭에 우산이 있어.

Listen and Talk A 2

G: This juice is _____ _____, Suho.

B: _____ _____? _____ you _____ _____ again?

G: I said, "This juice is _____ _____." It _____ "I'll _____ _____ the juice."

B: Oh. Thanks _____ _____.

G: _____ _____.

G: 수호야, 이 주스는 내 위에 있어.
B: 뭐라고 했어? 다시 한 번 말해 줄래?
G: "이 주스는 내 위에 있어."라고 했어. 그것은 "내가 그 주스를 낼게."라는 뜻이야.
B: 오. 정말 고마워.
G: 천만에.

Listen and Talk A 3

B: Everything _____ _____.

G: Yes. _____ you _____ _____ of my spaghetti?

B: No, _____. Spaghetti is _____ my cup of _____.

G: _____ your cup of _____? What _____ that _____?

B: It means "I _____ _____ _____."

G: Oh, I _____. You _____ _____ spaghetti.

B: 모든 것이 맛있어 보여.
G: 응. 내 스파게티 좀 먹을래?
B: 괜찮아. 스파게티는 나의 차 한 잔이 아니야.
G: 네 차 한 잔이 아니라고? 그게 무슨 뜻이니?
B: 그것은 "난 무언가를 좋아하지 않아." 라는 뜻이야.
G: 오, 알겠어. 넌 스파게티를 좋아하지 않는구나.

Listen and Talk A 4

G: I feel _____ _____ _____.

B: _____ _____, but _____ you please _____ _____?

G: I said, "I feel _____ _____ _____." It means "I _____ _____." I think I _____ _____ _____.

B: Oh. _____ _____ _____ buy some medicine before you _____ on the plane? You can _____ _____ at the store _____ _____.

G: I guess I _____.

G: 난 날씨 아래 있는 기분이야.
B: 미안하지만 다시 한 번 말해 줄래?
G: "나는 날씨 아래 있는 기분이야."라고 말했어. 그것은 "몸이 좋지 않아."라는 뜻이야. 난 감기에 걸린 것 같아.
B: 오, 비행기 타기 전에 약을 좀 사는 게 어때? 저기에 있는 가게에서 약을 살 수 있어.
G: 그래야겠다.

Listen and Talk B 1

A: Don't _____ _____ _____ _____.

B: _____ _____, but _____ _____ _____ _____ _____ _____?

A: I said, "Don't _____ _____ _____ _____."

B: _____ _____ _____ _____?

A: It _____ "Don't _____ _____."

A: 얼굴을 길쭉하게 만들지 마.
B: 미안하지만 다시 한 번 말해 줄래?
A: "얼굴을 길쭉하게 만들지 마."라고 했어.
B: 그게 무슨 뜻이니?
A: 그것은 "슬퍼하지 마."라는 뜻이야.

Listen and Talk B 2

M: _____ _____ _____.

W: _____ _____, but _____ _____ _____ _____ _____?

M: I said, "_____ _____ _____."

W: _____ _____ _____ _____?

M: It means "_____ _____."

M: 다리를 부러뜨려.
W: 미안하지만 다시 한 번 말해 줄래?
M: "다리를 부러뜨려."라고 했어.
W: 그게 무슨 뜻이니?
M: 그것은 "행운을 빌어."라는 뜻이야.

Listen and Talk B 3

M: I feel _____ _____ _____.

W: _____ _____, but _____ _____ _____ _____ _____ _____?

M: I said, "I feel _____ _____ _____."

W: _____ _____ _____ _____?

M: It means "I _____ _____ well."

M: 나는 날씨 아래 있는 기분이야.
W: 미안하지만 다시 한 번 말해 줄래?
M: "나는 날씨 아래 있는 기분이야."라고 했어.
W: 그게 무슨 뜻이니?
M: 그것은 "난 몸이 좋지 않아."라는 뜻이야.

Listen and Talk C

G: Thank you for everything, Jiho. I _____ _____ _____ _____ in Korea.

B: _____ _____. Please _____ _____ me again, Lucy.

G: I'd _____ _____, but before I do, I'd _____ _____ _____ you _____ _____ me in London.

B: Thanks. Anyway, _____'s too bad _____ you can't _____ to my soccer game tomorrow.

G: I'm sorry that I _____ _____. I'll _____ _____ _____ for you.

B: _____ _____, but _____ please _____ _____?

G: I said, "I'll _____ _____ _____ _____ for you." It means "I _____ _____ _____ _____ _____ _____."

B: Oh. Thanks. _____ a nice _____.

G: Thanks. I'll _____ _____ _____.

G: 지호야, 모든 게 고마웠어. 한국에서 정말 좋은 시간을 보냈어.
B: 천만에. 다음에 또 와줘, Lucy.
G: 그러고 싶지만, 그 전에 난 런던으로 널 초대하고 싶어.
B: 고마워. 어쨌든, 내일 네가 내 축구 시합에 올 수 없어서 너무 안타깝다.
G: 나도 더 오래 머물 수 없어서 유감이야. 너를 위해 내 손가락을 교차할게.
B: 미안한데, 다시 한 번 말해 줄래?
G: 나는 "너를 위해 내 손가락을 교차할게."라고 말했어. 그것은 "행운을 빌게."라는 뜻이야.
B: 아, 고마워. 즐거운 여행이 되길 바랄게.
G: 고마워. 연락할게.

Review 1

G: I'll _____ _____ _____ _____ for you.

B: I'm sorry, but _____ _____ _____ _____ _____?

G: I said, "I'll _____ _____ _____ _____ for you." It means "I _____ _____ _____ _____."

G: 너를 위해 내 손가락을 교차할게.
B: 미안하지만 다시 한 번 말해 줄래?
G: "너를 위해 내 손가락을 교차할게." 라고 했어. 그것은 "행운을 빌게."라 는 뜻이야.

Review 2

W: I _____ _____ _____ _____.

M: Excuse me, but _____ _____ _____ _____ _____ _____?

W: I said, "I _____ _____ _____ _____."

M: _____ _____ _____ _____?

W: It means "I _____ _____ _____." I think I _____ _____ _____.

M: Oh. _____ _____ _____ _____ some medicine? You can _____ _____ at the store _____ _____.

W: OK, I _____.

W: 저는 날씨 아래에 있는 기분이에요.
M: 죄송한데, 다시 한 번 말해 주시겠어 요?
W: "저는 날씨 아래에 있는 기분이에 요."라고 말했어요.
M: 그게 무슨 뜻인가요?
W: 그것은 "몸이 좋지 않다."라는 뜻이 에요. 감기에 걸린 것 같아요.
M: 오. 약을 좀 사는 게 어때요? 저기에 있는 가게에서 약을 살 수 있어요.
W: 네, 그럴게요.

Review 3

M: Look. It's raining _____ _____ _____.

W: _____ _____ _____ _____ _____?

M: It's raining _____ _____ _____.

W: _____ _____ _____ _____?

M: It _____ "It's _____ _____ _____."

M: 봐요. 고양이와 개처럼 비가 내리네 요.
W: 다시 한 번 말해 주시겠어요?
M: 고양이와 개처럼 비가 내려요.
W: 그게 무슨 뜻인가요?
M: 그것은 "비가 아주 많이 내린다."라 는 뜻이에요.

Review 4

G: This pizza _____ _____ _____, Suho.

B: _____ _____ _____ _____?

G: It means "I'll _____ _____ the pizza."

G: 수호야, 이 피자는 내 위에 있어.
B: 그게 무슨 뜻이니?
G: 그것은 "피자는 내가 살게."라는 뜻 이야.

대화문 Test

※ 다음 우리말에 맞도록 대화를 영어로 쓰시오.

Listen and Talk A 1

G: _____

B: _____

G: _____

B: _____

G: 봐. 고양이와 개처럼 비가 내려.
B: 고양이와 개처럼 비가 내린다고? 그게 무슨 뜻이니?
G: 그것은 "비가 아주 많이 내린다."라는 뜻이야.
B: 오, 걱정 마. 내 배낭에 우산이 있어.

Listen and Talk A 2

G: _____

B: _____

G: _____

B: _____

G: _____

G: 수호야, 이 주스는 내 위에 있어.
B: 뭐라고 했어? 다시 한 번 말해 줄래?
G: "이 주스는 내 위에 있어."라고 했어. 그것은 "내가 그 주스를 낼게."라는 뜻이야.
B: 오. 정말 고마워.
G: 천만에.

Listen and Talk A 3

B: _____

G: _____

B: _____

G: _____

B: _____

G: _____

B: 모든 것이 맛있어 보여.
G: 응. 내 스파게티 좀 먹을래?
B: 괜찮아. 스파게티는 나의 차 한 잔이 아니야.
G: 네 차 한 잔이 아니라고? 그게 무슨 뜻이니?
B: 그것은 "난 무언가를 좋아하지 않아." 라는 뜻이야.
G: 오, 알겠어. 넌 스파게티를 좋아하지 않는구나.

Listen and Talk A 4

G: _____

B: _____

G: _____

B: _____

G: _____

G: 난 날씨 아래 있는 기분이야.
B: 미안하지만 다시 한 번 말해 줄래?
G: "나는 날씨 아래 있는 기분이야."라고 말했어. 그것은 "몸이 좋지 않아."라는 뜻이야. 난 감기에 걸린 것 같아.
B: 오, 비행기 타기 전에 약을 좀 사는 게 어때? 저기에 있는 가게에서 약을 살 수 있어.
G: 그래야겠다.

Listen and Talk B 1

A: _____

B: _____

A: _____

B: _____

A: _____

Listen and Talk B 2

M: _____

W: _____

M: _____

W: _____

M: _____

Listen and Talk B 3

M: _____

W: _____

M: _____

W: _____

M: _____

Listen and Talk C

G: _____

B: _____

G: _____

B: _____

G: _____

B: _____

G: _____

B: _____

G: _____

A: 얼굴을 길쭉하게 만들지 마.
B: 미안하지만 다시 한 번 말해 줄래?
A: "얼굴을 길쭉하게 만들지 마."라고 했어.
B: 그게 무슨 뜻이니?
A: 그것은 "슬퍼하지 마."라는 뜻이야.

M: 다리를 부러뜨려.
W: 미안하지만 다시 한 번 말해 줄래?
M: "다리를 부러뜨려."라고 했어.
W: 그게 무슨 뜻이니?
M: 그것은 "행운을 빌어."라는 뜻이야.

M: 나는 날씨 아래 있는 기분이야.
W: 미안하지만 다시 한 번 말해 줄래?
M: "나는 날씨 아래 있는 기분이야."라고 했어.
W: 그게 무슨 뜻이니?
M: 그것은 "난 몸이 좋지 않아."라는 뜻이야.

G: 지호야, 모든 게 고마웠어. 한국에서 정말 좋은 시간을 보냈어.
B: 천만에. 다음에 또 와줘, Lucy.
G: 그러고 싶지만, 그 전에 난 런던으로 널 초대하고 싶어.
B: 고마워. 어쨌든, 내일 네가 내 축구 시합에 올 수 없어서 너무 안타깝다.
G: 나도 더 오래 머물 수 없어서 유감이야. 너를 위해 내 손가락을 교차할게.
B: 미안한데, 다시 한 번 말해 줄래?
G: 나는 "너를 위해 내 손가락을 교차할게."라고 말했어. 그것은 "행운을 빌게."라는 뜻이야.
B: 아, 고마워. 즐거운 여행이 되길 바랄게.
G: 고마워. 연락할게.

Review 1

G: _____

B: _____

G: _____

G: 너를 위해 내 손가락을 교차할게.
B: 미안하지만 다시 한 번 말해 줄래?
G: "너를 위해 내 손가락을 교차할게."
라고 했어. 그것은 "행운을 빌게."라
는 뜻이야.

Review 2

W: _____

M: _____

W: _____

M: _____

W: _____

M: _____

W: _____

W: 저는 날씨 아래에 있는 기분이에요.
M: 죄송한데, 다시 한 번 말해 주시겠어
요?
W: "저는 날씨 아래에 있는 기분이에
요."라고 말했어요.
M: 그게 무슨 뜻인가요?
W: 그것은 "몸이 좋지 않다."라는 뜻이
에요. 감기에 걸린 것 같아요.
M: 오. 약을 좀 사는 게 어때요? 저기에
있는 가게에서 약을 살 수 있어요.
W: 네, 그럴게요.

Review 3

M: _____

W: _____

M: _____

W: _____

M: _____

M: 봐요. 고양이와 개처럼 비가 내리네
요.
W: 다시 한 번 말해 주시겠어요?
M: 고양이와 개처럼 비가 내려요.
W: 그게 무슨 뜻인가요?
M: 그것은 "비가 아주 많이 내린다."라
는 뜻이에요.

Review 4

G: _____

B: _____

G: _____

G: 수호야, 이 피자는 내 위에 있어.
B: 그게 무슨 뜻이니?
G: 그것은 "피자는 내가 살게."라는 뜻
이야.

※ 다음 우리말과 일치하도록 빈칸에 알맞은 것을 골라 쓰시오.

1 **English** _____ **of** _____
A. Origin   B. Words   C. Foreign

2 English has often _____ _____ from _____ cultures or _____.
A. other   B. words   C. languages   D. borrowed

3 _____ are some _____ interesting stories.
A. examples   B. with   C. here

shampoo

4 The word *shampoo* _____ _____ the Hindi word *chāmpo*, which _____ "to _____."
A. from   B. means   C. comes   D. press

5 In India, the word _____ for a _____.
A. massage   B. used   C. head   D. was

6 British _____ in India _____ a bath _____ a head massage and _____ it to Britain in the 18th century.
A. experienced   B. introduced   C. traders   D. with

7 The _____ of the word *shampoo* changed a _____ times after it first _____ English _____ 1762.
A. entered   B. few   C. meaning   D. around

8 In the 19th _____, *shampoo* got its _____ meaning of "_____ the _____."
A. washing   B. present   C. hair   D. century

9 _____ after that, the word began to _____ for a special soap for the hair.
A. used   B. shortly   C. also   D. be

robot

10 The word *robot* comes from the _____ *R.U.R.*, _____ was _____ in 1920 _____ a Czech writer Karel Čapek.
A. written   B. play   C. by   D. which

11 In the play, robots are machines that _____.
A. like   B. look   C. humans

12 They _____ _____ to _____ for humans and are _____ in a factory.
A. work   B. produced   C. are   D. designed

13 It is interesting that the _____ _____ the word *robot* didn't come from Karel Čapek _____.
A. himself   B. of   C. idea   D. using

14 He originally _____ the machines in his play *labori* _____ the Latin word "_____."
A. for   B. called   C. from   D. work

1 외국어에서 유래된 영어 단어

2 영어는 종종 다른 문화나 언어에서 단어를 빌려왔다.

3 여기 재미있는 이야기가 있는 몇 개의 예가 있다.

샴푸

4 *shampoo*라는 단어는 힌디어 *chāmpo*에서 왔고, '누르다'라는 의미이다.

5 인도에서 그 단어는 머리 마사지라는 의미로 쓰였다.

6 인도에 있는 영국 상인들은 머리 마사지를 함께하는 목욕을 경험했고 마사지를 18세기에 영국에 소개했다.

7 *shampoo*라는 단어의 의미는 그 단어가 1762년쯤 영어에 처음으로 들어온 이후 몇 번 바뀌었다.

8 19세기에, *shampoo*는 '머리 감기'라는 현재의 의미를 갖게 되었다.

9 그 후 얼마 지나지 않아, 그 단어는 머리에 사용하는 특별한 비누에도 쓰이기 시작했다.

로봇

10 *robot*이라는 단어는 "*R.U.R.*"에서 왔는데, 그 연극은 1920년 체코의 작가 Karel Čapek에 의해 쓰였다.

11 그 연극에서 로봇은 인간처럼 생긴 기계이다.

12 그들은 인간을 위해 일하도록 설계되고, 공장에서 생산된다.

13 *robot*이라는 단어를 사용하려는 생각이 Karel Čapek 자신에게서 나온 게 아니었다는 것이 흥미롭다.

14 그는 원래 자신의 연극에서 그 기계들을 '일'을 의미하는 라틴어에서 온 *labori*라고 불렀다.

15 _____, his brother suggested *roboti*, which means "_____ workers" _____ _____.

A. slave   B. Czech   C. however   D. in

16 Karel Čapek liked the _____ and decided _____ the _____ *roboti*.

A. use   B. idea   C. to   D. word

17 In 1938, the _____ was _____ a science _____ show on television in Britain.

A. fiction   B. made   C. play   D. into

hurricane

18 The word *hurricane* _____ from the Spanish word *huracán*, which _____ the _____ of a Mayan god.

A. from   B. comes   C. name   D. originates

19 In the Mayan _____ _____, Huracán is the weather god of wind, storm, and fire, and he is one of the three _____ who _____ humans.

A. gods   B. myth   C. creation   D. created

20 _____, the first humans _____ the gods, _____ Huracán _____ a great flood.

A. so   B. however   C. caused   D. angered

21 The first _____ _____ the Mayan _____ was in 1517.

A. civilization   B. contact   C. Spanish   D. with

22 Spanish explorers who were _____ _____ the Caribbean experienced a hurricane and _____ _____ the word for it from the people in the area.

A. through   B. up   C. passing   D. picked

23 _____ English, one of the _____ _____ of *hurricane* was in a play _____ Shakespeare in 1608.

A. by   B. uses   C. early   D. in

hamburger

24 The _____ *hamburger* _____ comes _____ Hamburg, Germany's _____ city.

A. originally   B. word   C. second-largest   D. from

25 *Hamburger* _____ "people or _____ from Hamburg" _____.

A. things   B. means   C. German   D. in

26 The _____ of the first hamburger is _____.

A. clear   B. origin   C. not

27 However, it is _____ _____ the hamburger was invented in a small town in Texas, USA, sometime _____ 1885 _____ 1904.

A. between   B. believed   C. and   D. that

28 A cook _____ a Hamburg-style steak between two _____ of bread, and people started to call _____ _____ a hamburger.

A. slices   B. food   C. placed   D. such

---

15 하지만, 그의 형이 *roboti*를 제안했는데, *roboti*는 체코어로 '노예 근로자들'을 의미한다.

16 Karel Čapek은 그 아이디어가 마음에 들어 *roboti*라는 단어를 사용하기로 결정했다.

17 1938년에 그 연극은 영국 TV에서 공상 과학물로 만들어졌다.

태풍

18 *hurricane*이라는 단어는 스페인어 단어 *huracán*에서 왔고, 그것은 마야 신의 이름에서 유래한다.

19 마야의 창조 신화에서, Huracán은 바람, 폭풍우, 그리고 불에 관한 날씨의 신이며, 그는 인간을 창조한 세 명의 신들 중 한 명이다.

20 하지만, 최초의 인간들이 신들을 화나게 해서 Huracán은 거대한 홍수를 일으켰다.

21 스페인이 마야 문명과 했던 첫 접촉은 1517년이었다.

22 카리브 제도를 지나던 스페인 탐험가들이 허리케인을 겪었고, 그 지역 사람들로부터 그것을 의미하는 단어를 듣게 되었다.

23 영어에서 일찍이 *hurricane*을 사용한 것 중 하나는 1608년 셰익스피어에 의한 희곡에서였다.

햄버거

24 *hamburger*라는 단어는 원래 독일에서 두 번째로 큰 도시인 함부르크에서 왔다.

25 *hamburger*는 독일어로 '함부르크 출신의 사람 또는 사물'을 의미한다.

26 최초의 햄버거의 기원은 분명하지 않다.

27 하지만 햄버거는 1885년에서 1904년 사이의 언젠가 미국 텍사스에 있는 작은 마을에서 발명되었다고 믿어진다.

28 한 요리사가 빵 두 조각 사이에 함부르크 스타일의 스테이크를 넣었고, 사람들은 그런 음식을 햄버거라고 부르기 시작했다.

※ 다음 우리말과 일치하도록 빈칸에 알맞은 말을 쓰시오.

1 English _____ of _____ _____

2 English _____ _____ _____ _____ from _____ _____ or languages.

3 Here _____ some examples _____ _____ _____ _____ .

shampoo

4 The word *shampoo* _____ _____ the Hindi word *chāmpo*, _____ means "_____ _____ ."

5 In India, the word _____ _____ for a head massage.

6 British traders in India experienced a bath _____ _____ _____ _____ and _____ it _____ Britain in the 18th century.

7 The meaning of the word *shampoo* changed _____ _____ _____ after it first _____ English _____ 1762.

8 In the 19th century, *shampoo* got its _____ meaning of "_____ _____ _____ ."

9 _____ _____ _____ _____ , the word began _____ _____ _____ _____ a special soap for the hair.

robot

10 The word *robot* comes from the play *R.U.R.*, which _____ _____ in 1920 by a _____ _____ Karel Čapek.

11 In the play, robots are machines that _____ _____ humans.

12 They _____ _____ _____ for humans and _____ _____ in a factory.

13 _____ is interesting that _____ _____ _____ _____ the word *robot* didn't _____ _____ Karel Čapek _____ .

14 He _____ _____ the machines in his play *labori* _____ the Latin word _____ "work."

1 외국어에서 유래된 영어 단어

2 영어는 종종 다른 문화나 언어에서 단어를 빌려왔다.

3 여기 재미있는 이야기가 있는 몇 개의 예가 있다.

샴푸

4 *shampoo*라는 단어는 힌디어 *chāmpo*에서 왔고, '누르다'라는 의미이다.

5 인도에서 그 단어는 머리 마사지라는 의미로 쓰였다.

6 인도에 있는 영국 상인들은 머리 마사지를 함께하는 목욕을 경험했고 마사지를 18세기에 영국에 소개했다.

7 *shampoo*라는 단어의 의미는 그 단어가 1762년쯤 영어에 처음으로 들어온 이후 몇 번 바뀌었다.

8 19세기에, *shampoo*는 '머리 감기'라는 현재의 의미를 갖게 되었다.

9 그 후 얼마 지나지 않아, 그 단어는 머리에 사용하는 특별한 비누에도 쓰이기 시작했다.

로봇

10 *robot*이라는 단어는 "*R.U.R.*"에서 왔는데, 그 연극은 1920년 체코의 작가 Karel Čapek에 의해 쓰였다.

11 그 연극에서 로봇은 인간처럼 생긴 기계이다.

12 그들은 인간을 위해 일하도록 설계되고, 공장에서 생산된다.

13 *robot*이라는 단어를 사용하려는 생각이 Karel Čapek 자신에게서 나온 게 아니었다는 것이 흥미롭다.

14 그는 원래 자신의 연극에서 그 기계들을 '일'을 의미하는 라틴어에서 온 *labori*라고 불렀다.

15 _____, his brother _____ *roboti*, _____ means "slave workers" _____ _____.

16 Karel Čapek liked the idea and _____ _____ _____ the word *roboti*.

17 In 1938, the play _____ _____ _____ a science fiction show _____ _____ in Britain.

hurricane

18 The word *hurricane* _____ _____ the Spanish word *huracán*, which _____ _____ the name of a Mayan god.

19 In the Mayan _____ _____, Huracán is the weather god of wind, storm, and fire, and he is _____ _____ _____ _____ _____ who _____ _____.

20 However, the first humans _____ the gods, _____ Huracán _____ a great _____.

21 The first _____ _____ _____ the Mayan _____ was in 1517.

22 Spanish _____ who _____ _____ _____ the Caribbean experienced a hurricane and _____ _____ the word _____ _____ from the people in the area.

23 _____ _____, one of the _____ _____ of *hurricane* was in a play _____ Shakespeare in 1608.

hamburger

24 The word *hamburger* _____ _____ _____ Hamburg, Germany's _____ city.

25 *Hamburger* means "people or things _____ Hamburg" _____ _____.

26 The origin of the first hamburger _____ _____ _____.

27 However, _____ _____ _____ _____ the hamburger was invented in a small town in Texas, USA, sometime _____ 1885 _____ 1904.

28 A cook _____ a _____ steak between _____ _____ _____ _____, and people started to _____ _____ _____ a hamburger.

15 하지만, 그의 형이 *roboti*를 제안했는데, *roboti*는 체코어로 '노예 근로자들'을 의미한다.

16 Karel Čapek은 그 아이디어가 마음에 들어 *roboti*라는 단어를 사용하기로 결정했다.

17 1938년에 그 연극은 영국 TV에서 공상 과학물로 만들어졌다.

태풍

18 *hurricane*이라는 단어는 스페인어 단어 *huracán*에서 왔고, 그것은 마야 신의 이름에서 유래한다.

19 마야의 창조 신화에서, Huracán은 바람, 폭풍우, 그리고 불에 관한 날씨의 신이며, 그는 인간을 창조한 세 명의 신들 중 한 명이다.

20 하지만, 최초의 인간들이 신들을 화나게 해서 Huracán은 거대한 홍수를 일으켰다.

21 스페인이 마야 문명과 했던 첫 접촉은 1517년이었다.

22 카리브 제도를 지나던 스페인 탐험가들이 허리케인을 겪었고, 그 지역 사람들로부터 그것을 의미하는 단어를 듣게 되었다.

23 영어에서 일찍이 *hurricane*을 사용한 것 중 하나는 1608년 셰익스피어에 의한 희곡에서였다.

햄버거

24 *hamburger*라는 단어는 원래 독일에서 두 번째로 큰 도시인 함부르크에서 왔다.

25 *hamburger*는 독일어로 '함부르크 출신의 사람 또는 사물'을 의미한다.

26 최초의 햄버거의 기원은 분명하지 않다.

27 하지만 햄버거는 1885년에서 1904년 사이의 언젠가 미국 텍사스에 있는 작은 마을에서 발명되었다고 믿어진다.

28 한 요리사가 빵 두 조각 사이에 함부르크 스타일의 스테이크를 넣었고, 사람들은 그런 음식을 햄버거라고 부르기 시작했다.

※ 다음 문장을 우리말로 쓰시오.

1 English Words of Foreign Origin

➡ _____

2 English has often borrowed words from other cultures or languages.

➡ _____

3 Here are some examples with interesting stories.

➡ _____

shampoo 샴푸

4 The word *shampoo* comes from the Hindi word *chāmpo*, which means "to press."

➡ _____

5 In India, the word was used for a head massage.

➡ _____

6 British traders in India experienced a bath with a head massage and introduced it to Britain in the 18th century.

➡ _____

7 The meaning of the word *shampoo* changed a few times after it first entered English around 1762.

➡ _____

8 In the 19th century, *shampoo* got its present meaning of "washing the hair."

➡ _____

9 Shortly after that, the word began to be also used for a special soap for the hair.

➡ _____

robot 로봇

10 The word *robot* comes from the play *R.U.R.*, which was written in 1920 by a Czech writer Karel Čapek.

➡ _____

11 In the play, *robots* are machines that look like humans.

➡ _____

12 They are designed to work for humans and are produced in a factory.

➡ _____

13 It is interesting that the idea of using the word *robot* didn't come from Karel Čapek himself.

➡ _____

14 He originally called the machines in his play *labori* from the Latin word for "work."

➡ _____

15 However, his brother suggested *roboti*, which means "slave workers" in Czech.

➡ _____

16 Karel Čapek liked the idea and decided to use the word *roboti*.

➡ _____

17 In 1938, the play was made into a science fiction show on television in Britain.

➡ _____

hurricane 태풍

18 The word *hurricane* comes from the Spanish word *huracán*, which originates from the name of a Mayan god.

➡ _____

19 In the Mayan creation myth, Huracán is the weather god of wind, storm, and fire, and he is one of the three gods who created humans.

➡ _____
_____

20 However, the first humans angered the gods, so Huracán caused a great flood.

➡ _____

21 The first Spanish contact with the Mayan civilization was in 1517.

➡ _____

22 Spanish explorers who were passing through the Caribbean experienced a hurricane and picked up the word for it from the people in the area.

➡ _____
_____

23 In English, one of the early uses of *hurricane* was in a play by Shakespeare in 1608.

➡ _____

hamburger 햄버거

24 The word *hamburger* originally comes from Hamburg, Germany's second-largest city.

➡ _____

25 *Hamburger* means "people or things from Hamburg" in German.

➡ _____

26 The origin of the first hamburger is not clear.

➡ _____

27 However, it is believed that the hamburger was invented in a small town in Texas, USA, sometime between 1885 and 1904.

➡ _____

28 A cook placed a Hamburg-style steak between two slices of bread, and people started to call such food a hamburger.

➡ _____

※ 다음 괄호 안의 단어들을 우리말에 맞도록 바르게 배열하시오.

1 ▶ (Words / English / of / Origin / Foreign)

➡ _____

2 ▶ (has / English / borrowed / often / from / words / cultures / other / languages. / or)

➡ _____

3 ▶ (are / here / examples / some / interesting / with / stories.)

➡ _____

shampoo

4 ▶ (word / the / comes / *shampoo* / from / Hindi / the / word / *chāmpo*, / means / which / press." / "to)

➡ _____
_____

5 ▶ (India, / in / word / the / used / was / a / for / massage. / head)

➡ _____

6 ▶ (traders / British / India / in / a / experienced / bath / a / with / massage / heard / and / it / introduced / to / Britain / the / in / century. / 18th)

➡ _____
_____

7 ▶ (meaning / the / the / of / *shampoo* / word / changed / few / a / after / times / first / it / English / entered / 1762. / around)

➡ _____
_____

8 ▶ (the / in / century, / 19th / *shampoo* / got / present / its / of / meaning / the / hair." / "washing)

➡ _____

9 ▶ (after / shortly / that, / word / the / to / began / be / used / also / for / special / a / soap / the / hair. / for)

➡ _____
_____

robot

10 ▶ (word / the / comes / *robot* / from / play / the / *R.U.R.*, / was / which / in / written / 1920 / by / Czech / a / Karel / writer / Čapek.)

➡ _____
_____

---

1 외국어에서 유래된 영어 단어

2 영어는 종종 다른 문화나 언어에서 단어를 빌려왔다.

3 여기 재미있는 이야기가 있는 몇 개의 예가 있다.

샴푸

4 *shampoo*라는 단어는 힌디어 *chāmpo*에서 왔고, '누르다'라는 의미이다.

5 인도에서 그 단어는 머리 마사지라는 의미로 쓰였다.

6 인도에 있는 영국 상인들은 머리 마사지를 함께하는 목욕을 경험했고 마사지를 18세기에 영국에 소개했다.

7 *shampoo*라는 단어의 의미는 그 단어가 1762년쯤 영어에 처음으로 들어온 이후 몇 번 바뀌었다.

8 19세기에, *shampoo*는 '머리 감기'라는 현재의 의미를 갖게 되었다.

9 그 후 얼마 지나지 않아, 그 단어는 머리에 사용하는 특별한 비누에도 쓰이기 시작했다.

로봇

10 *robot*이라는 단어는 "*R.U.R.*"에서 왔는데, 그 연극은 1920년 체코의 작가 Karel Čapek에 의해 쓰였다.

11 (the / in / play, / are / robots / that / machines / like / look / humans.)

➡ _____

12 (are / they / designed / work / to / humans / for / and / produced / are / a / in / factory.)

➡ _____

13 (is / it / that / interesting / the / idea / using / of / the / *robot* / word / come / didn't / from / Karel / himself. / Čapek)

➡ _____
_____

14 (originally / he / the / called / machines / his / in / play / from / *labori* / the / word / Latin / "work." / for)

➡ _____
_____

15 (his / however, / brother / *roboti,* / suggested / means / which / workers" / "slave / Czech. / in)

➡ _____
_____

16 (Čapek / Karel / the / liked / idea / and / decided / use / to / word / the / *roboti.*)

➡ _____

17 (1938, / in / play / the / was / into / made / a / fiction / science / on / show / Britain. / in / television)

➡ _____
_____

hurricane

18 (word / the / comes / *hurricane* / from / the / word / Spanish / *huracán,* / originates / which / the / from / of / name / Mayan / a / god.)

➡ _____
_____

19 (the / in / creation / Mayan / myth, / Huracán / the / is / god / weather / wind, / of / and / storm, / fire, / he / and / is / of / one / three / the / who / gods / humans. / created)

➡ _____
_____

20 (the / however, / first / angered / humans / gods, / the / so / caused / Huracán / great / a / flood.)

➡ _____
_____

11 그 연극에서 로봇은 인간처럼 생긴 기계이다.

12 그들은 인간을 위해 일하도록 설계되고, 공장에서 생산된다.

13 *robot*이라는 단어를 사용하려는 생각이 Karel Čapek 자신에게서 나온 게 아니었다는 것이 흥미롭다.

14 그는 원래 자신의 연극에서 그 기계들을 '일'을 의미하는 라틴어에서 온 *labori*라고 불렀다.

15 하지만, 그의 형이 *roboti*를 제안했는데, *roboti*는 체코어로 '노예 근로자들'을 의미한다.

16 Karel Čapek은 그 아이디어가 마음에 들어 *roboti*라는 단어를 사용하기로 결정했다.

17 1938년에 그 연극은 영국 TV에서 공상 과학물로 만들어졌다.

태풍

18 *hurricane*이라는 단어는 스페인어 단어 *huracán*에서 왔고, 그것은 마야 신의 이름에서 유래한다.

19 마야의 창조 신화에서, Huracán은 바람, 폭풍우, 그리고 불에 관한 날씨의 신이며, 그는 인간을 창조한 세 명의 신들 중 한 명이다.

20 하지만, 최초의 인간들이 신들을 화나게 해서 Huracán은 거대한 홍수를 일으켰다.

21 (first / the / contact / Spanish / the / with / civilization / Mayan / in / was / 1517.)

➡ _____

22 (explorers / Spanish / were / who / through / passing / the / experienced / Caribbean / hurricane / a / and / up / picked / the / for / word / from / it / people / the / area. / the / in)

➡ _____

_____

23 (English, / in / of / one / early / the / of / uses / was / hurricane / in / play / a / Shakespeare / by / 1608. / in)

➡ _____

_____

hamburger

24 (word / the / originally / *hamburger* / comes / Hamburg, / from / Germany's / city. / second-largest)

➡ _____

_____

25 (means / *hamburger* / or / "people / things / Hamburg" / from / German. / in)

➡ _____

_____

26 (origin / the / of / first / the / hamburger / not / clear. / is)

➡ _____

27 (it / however, / is / that / believed / the / was / hamburger / invented / a / in / town / small / in / USA, / Texas, / between / sometime / 1904. / and / 1885)

➡ _____

_____

28 (cook / a / placed / a / steak / Hamburg-style / two / between / of / slices / bread, / and / started / people / call / to / food / such / hamburger, / a)

➡ _____

_____

21 스페인이 마야 문명과 했던 첫 접촉은 1517년이었다.

22 카리브 제도를 지나던 스페인 탐험가들이 허리케인을 겪었고, 그 지역 사람들로부터 그것을 의미하는 단어를 듣게 되었다.

23 영어에서 일찍이 *hurricane*을 사용한 것 중 하나는 1608년 셰익스피어에 의한 희곡에서였다.

햄버거

24 *hamburger*라는 단어는 원래 독일에서 두 번째로 큰 도시인 함부르크에서 왔다.

25 *hamburger*는 독일어로 '함부르크 출신의 사람 또는 사물'을 의미한다.

26 최초의 햄버거의 기원은 분명하지 않다.

27 하지만 햄버거는 1885년에서 1904년 사이의 언젠가 미국 텍사스에 있는 작은 마을에서 발명되었다고 믿어진다.

28 한 요리사가 빵 두 조각 사이에 함부르크 스타일의 스테이크를 넣었고, 사람들은 그런 음식을 햄버거라고 부르기 시작했다.

※ 다음 우리말을 영어로 쓰시오.

1 외국어에서 유래된 영어 단어

➡ _____

2 영어는 종종 다른 문화나 언어에서 단어를 빌려왔다.

➡ _____

3 여기 재미있는 이야기가 있는 몇 개의 예가 있다.

➡ _____

shampoo 샴푸

4 shampoo라는 단어는 힌디어 *chāmpo*에서 왔고, '누르다'라는 의미이다.

➡ _____

5 인도에서 그 단어는 머리 마사지라는 의미로 쓰였다.

➡ _____

6 인도에 있는 영국 상인들은 머리 마사지를 함께하는 목욕을 경험했고 마사지를 18세기에 영국에 소개했다.

➡ _____

_____

7 *shampoo*라는 단어의 의미는 그 단어가 1762년쯤 영어에 처음으로 들어온 이후 몇 번 바뀌었다.

➡ _____

8 19세기에, *shampoo*는 '머리 감기'라는 현재의 의미를 갖게 되었다.

➡ _____

9 그 후 얼마 지나지 않아, 그 단어는 머리에 사용하는 특별한 비누에도 쓰이기 시작했다.

➡ _____

robot 로봇

10 robot이라는 단어는 "*R.U.R.*"에서 왔는데, 그 연극은 1920년 체코의 작가 Karel Čapek에 의해 쓰였다.

➡ _____

11 그 연극에서 로봇은 인간처럼 생긴 기계이다.

➡ _____

12 그들은 인간을 위해 일하도록 설계되고, 공장에서 생산된다.

➡ _____

13 robot이라는 단어를 사용하려는 생각이 Karel Čapek 자신에게서 나온 게 아니었다는 것이 흥미롭다.

➡ _____

14 그는 원래 자신의 연극에서 그 기계들을 '일'을 의미하는 라틴어에서 온 *labori*라고 불렀다.

➡ _____

15 하지만, 그의 형이 roboti를 제안했는데, *roboti*는 체코어로 '노예 근로자들'을 의미한다.
➡ _____

16 Karel Čapek은 그 아이디어가 마음에 들어 *roboti*라는 단어를 사용하기로 결정했다.
➡ _____

17 1938년에 그 연극은 영국 TV에서 공상 과학물로 만들어졌다.
➡ _____

hurricane 태풍

18 hurricane이라는 단어는 스페인어 단어 *huracán*에서 왔고, 그것은 마야 신의 이름에서 유래한다.
➡ _____

19 마야의 창조 신화에서, Huracán은 바람, 폭풍우, 그리고 불에 관한 날씨의 신이며, 그는 인간을 창조한 세 명의 신들 중 한 명이다.
➡ _____
_____

20 하지만, 최초의 인간들이 신들을 화나게 해서 Huracán은 거대한 홍수를 일으켰다.
➡ _____

21 스페인이 마야 문명과 했던 첫 접촉은 1517년이었다.
➡ _____

22 카리브 제도를 지나던 스페인 탐험가들이 허리케인을 겪었고, 그 지역 사람들로부터 그것을 의미하는 단어를 듣게 되었다.
➡ _____
_____

23 영어에서 일찍이 *hurricane*을 사용한 것 중 하나는 1608년 셰익스피어의 희곡에서였다.
➡ _____

hamburger 햄버거

24 *hamburger*라는 단어는 원래 독일에서 두 번째로 큰 도시인 함부르크에서 왔다.
➡ _____

25 *hamburger*는 독일어로 '함부르크 출신의 사람 또는 사물'을 의미한다.
➡ _____

26 최초의 햄버거의 기원은 분명하지 않다.
➡ _____

27 하지만 햄버거는 1885년에서 1904년 사이의 언젠가 미국 텍사스에 있는 작은 마을에서 발명되었다고 믿어진다.
➡ _____

28 한 요리사가 빵 두 조각 사이에 함부르크 스타일의 스테이크를 넣었고, 사람들은 그런 음식을 햄버거라고 부르기 시작했다.
➡ _____
_____

구석구석 지문 Test

※ 다음 우리말과 일치하도록 빈칸에 알맞은 말을 쓰시오.

After You Read A

1. Online _____

2. English words _____ _____ _____ or _____

3. shampoo: It _____ _____ the Hindi word *chāmpo*, _____
   means "_____."

4. robot: It comes from *roboti*, _____ means "_____"
   _____ _____.

5. hurricane: It comes from _____ _____, *huracán*, _____
   _____ _____ the name of a Mayan god.

6. hamburger: It comes from _____, _____ _____
   _____ _____.

Around the World

1. 1. Many _____ _____ about law _____ _____ _____ _____.

2. Examples _____ words _____ _____ _____ and _____.

3. 2. _____ _____ _____ _____ _____ _____ about music
   _____ come from Italian.

4. _____ _____, piano and violin _____ _____ _____.

5. 3. Many English words for _____ come from _____.

6. _____ _____, tomato _____ _____ *tomate* and potato
   comes from *patata* _____ _____.

Think and Write Step 2

1. The _____ of the _____

2. The word *sandwich* _____ _____ John Montagu, _____ was
   _____ _____ _____ of Sandwich.

3. He _____ _____ meat between _____ _____ _____
   _____ because he could play a card game _____ _____
   _____.

4. People _____ _____ it was a great idea and began to call
   _____ _____ _____ him.

---

1. 온라인 사전
2. 다른 문화나 언어에서 온 영어 단어들
3. 샴푸: 그것은 힌디어 *chāmpo*에서 왔는데, '누르다'를 의미한다.
4. 로봇: 그것은 *roboti*에서 왔는데, *roboti*는 체코어로 '노예 근로자들'을 의미한다.
5. 허리케인: 그것은 스페인어 *huracán*에서 왔는데, 마야 신의 이름에서 유래된다.
6. 햄버거: 그것은 독일에서 두 번째로 큰 도시인 함부르크에서 왔다.

1. 1. 법에 관한 많은 영어 단어들은 프랑스어에서 왔다.
2. judge(판사)와 justice(정의)와 같은 단어들을 예로 들 수 있다.
3. 2. 이탈리아어에서 온 음악에 관한 많은 영어 단어들이 있다.
4. 예를 들어, piano(피아노)와 violin(바이올린) 등이 있다.
5. 3. 채소에 관한 많은 영어 단어들은 스페인어에서 왔다.
6. 예를 들어, tomato(토마토)는 *tomate*에서 왔고, potato(감자)는 *patata*에서 왔다.

1. 단어 sandwich의 유래
2. 단어 sandwich는 John Montagu에게서 유래했는데, 그는 샌드위치 백작 4세였다.
3. 그는 먹는 동안에 카드게임을 할 수 있었기 때문에 빵 두 조각 사이에 고기를 끼워서 먹는 것을 즐겼다.
4. 사람들은 그것을 좋은 생각이라고 여겼고, 그의 이름을 따서 그런 음식을 샌드위치라고 부르기 시작했다.

※ 다음 우리말을 영어로 쓰시오.

After You Read A

1. 온라인 사전
   ➡ _____

2. 다른 문화나 언어에서 온 영어 단어들
   ➡ _____

3. 샴푸: 그것은 힌디어 chāmpo에서 왔는데, '누르다'를 의미한다.
   ➡ _____

4. 로봇: 그것은 roboti에서 왔는데, roboti는 체코어로 '노예 근로자들'을 의미한다.
   ➡ _____

5. 허리케인: 그것은 스페인어 huracán에서 왔는데, 마야 신의 이름에서 유래된다.
   ➡ _____

6. 햄버거: 그것은 독일에서 두 번째로 큰 도시인 함부르크에서 왔다
   ➡ _____

Around the World

1. 1. 법에 관한 많은 영어 단어들은 프랑스어에서 왔다.
   ➡ _____

2. judge(판사)와 justice(정의)와 같은 단어들을 예로 들 수 있다.
   ➡ _____

3. 2. 이탈리아어에서 온 음악에 관한 많은 영어 단어들이 있다.
   ➡ _____

4. 예를 들어, piano(피아노)와 violin(바이올린) 등이 있다
   ➡ _____

5. 3. 채소에 관한 많은 영어 단어들은 스페인어에서 왔다.
   ➡ _____

6. 예를 들어, tomato(토마토)는 tomate에서 왔고, potato(감자)는 patata에서 왔다.
   ➡ _____

1. 단어 sandwich의 유래
   ➡ _____

2. 단어 sandwich는 John Montagu에게서 유래했는데, 그는 샌드위치 백작 4세였다.
   ➡ _____

3. 그는 먹는 동안에 카드게임을 할 수 있었기 때문에 빵 두 조각 사이에 고기를 끼워서 먹는 것을 즐겼다.
   ➡ _____

4. 사람들은 그것을 좋은 생각이라고 여겼고, 그의 이름을 따서 그런 음식을 샌드위치라고 부르기 시작했다.
   ➡ _____

※ 다음 영어를 우리말로 쓰시오.

01 tight

02 refund

03 balance

04 case

05 charity

06 comfortable

07 receipt

08 pocket money

09 remaining

10 correct

11 budget

12 couch

13 divide

14 return

15 exchange

16 although

17 save

18 donate

19 effort

20 lastly

21 allowance

22 majority

23 medicine

24 instead

25 price

26 manage

27 work

28 receive

29 loose

30 result

31 survey

32 recently

33 while

34 already

35 get a refund

36 would like to

37 take care of

38 right away

39 use up

40 have difficulty (in) -ing

41 carry around

42 on sale

43 have money back

※ 다음 우리말을 영어로 쓰시오.

01 환불; 환불받다

02 비록 ~이지만

03 가격

04 편안한

05 소파

06 반품하다

07 노력

08 매주의, 주간의

09 바로 잡다

10 그 대신에

11 예산

12 교환; 교환하다

13 자선 단체

14 마지막으로

15 남아 있는

16 기부하다

17 결과

18 헐렁한, 느슨한

19 영수증

20 대다수

21 지폐

22 균형, 통장의 잔액

23 용돈

24 나누다

25 받다

26 빠듯한, 꽉 조이는[딱 붙는]

27 비가 내리는

28 이미, 벌써

29 의약품

30 최근에

31 사례, 경우

32 관리하다

33 저축하다, 구하다

34 설문조사

35 즉시

36 환불받다

37 노력을 필요로 하다

38 그 자리에서, 현장에서

39 가지고 다니다

40 ~하기를 원하다, 좋아하다

41 교환받다

42 마음을 바꾸다

43 ~을 돌보다, ~을 처리하다

※ 다음 영영풀이에 알맞은 단어를 <보기>에서 골라 쓴 후, 우리말 뜻을 쓰시오.

1 _____ : not firmly fastened in place: _____

2 _____ : a substance used for treating illness: _____

3 _____ : to give money to a group that needs help: _____

4 _____ : most of the people or things in a group: _____

5 _____ : a sum of money which is returned to you: _____

6 _____ : an opinion you give someone about what they should do: _____

7 _____ : to make something right or to make it work the way it should: _____

8 _____ : an amount money that a person or company can spend: _____

9 _____ : left over after a part has been taken, used, or lost: _____

10 _____ : the amount of money that you have in your bank account: _____

11 _____ : hard work that you do when you are trying to achieve something: _____

12 _____ : the act of giving someone something and receiving something else from them: _____

13 _____ : money given by parents to a child regularly that the child can spend: _____

14 _____ : a piece of paper that shows you have paid for something: _____

15 _____ : a comfortable piece of furniture big enough for two or three people to sit on: _____

16 _____ : an organization that gives money, goods, or help to people who are poor, sick, etc.: _____

보기	advice	correct	charity	receipt
	medicine	donate	remaining	balance
	budget	refund	couch	allowance
	loose	majority	effort	exchange

※ 다음 우리말과 일치하도록 빈칸에 알맞은 말을 쓰시오.

Listen and Talk A 1

W: Hello. May I _____ _____ ?
B: Yes, please. I'd _____ _____ _____ a _____ for this watch.
W: OK. Was there anything _____ _____ it?
B: No, I just _____ my _____ . Can I _____ my money _____ ?
W: OK. I'll _____ _____ _____ it _____ _____ .

해석

W: 안녕하세요. 무엇을 도와드릴까요?
B: 네, 이 손목시계를 환불받고 싶어서요.
W: 알겠습니다. 시계에 무슨 문제가 있었나요?
B: 아니요, 그냥 마음이 바뀌었어요. 돈을 돌려받을 수 있을까요?
W: 네. 지금 바로 처리해드리겠습니다.

Listen and Talk A 2

W: Hello. Do you _____ _____ _____ ?
B: Yes. I'd _____ _____ _____ this smartphone case.
W: _____ _____ . Do you have the _____ _____ you?
B: _____ _____ _____ . I bought _____ three days ago.
W: Oh, then _____ _____ .

W: 안녕하세요. 도움이 필요하신가요?
B: 네. 이 스마트폰 케이스를 환불받고 싶어요.
W: 어디 봅시다. 영수증을 가지고 계시나요?
B: 여기 있습니다. 3일 전에 구매했어요.
W: 아, 그렇다면 가능합니다.

Listen and Talk A 3

W: Hello. Are you _____ _____ anything _____ ?
B: No, I'm not. I'd _____ _____ _____ this T-shirt. It's too small.
W: Sure. What size _____ _____ _____ ?
B: Large, please.
W: _____ _____ _____ .
B: Thank you.

W: 안녕하세요. 특별히 찾으시는 것 있으세요?
B: 아니요. 저는 이 티셔츠를 교환하고 싶어서요. 너무 작아요.
W: 네. 어떤 사이즈를 원하세요?
B: 큰 사이즈로 주세요.
W: 여기 있습니다.
B: 감사합니다.

Listen and Talk A 4

W: Hello. _____ can I _____ _____ _____ ?
B: Can I _____ this black umbrella _____ a _____ color?
W: Sure. _____ color _____ you _____ ?
B: _____ _____ a _____ _____ , please.
W: OK. _____ _____ _____ .

W: 안녕하세요. 무엇을 도와드릴까요?
B: 이 검은색 우산을 다른 색으로 교환할 수 있을까요?
W: 물론이죠. 어떤 색을 원하세요?
B: 저는 노란색을 원해요.
W: 알겠습니다. 여기 있습니다.

Listen and Talk B 1

A: Hello. _____ _____ _____ _____?
B: Yes, please. _____ _____ _____ _____ this bag.
A: Sure. _____ would you like to exchange _____ _____?
B: I'd _____ _____ exchange _____ _____ a cap.
A: OK.

A: 안녕하세요. 무엇을 도와드릴까요?
B: 네. 이 가방을 교환하고 싶어요.
A: 네. 무엇으로 교환하고 싶으세요?
B: 저는 모자로 교환하고 싶어요.
A: 알겠습니다.

Listen and Talk B 2

A: Hello. _____ _____ help you?
B: Yes, please. I'd like to _____ _____ _____ _____ this bag.
A: Sure. Do you have the _____?
B: Yes, I _____. _____ _____ _____.

A: 안녕하세요. 무엇을 도와드릴까요?
B: 네. 이 가방을 환불받고 싶어요.
A: 물론이죠. 영수증을 가지고 계시나요?
B: 네. 여기 있습니다.

Listen and Talk C

M: Hello. _____ _____ _____ _____?
G: Yes, please. I'd like to _____ _____ _____ _____ this cap.
M: Do you have the _____?
G: No, I _____. I _____ _____ _____ a gift.
M: If you don't have the receipt, then, _____ not possible _____ _____ a _____.
G: _____ _____. Then, can I _____ it _____ _____?
M: Yes, you _____. What _____ _____ _____ _____?
G: I _____ _____ _____ this blue bag.
M: _____ _____ _____ _____ .... The _____ is the _____, so you can just _____ _____.
G: Thank you.

M: 안녕하세요. 도와드릴까요?
G: 네. 이 모자를 환불받고 싶어요.
M: 영수증을 가지고 있나요?
G: 아니요. 선물로 받았어요.
M: 영수증이 없으면, 환불은 가능하지 않아요.
G: 알겠어요. 그럼, 다른 것으로 교환할 수 있나요?
M: 네, 가능해요. 어떤 것을 원하시나요?
G: 이 파란색 가방을 갖고 싶어요.
M: 한번 볼게요…. 가격이 같으니까 그것을 가져가셔도 돼요.
G: 고맙습니다.

Listen and Talk D

G: I _____ this red skirt _____ _____. I like the skirt, but my sister says that the color doesn't _____ _____ _____ me. I _____ _____ I should _____ _____ _____ a different color.
B: It's _____ _____ _____ but I think it's fine.

G: 나는 지난주에 이 빨간색 치마를 샀어. 나는 치마가 마음에 드는데 내 여동생은 색깔이 나에게 잘 어울리지 않는대. 이걸 다른 색으로 교환을 해야 할지 고민이야.
B: 네가 하고 싶은 대로 하렴. 하지만 내 생각엔 괜찮은 것 같아.

Talk and Play

A: _____ _____. I'd like to _____ this T-shirt _____ these pants.
B: OK. Is there _____ _____ _____ it?
A: I _____ _____ the color.
B: I see.

A: _____ _____. I'd like to _____ this cap.
B: OK. Is there _____ _____ with it?
A: I don't like the color.
B: I see.

실례합니다. 이 티셔츠를 이 바지로 교환하고 싶어요.
네. 티셔츠에 무슨 문제가 있나요?
색이 마음에 들지 않아요.
알겠습니다.

실례합니다. 저는 이 모자를 환불받고 싶어요.
네. 모자에 무슨 문제가 있나요?
색이 마음에 들지 않아요.
알겠습니다.

Review 1

W: Hello. _____?
B: Yes, please. _____ this baseball glove.
W: OK. Was there _____ it?
B: No, I just _____ my _____. Can I _____ my money _____?
W: OK. _____.

안녕하세요. 무엇을 도와드릴까요?
네. 이 야구 글러브를 환불받고 싶어서요.
알겠어요. 그것에 무슨 문제가 있었나요?
아니요. 그냥 마음이 바뀌었어요. 제 돈을 돌려받을 수 있을까요?
네. 여기 있습니다.

Review 2

M: Hello. _____?
W: Yes, please. _____ this yellow T-shirt. It's _____ me.
M: Sure. What size _____?
W: _____ size, please. Oh! Can I _____ red?
M: OK. _____.

안녕하세요. 무엇을 도와드릴까요?
네. 이 노란색 티셔츠를 교환하고 싶어요. 저에게는 너무 작네요.
네. 어떤 사이즈로 교환하고 싶으신가요?
중간 사이즈로 주세요. 오! 빨간색 티셔츠로 바꿀 수 있을까요?
네. 여기 있습니다.

Review 3

M: Hello. _____ I _____ you?
G: Yes, please. Can I _____ this hat?
M: I'm _____.
G: Then, can I _____ this hat _____ the gloves _____ there?
M: Yes, you _____.

안녕하세요. 무엇을 도와드릴까요?
네. 이 모자를 환불받을 수 있을까요?
최송하지만 안 됩니다.
그렇다면 이 모자를 저기에 있는 장갑으로 교환할 수 있을까요?
네. 가능합니다.

Review 4

A: Hello. _____ I _____ you?
B: I'd like to _____ this cap.
A: Sure. Do you have the _____?
B: Yes, I _____. _____.

안녕하세요. 무엇을 도와드릴까요?
네. 이 모자를 환불받고 싶어요.
물론이죠. 영수증을 가지고 계시나요?
네. 여기 있습니다.

대화문 Test

※ 다음 우리말에 맞도록 대화를 영어로 쓰시오.

Listen and Talk A 1

W: _____

B: _____

W: _____

B: _____

W: _____

Listen and Talk A 2

W: _____

B: _____

W: _____

B: _____

W: _____

Listen and Talk A 3

W: _____

B: _____

W: _____

B: _____

W: _____

B: _____

Listen and Talk A 4

W: _____

B: _____

W: _____

B: _____

W: _____

해석

W: 안녕하세요. 무엇을 도와드릴까요?
B: 네, 이 손목시계를 환불받고 싶어서요.
W: 알겠습니다. 시계에 무슨 문제가 있었나요?
B: 아니요, 그냥 마음이 바뀌었어요. 돈을 돌려받을 수 있을까요?
W: 네. 지금 바로 처리해드리겠습니다.

W: 안녕하세요. 도움이 필요하신가요?
B: 네. 이 스마트폰 케이스를 환불받고 싶어요.
W: 어디 봅시다. 영수증을 가지고 계시나요?
B: 여기 있습니다. 3일 전에 구매했어요.
W: 아, 그렇다면 가능합니다.

W: 안녕하세요. 특별히 찾으시는 것 있으세요?
B: 아니요. 저는 이 티셔츠를 교환하고 싶어서요. 너무 작아요.
W: 네. 어떤 사이즈를 원하세요?
B: 큰 사이즈로 주세요.
W: 여기 있습니다.
B: 감사합니다.

W: 안녕하세요. 무엇을 도와드릴까요?
B: 이 검은색 우산을 다른 색으로 교환할 수 있을까요?
W: 물론이죠. 어떤 색을 원하세요?
B: 저는 노란색을 원해요.
W: 알겠습니다. 여기 있습니다.

Listen and Talk B 1

A: _____

B: _____

A: _____

B: _____

A: _____

A: 안녕하세요. 무엇을 도와드릴까요?
B: 네. 이 가방을 교환하고 싶어요.
A: 네. 무엇으로 교환하고 싶으세요?
B: 저는 모자로 교환하고 싶어요.
A: 알겠습니다.

Listen and Talk B 2

A: _____

B: _____

A: _____

B: _____

A: 안녕하세요. 무엇을 도와드릴까요?
B: 네. 이 가방을 환불받고 싶어요.
A: 물론이죠. 영수증을 가지고 계시나요?
B: 네. 여기 있습니다.

Listen and Talk C

M: _____

G: _____

M: _____

G: _____

M: _____

G: _____

M: _____

G: _____

M: _____

G: _____

M: 안녕하세요. 도와드릴까요?
G: 네. 이 모자를 환불받고 싶어요.
M: 영수증을 가지고 있나요?
G: 아니요. 선물로 받았어요.
M: 영수증이 없으면, 환불은 가능하지 않아요.
G: 알겠어요. 그럼, 다른 것으로 교환할 수 있나요?
M: 네, 가능해요. 어떤 것을 원하시나요?
G: 이 파란색 가방을 갖고 싶어요.
M: 한번 볼게요…. 가격이 같으니까 그것을 가져가셔도 돼요.
G: 고맙습니다.

Listen and Talk D

G: _____

_____

B: _____

G: 나는 지난주에 이 빨간색 치마를 샀어. 나는 치마가 마음에 드는데 내 여동생은 색깔이 나에게 잘 어울리지 않는대. 이걸 다른 색으로 교환을 해야 할지 고민이야.
B: 네가 하고 싶은 대로 하렴, 하지만 내 생각엔 괜찮은 것 같아.

Talk and Play

A: _____

B: _____

A: _____

B: _____

A: _____

B: _____

A: _____

B: _____

Review 1

W: _____

B: _____

W: _____

B: _____

W: _____

Review 2

M: _____

W: _____

M: _____

W: _____

M: _____

Review 3

M: _____

G: _____

M: _____

G: _____

M: _____

Review 4

A: _____

B: _____

A: _____

B: _____

A: 실례합니다. 이 티셔츠를 이 바지로 교환하고 싶어요.
B: 네. 티셔츠에 무슨 문제가 있나요?
A: 색이 마음에 들지 않아요.
B: 알겠습니다.

A: 실례합니다. 저는 이 모자를 환불받고 싶어요.
B: 네. 모자에 무슨 문제가 있나요?
A: 색이 마음에 들지 않아요.
B: 알겠습니다.

W: 안녕하세요. 무엇을 도와드릴까요?
B: 네. 이 야구 글러브를 환불받고 싶어서요.
W: 알겠어요. 그것에 무슨 문제가 있었나요?
B: 아니요. 그냥 마음이 바뀌었어요. 제 돈을 돌려받을 수 있을까요?
W: 네. 여기 있습니다.

M: 안녕하세요. 무엇을 도와드릴까요?
W: 네. 이 노란색 티셔츠를 교환하고 싶어요. 저에게는 너무 작네요.
M: 네. 어떤 사이즈로 교환하고 싶으신가요?
W: 중간 사이즈로 주세요. 오! 빨간색 티셔츠로 바꿀 수 있을까요?
M: 네. 여기 있습니다.

M: 안녕하세요. 무엇을 도와드릴까요?
G: 네. 이 모자를 환불받을 수 있을까요?
M: 죄송하지만 안 됩니다.
G: 그렇다면 이 모자를 저기에 있는 장갑으로 교환할 수 있을까요?
M: 네. 가능합니다.

A: 안녕하세요. 무엇을 도와드릴까요?
B: 네. 이 모자를 환불받고 싶어요.
A: 물론이죠. 영수증을 가지고 계시나요?
B: 네. 여기 있습니다.

※ 다음 우리말과 일치하도록 빈칸에 알맞은 것을 골라 쓰시오.

1 _____ _____ **Money**
A. Dr.　　　　　B. Ask

2 **The** _____ **Middle School** _____
A. Times　　　　B. Green

3 _____ Spending _____
A. Habits　　　　B. Teens'

4 _____ _____ are you _____ your money?
A. smart　　　B. with　　　C. how

5 These are the _____ of a _____ of 100 _____ at Green Middle School.
A. survey　　　B. results　　　C. students

6 We first _____ students "Are you _____ your money?"
A. with　　　B. asked　　　C. smart

7 _____ Graph 1 _____, 70% answered "No" _____ 30% answered "Yes."
A. while　　　B. as　　　C. shows

8 We then asked the students who answered "No" _____ their _____ money _____ _____.
A. biggest　　B. is　　C. worry　　D. what

9 As Graph 2 shows, 60% think they don't have _____ _____ while 28% think they have _____ _____ money.
A. allowance　B. saving　C. enough　D. difficulty

10 _____, 12% said they _____ money _____ things they didn't _____.
A. spent　　B. need　　C. lastly　　D. on

11 Our _____ shows that the _____ of students think they are not _____ _____ their money.
A. majority　B. survey　C. with　D. smart

12 _____ money is not easy, and _____ a smart spender _____ _____.
A. takes　B. managing　C. effort　D. becoming

13 Do you _____ any _____ _____?
A. money　　B. worries　　C. have

14 _____ _____ _____ Dr. Money.
A. with　　B. let's　　C. talk

15 _____ _____.
A. Jason　　B. I'm

16 I get a _____ _____, but I _____ have _____.
A. allowance   B. enough   C. weekly   D. never

17 _____ Thursday, _____ of my money _____ _____.
A. gone   B. by   C. all   D. is

18 I don't know _____ _____ _____ this problem.
A. to   B. how   C. solve

19 Hi, _____ _____ _____.
A. Dr.   B. Money   C. I'm

20 _____ look _____ your _____ _____.
A. spending   B. let's   C. diary   D. at

21 You _____ most of your money _____ the _____ of the week.
A. up   B. beginning   C. used   D. at

22 _____ my _____.
A. tip   B. here's

23 Don't _____ _____ all of your _____ _____.
A. around   B. weekly   C. allowance   D. carry

24 _____ the money _____ _____.
A. into   B. divide   C. days

25 Then _____ only the money you need _____ _____.
A. for   B. day   C. each   D. carry

26 Hello, _____ _____.
A. Money   B. Dr.

27 _____ _____.
A. Steve   B. I'm

28 I _____ _____ _____ money.
A. difficulty   B. have   C. saving

29 For example, I've _____ _____ to go to my favorite singer's concert _____ the _____ two months.
A. last   B. saving   C. for   D. been

30 _____, I _____ don't have _____ _____.
A. still   B. however   C. money   D. enough

31 I don't know _____ _____ _____.
A. to   B. do   C. what

32 _____ _____.
A. see   B. let's

33 In the _____ _____ weeks, you _____ 80% of your allowance and only _____ 20%.
A. saved   B. few   C. spent   D. last

34 I _____ you've _____ _____ too much.
A. been   B. think   C. spending

16 저는 매주 용돈을 받지만, 절대로 충분하지 않아요.

17 목요일쯤이면 용돈이 모두 사라져요.

18 이 문제를 해결할 방법을 모르겠어요.

19 안녕하세요, Dr. Money입니다.

20 용돈 기입장을 한번 봅시다.

21 주의 초반에 용돈의 대부분을 다 썼군요.

22 이게 내 조언이에요.

23 일주일 용돈 전부를 가지고 다니지 마세요.

24 용돈을 하루 단위로 나누세요.

25 그리고 하루에 필요한 돈만 들고 다니세요.

26 안녕하세요, Dr. Money.

27 저는 Steve예요.

28 저는 돈을 모으기가 어려워요.

29 예를 들면, 저는 좋아하는 가수의 콘서트에 가려고 지난 두 달 동안 돈을 저축해 오고 있어요.

30 하지만 저는 여전히 충분한 돈을 가지고 있지 않아요.

31 어떻게 해야 할지 모르겠어요.

32 어디 봅시다.

33 지난 몇 주에 용돈의 80%를 사용하고 20%만을 저축했군요.

34 나는 Steve가 돈을 너무 많이 써 왔다고 생각해요.

35 To _____ money, you _____ to have a _____ _____.

    A. tighter   B. save   C. budget   D. need

36 _____ _____, you can _____ the 50%-40%-10% _____.

    A. follow   B. rule   C. example   D. for

37 _____ 50%, spend 40%, and _____ the _____ 10% to _____.

    A. remaining   B. donate   C. charity   D. save

38 _____ the _____, you can _____ your money better.

    A. following   B. manage   C. by   D. rule

39 Then you can _____ money _____ to _____ the _____.

    A. faster   B. save   C. ticket   D. buy

40 _____ _____.

    A. Minji   B. I'm

41 I like to _____ things _____ _____.

    A. sale   B. buy   C. on

42 If something's on _____, I _____ it _____ I don't _____ it.

    A. although   B. buy   C. sale   D. need

43 _____ week, I _____ two T-shirts on _____, but I _____ have many.

    A. already   B. bought   C. last   D. sale

44 _____ things on sale is _____ if you _____ things you _____.

    A. buy   B. buying   C. need   D. good

45 In your _____, the problem is _____ you buy _____ you don't _____ need.

    A. case   B. even   C. things   D. that

46 _____ some _____.

    A. advice   B. here's

47 _____ you buy _____, ask _____, "Do I really need this?"

    A. yourself   B. before   C. something

48 Also, before you _____ _____, _____ a shopping _____.

    A. shopping   B. list   C. make   D. go

49 Don't buy _____ that aren't _____ the list even _____ they're on _____.

    A. on   B. items   C. if   D. sale

50 Then you _____ _____ things _____ the _____.

    A. spot   B. won't   C. on   D. buy

35 돈을 모으기 위해서, 더 빠듯한 예산을 세우는 것이 필요해요.

36 예를 들어, Steve는 50%-40%-10%의 규칙을 따를 수 있어요.

37 50%를 저축하고, 40%를 쓰고, 남아 있는 10%를 자선 단체에 기부하세요.

38 이 규칙을 따름으로써 돈을 더 잘 관리할 수 있어요.

39 그러면 그 티켓을 사기 위해 돈을 더 빨리 모을 수 있답니다.

40 저는 민지입니다.

41 저는 할인 판매하는 물건을 사는 것을 좋아해요.

42 어떤 물건이 할인 판매를 하면 저는 그것이 필요하지 않더라도 사요.

43 지난주에는 할인 판매하는 티셔츠 두 장을 샀지만 이미 많이 가지고 있었어요.

44 민지가 필요한 물건을 산다면 할인 판매하는 물건을 사는 것은 좋습니다.

45 민지의 경우에, 문제점은 필요하지 않은 물건도 산다는 거예요.

46 여기 몇 가지 조언이 있어요.

47 민지는 무언가를 사기 전에 "이것이 정말 필요한가?"라고 스스로에게 물어보세요.

48 또한 쇼핑하러 가기 전에 쇼핑 목록을 만드세요.

49 만약 물건들이 할인 판매 중이라고 해도 목록에 없는 물건들은 사지 마세요.

50 그러면 즉석에서 물건을 사지 않게 될 거예요.

※ 다음 우리말과 일치하도록 빈칸에 알맞은 것을 골라 쓰시오.

1 _____ **Dr.** _____

2 **The Green** _____ _____ _____

3 **Teens'** _____ _____

4 _____ _____ are you _____ your money?

5 These are the _____ of _____ _____ of 100 students at Green Middle School.

6 We first asked students "Are you _____ _____ your money?"

7 _____ Graph 1 _____, 70% answered "No" _____ 30% answered "Yes."

8 We then _____ the students who _____ "No" what their _____ _____ _____ is.

9 _____ Graph 2 _____, 60% _____ they don't have _____ _____ 28% think they _____ _____ _____ money.

10 _____, 12% said they _____ money _____ things they _____ _____.

11 Our survey _____ that _____ _____ of students think they are not _____ _____ their money.

12 _____ money is not easy, and _____ a smart spender _____ effort.

13 Do you have any _____ _____?

14 _____ _____ _____ Dr. Money.

15 _____ Jason.

1 Dr. Money에게 물어보세요.

2 그린 중학교 타임스

3 10대들의 소비 습관

4 당신은 돈에 관해 얼마나 현명한가?

5 이것은 Green 중학교 학생 100명의 설문 조사 결과이다.

6 우리는 먼저 학생들에게 "당신은 돈에 관하여 현명한가?"라고 물었다.

7 그래프 1이 보여 주듯이, 30%가 "예"라고 대답한 반면 70%가 "아니요"라고 답했다.

8 그 다음 우리는 "아니요"라고 대답한 학생들에게 그들의 돈에 대한 가장 큰 고민이 무엇인지 물었다.

9 그래프 2가 보여주듯이 28%가 자신들이 돈을 모으는 것에 어려움이 있다고 생각하는 반면, 60%는 충분한 용돈을 받지 못한다고 생각한다.

10 마지막으로, 12%는 필요하지 않은 것에 돈을 소비했다고 말했다.

11 우리의 설문 조사는 대다수의 학생들이 자신들이 돈에 관련하여 현명하지 못하다고 생각한다는 것을 보여준다.

12 돈을 관리하는 것은 쉽지 않고 현명한 소비자가 되는 것에는 노력이 필요하다.

13 여러분은 돈과 관련된 걱정거리가 있는가?

14 Dr. Money와 이야기해 보자.

15 저는 Jason이에요.

16 I get a _____ _____, but I never have _____.

17 _____ Thursday, all of my money _____ _____.

18 I don't know _____ _____ _____ this problem.

19 Hi, _____ Dr. Money.

20 Let's _____ _____ your _____ _____.

21 You _____ _____ most of your money _____ _____
_____ _____ _____.

22 Here's _____ _____.

23 Don't _____ _____ all of your _____ _____.

24 _____ the money _____ days.

25 Then _____ only the money you need _____ _____
_____.

26 _____, Dr. Money.

27 _____ Steve.

28 I _____ _____ _____ money.

29 For example, _____ _____ _____ to go to my favorite
singer's concert _____ _____ _____ _____ _____.

30 _____, I _____ have _____ _____.

31 I don't know _____ _____ _____.

32 _____ _____.

33 _____ _____ _____ _____ weeks, you spent 80% of
your _____ and only _____ 20%.

34 I think _____ _____ _____ too much.

---

16 저는 매주 용돈을 받지만, 절대로 충분하지 않아요.

17 목요일쯤이면 용돈이 모두 사라져요.

18 이 문제를 해결할 방법을 모르겠어요.

19 안녕하세요, Dr. Money입니다.

20 용돈 기입장을 한번 봅시다.

21 주의 초반에 용돈의 대부분을 다 썼군요.

22 이게 내 조언이에요.

23 일주일 용돈 전부를 가지고 다니지 마세요.

24 용돈을 하루 단위로 나누세요.

25 그리고 하루에 필요한 돈만 들고 다니세요.

26 안녕하세요, Dr. Money.

27 저는 Steve예요.

28 저는 돈을 모으기가 어려워요.

29 예를 들면, 저는 좋아하는 가수의 콘서트에 가려고 지난 두 달 동안 돈을 저축해 오고 있어요.

30 하지만 저는 여전히 충분한 돈을 가지고 있지 않아요.

31 어떻게 해야 할지 모르겠어요.

32 어디 봅시다.

33 지난 몇 주에 용돈의 80%를 사용하고 20%만을 저축했군요.

34 나는 Steve가 돈을 너무 많이 써 왔다고 생각해요.

35 _____ _____ money, you need to _____ _____ _____
_____.

36 For example, you can _____ _____ _____ _____.

37 _____ 50%, spend 40%, and _____ _____ _____ 10%
to _____.

38 _____ _____ the rule, you can _____ your money
_____.

39 Then you can save money _____ _____ _____ the ticket.

40 _____ Minji.

41 I like to buy things _____ _____.

42 If something's _____ _____, I buy it _____ I don't need
it.

43 Last week, I _____ two T-shirts on sale, but I _____
_____ many.

44 _____ things on sale _____ good if you buy _____
_____ _____.

45 _____ _____ _____, the problem is that you buy things
you _____ _____ _____.

46 _____ some _____.

47 Before you buy something, _____ _____, "Do I really need
this?"

48 Also, before you _____ _____, _____ a shopping list.

49 _____ _____ items that aren't _____ _____ _____
even if they're on sale.

50 Then you _____ _____ things _____ _____ _____.

35 돈을 모으기 위해서, 더 빠듯한 예산을 세우는 것이 필요해요.

36 예를 들어, Steve는 50%-40%-10%의 규칙을 따를 수 있어요.

37 50%를 저축하고, 40%를 쓰고, 남아 있는 10%를 자선 단체에 기부하세요.

38 이 규칙을 따름으로써 돈을 더 잘 관리할 수 있어요.

39 그러면 그 티켓을 사기 위해 돈을 더 빨리 모을 수 있답니다.

40 저는 민지입니다.

41 저는 할인 판매하는 물건을 사는 것을 좋아해요.

42 어떤 물건이 할인 판매를 하면 저는 그것이 필요하지 않더라도 사요.

43 지난주에는 할인 판매하는 티셔츠 두 장을 샀지만 이미 많이 가지고 있었어요.

44 민지가 필요한 물건을 산다면 할인 판매하는 물건을 사는 것은 좋습니다.

45 민지의 경우에, 문제점은 필요하지 않은 물건도 산다는 거예요.

46 여기 몇 가지 조언이 있어요.

47 민지는 무언가를 사기 전에 "이것이 정말 필요한가?"라고 스스로에게 물어보세요.

48 또한 쇼핑하러 가기 전에 쇼핑 목록을 만드세요.

49 만약 물건들이 할인 판매 중이라고 해도 목록에 없는 물건들은 사지 마세요.

50 그러면 즉석에서 물건을 사지 않게 될 거예요.

※ 다음 문장을 우리말로 쓰시오.

1 Ask Dr. Money

➡ _____

2 The Green Middle School Times

➡ _____

3 Teens' Spending Habits

➡ _____

4 How smart are you with your money?

➡ _____

5 These are the results of a survey of 100 students at Green Middle School.

➡ _____

6 We first asked students "Are you smart with your money?"

➡ _____

7 As Graph 1 shows, 70% answered "No" while 30% answered "Yes."

➡ _____

8 We then asked the students who answered "No" what their biggest money worry is.

➡ _____

9 As Graph 2 shows, 60% think they don't have enough allowance while 28% think they have difficulty saving money.

➡ _____

➡ _____

10 Lastly, 12% said they spent money on things they didn't need.

➡ _____

11 Our survey shows that the majority of students think they are not smart with their money.

➡ _____

12 Managing money is not easy, and becoming a smart spender takes effort.

➡ _____

13 Do you have any money worries?

➡ _____

14 Let's talk with Dr. Money.

➡ _____

15 I'm Jason.

➡ _____

16 I get a weekly allowance, but I never have enough.

➡ _____

17 By Thursday, all of my money is gone.

➡ _____

18 I don't know how to solve this problem.

➡ _____

19 Hi, I'm Dr. Money.

➡ _____

20 Let's look at your spending diary.

➡ _____

21 You used up most of your money at the beginning of the week.

➡ _____

22 Here's my tip.

➡ _____

23 Don't carry around all of your weekly allowance.

➡ _____

24 Divide the money into days.

➡ _____

25 Then carry only the money you need for each day.

➡ _____

26 Hello, Dr. Money.

➡ _____

27 I'm Steve.

➡ _____

28 I have difficulty saving money.

➡ _____

29 For example, I've been saving to go to my favorite singer's concert for the last two months.

➡ _____

30 However, I still don't have enough money.

➡ _____

31 I don't know what to do.

➡ _____

32 Let's see.

➡ _____

33 In the last few weeks, you spent 80% of your allowance and only saved 20%.

➡ _____

34 I think you've been spending too much.

➡ _____

35 To save money, you need to have a tighter budget.

➡ _____

36 For example, you can follow the 50%-40%-10% rule.

➡ _____

37 Save 50%, spend 40%, and donate the remaining 10% to charity.

➡ _____

38 By following the rule, you can manage your money better.

➡ _____

39 Then you can save money faster to buy the ticket.

➡ _____

40 I'm Minji.

➡ _____

41 I like to buy things on sale.

➡ _____

42 If something's on sale, I buy it although I don't need it.

➡ _____

43 Last week, I bought two T-shirts on sale, but I already have many.

➡ _____

44 Buying things on sale is good if you buy things you need.

➡ _____

45 In your case, the problem is that you buy things you don't even need.

➡ _____

46 Here's some advice.

➡ _____

47 Before you buy something, ask yourself, "Do I really need this?"

➡ _____

48 Also, before you go shopping, make a shopping list.

➡ _____

49 Don't buy items that aren't on the list even if they're on sale.

➡ _____

50 Then you won't buy things on the spot.

➡ _____

※ 다음 괄호 안의 단어들을 우리말에 맞도록 바르게 배열하시오.

1 (Dr. / ask / Money)
➡ _____

2 (Green / The / School / Middle / Times)
➡ _____

3 (Spending / Teens' / Habits)
➡ _____

4 (smart / how / you / are / with / money? / your)
➡ _____

5 (are / these / results / the / a / of / survey / 100 / of / at / students / Middle / Green / School.)
➡ _____

6 (first / we / students / asked / you / "are / smart / your / with / money?")
➡ _____

7 (Graph / as / shows, / 1 / answered / 70% / while / "No" / answered / 30% / "Yes.")
➡ _____

8 (then / we / the / asked / students / answered / who / "No" / their / what / money / biggest / is. / worry)
➡ _____

9 (Graph / as / shows, / 2 / think / 60% / they / have / don't / allowance / enough / 28% / while / think / have / they / saving / difficulty / money.)
➡ _____

10 (12% / lastly, / they / said / spent / on / money / they / things / need. / didn't)
➡ _____

11 (survey / our / that / shows / the / of / majority / students / they / think / not / are / with / smart / money. / their)
➡ _____

12 (money / managing / not / is / easy, / becoming / and / smart / a / spender / effort. / takes)
➡ _____

13 (you / do / any / have / worries? / money)
➡ _____

14 (talk / let's / Dr. / with / Money.)
➡ _____

15 (Jason. / I'm)
➡ _____

1 Dr. Money에게 물어보세요.

2 그린 중학교 타임스

3 10대들의 소비 습관

4 당신은 돈에 관해 얼마나 현명한가?

5 이것은 Green 중학교 학생 100명의 설문 조사 결과이다.

6 우리는 먼저 학생들에게 "당신은 돈에 관하여 현명한가?"라고 물었다.

7 그래프 1이 보여 주듯이, 30%가 "예"라고 대답한 반면 70%가 "아니요"라고 답했다.

8 그 다음 우리는 "아니요"라고 대답한 학생들에게 그들의 돈에 대한 가장 큰 고민이 무엇인지 물었다.

9 그래프 2가 보여주듯이 28%가 자신들이 돈을 모으는 것에 어려움이 있다고 생각하는 반면, 60%는 충분한 용돈을 받지 못한다고 생각한다.

10 마지막으로, 12%는 필요하지 않은 것에 돈을 소비했다고 말했다.

11 우리의 설문 조사는 대다수의 학생들이 자신들이 돈에 관련하여 현명하지 못하다고 생각한다는 것을 보여준다.

12 돈을 관리하는 것은 쉽지 않고 현명한 소비자가 되는 것에는 노력이 필요하다.

13 여러분은 돈과 관련된 걱정거리가 있는가?

14 Dr. Money와 이야기해 보자.

15 저는 Jason이에요.

16 (get / I / weekly / a / allowance, / I / but / never / enough. / have)
➡ _____

17 (Thursday, / by / of / all / money / my / gone. / is)
➡ _____

18 (don't / I / how / know / solve / to / problem. / this)
➡ _____

19 (I'm / hi, /. Money. / Dr.)
➡ _____

20 (look / let's / your / at / diary. / spending)
➡ _____

21 (used / you / most / up / your / of / at / money / the / of / beginning / week. / the)
➡ _____

22 (my / tip. / here's)
➡ _____

23 (carry / don't / all / around / of / weekly / your / allowance.)
➡ _____

24 (the / divide / into / money / days.)
➡ _____

25 (carry / then / the / only / you / money / for / need / day. / each)
➡ _____

26 (Dr. / hello, / Money.)
➡ _____

27 (Steve. / I'm)
➡ _____

28 (have / I / saving / difficulty / money.)
➡ _____

29 (example, / for / been / I've / to / saving / to / go / my / singer's / favorite / for / concert / the / two / last / months.)
➡ _____

30 (I / however, / don't / still / have / money. / enough)
➡ _____

31 (don't / I / what / know / do. / to)
➡ _____

32 (see. / let's)
➡ _____

33 (the / in / few / last / weeks, / spent / you / of / 80% / allowance / your / and / saved / 20%. / only)
➡ _____

34 (think / I / been / you've / too / spending / much.)
➡ _____

16 저는 매주 용돈을 받지만, 절대로 충분하지 않아요.

17 목요일쯤이면 용돈이 모두 사라져요.

18 이 문제를 해결할 방법을 모르겠어요.

19 안녕하세요, Dr. Money입니다.

20 용돈 기입장을 한번 봅시다.

21 주의 초반에 용돈의 대부분을 다 썼군요.

22 이게 내 조언이에요.

23 일주일 용돈 전부를 가지고 다니지 마세요.

24 용돈을 하루 단위로 나누세요.

25 그리고 하루에 필요한 돈만 들고 다니세요.

26 안녕하세요, Dr. Money.

27 저는 Steve예요.

28 저는 돈을 모으기가 어려워요.

29 예를 들면, 저는 좋아하는 가수의 콘서트에 가려고 지난 두 달 동안 돈을 저축해 오고 있어요.

30 하지만 저는 여전히 충분한 돈을 가지고 있지 않아요.

31 어떻게 해야 할지 모르겠어요.

32 어디 봅시다.

33 지난 몇 주에 용돈의 80%를 사용하고 20%만을 저축했군요.

34 나는 Steve가 돈을 너무 많이 써 왔다고 생각해요.

35 (save / to / money, / need / you / have / to / tighter / budget. / a)
➡ _____

36 (example, / for / can / you / the / follow / rule. / 50%-40%-10%)
➡ _____

37 (50%, / save / 40%, / spend / and / the / donate / 10% / remaining / charity. / to)
➡ _____

38 (following / by / rule, / the / can / you / manage / money / your / better.)
➡ _____

39 (you / then / save / can / faster / money / buy / to / ticket. / the)
➡ _____

40 (Minji. / I'm)
➡ _____

41 (like / I / buy / to / on / things / sale.)
➡ _____

42 (somethiong / if / sale, / on / buy / I / although / it / I / need / don't / it.)
➡ _____

43 (week, / last / bought / I / T-shirts / two / sale, / on / I / but / have / already / many.)
➡ _____

44 (things / buying / sale / on / good / is / you / if / things / buy / need. / you)
➡ _____

45 (your / in / case, / problem / the / that / is / buy / you / things / don't / you / need. / even)
➡ _____

46 (some / here's / advice.)
➡ _____

47 (you / before / something, / buy / yourself, / ask / I / "do / need / this?" / really)
➡ _____

48 (before / also / go / you / shopping, / a / make / list. / shopping)
➡ _____

49 (buy / don't / that / items / on / aren't / the / even / list / they're / if / sale. / on)
➡ _____

50 (you / then / buy / won't / on / things / spot. / the)
➡ _____

---

35 돈을 모으기 위해서, 더 빠듯한 예산을 세우는 것이 필요해요.

36 예를 들어, Steve는 50%-40%-10%의 규칙을 따를 수 있어요.

37 50%를 저축하고, 40%를 쓰고, 남아 있는 10%를 자선 단체에 기부하세요.

38 이 규칙을 따름으로써 돈을 더 잘 관리할 수 있어요.

39 그러면 그 티켓을 사기 위해 돈을 더 빨리 모을 수 있답니다.

40 저는 민지입니다.

41 저는 할인 판매하는 물건을 사는 것을 좋아해요.

42 어떤 물건이 할인 판매를 하면 저는 그것이 필요하지 않더라도 사요.

43 지난주에는 할인 판매하는 티셔츠 두 장을 샀지만 이미 많이 가지고 있었어요.

44 민지가 필요한 물건을 산다면 할인 판매하는 물건을 사는 것은 좋습니다.

45 민지의 경우에, 문제점은 필요하지 않은 물건도 산다는 거예요.

46 여기 몇 가지 조언이 있어요.

47 민지는 무언가를 사기 전에 "이것이 정말 필요한가?"라고 스스로에게 물어보세요.

48 또한 쇼핑하러 가기 전에 쇼핑 목록을 만드세요.

49 만약 물건들이 할인 판매 중이라고 해도 목록에 없는 물건들은 사지 마세요.

50 그러면 즉석에서 물건을 사지 않게 될 거예요.

※ 다음 우리말을 영어로 쓰시오.

1 Dr. Money에게 물어보세요.

➡ _____

2 그린 중학교 타임스

➡ _____

3 10대들의 소비 습관

➡ _____

4 당신은 돈에 관해 얼마나 현명한가?

➡ _____

5 이것은 Green 중학교 학생 100명의 설문 조사 결과이다.

➡ _____

6 우리는 먼저 학생들에게 "당신은 돈에 관하여 현명한가?"라고 물었다.

➡ _____

7 그래프 1이 보여 주듯이, 30%가 "예"라고 대답한 반면 70%가 "아니요"라고 답했다.

➡ _____

8 그 다음 우리는 "아니요"라고 대답한 학생들에게 그들의 돈에 대한 가장 큰 고민이 무엇인지 물었다.

➡ _____

9 그래프 2가 보여주듯이 28%가 자신들이 돈을 모으는 것에 어려움이 있다고 생각하는 반면, 60%는 충분한 용돈을 받지 못한다고 생각한다.

➡ _____

_____

10 마지막으로, 12%는 필요하지 않은 것에 돈을 소비했다고 말했다.

➡ _____

11 우리의 설문 조사는 대다수의 학생들이 자신들이 돈에 관련하여 현명하지 못하다고 생각한다는 것을 보여준다.

➡ _____

12 돈을 관리하는 것은 쉽지 않고 현명한 소비자가 되는 것에는 노력이 필요하다.

➡ _____

13 여러분은 돈과 관련된 걱정거리가 있는가?

➡ _____

14 Dr. Money와 이야기해 보자.

➡ _____

15 저는 Jason이에요.

➡ _____

16 저는 매주 용돈을 받지만, 절대로 충분하지 않아요.

➡ _____

17 목요일쯤이면 용돈이 모두 사라져요.

➡ _____

18 이 문제를 해결할 방법을 모르겠어요.

➡ _____

19 안녕하세요, Dr. Money입니다.

➡ _____

20 용돈 기입장을 한번 봅시다.

➡ _____

21 주의 초반에 용돈의 대부분을 다 썼군요.

➡ _____

22 이게 내 조언이에요.

➡ _____

23 일주일 용돈 전부를 가지고 다니지 마세요.

➡ _____

24 용돈을 하루 단위로 나누세요.

➡ _____

25 그리고 하루에 필요한 돈만 들고 다니세요.

➡ _____

26 안녕하세요, Dr. Money.

➡ _____

27 저는 Steve예요.

➡ _____

28 저는 돈을 모으기가 어려워요.

➡ _____

29 예를 들면, 저는 좋아하는 가수의 콘서트에 가려고 지난 두 달 동안 돈을 저축해 오고 있어요.

➡ _____

30 하지만 저는 여전히 충분한 돈을 가지고 있지 않아요.

➡ _____

31 어떻게 해야 할지 모르겠어요.

➡ _____

32 어디 봅시다.

➡ _____

33 지난 몇 주에 용돈의 80%를 사용하고 20%만을 저축했군요.
➡ _____

34 나는 Steve가 돈을 너무 많이 써 왔다고 생각해요.
➡ _____

35 돈을 모으기 위해서, 더 빠듯한 예산을 세우는 것이 필요해요.
➡ _____

36 예를 들어, Steve는 50%-40%-10%의 규칙을 따를 수 있어요.
➡ _____

37 50%를 저축하고, 40%를 쓰고, 남아 있는 10%를 자선 단체에 기부하세요.
➡ _____

38 이 규칙을 따름으로써 돈을 더 잘 관리할 수 있어요.
➡ _____

39 그러면 그 티켓을 사기 위해 돈을 더 빨리 모을 수 있답니다.
➡ _____

40 저는 민지입니다.
➡ _____

41 저는 할인 판매하는 물건을 사는 것을 좋아해요.
➡ _____

42 어떤 물건이 할인 판매를 하면 저는 그것이 필요하지 않더라도 사요.
➡ _____

43 지난주에는 할인 판매하는 티셔츠 두 장을 샀지만 이미 많이 가지고 있었어요.
➡ _____

44 민지가 필요한 물건을 산다면 할인 판매하는 물건을 사는 것은 좋습니다.
➡ _____

45 민지의 경우에, 문제점은 필요하지 않은 물건도 산다는 거예요.
➡ _____

46 여기 몇 가지 조언이 있어요.
➡ _____

47 민지는 무언가를 사기 전에 "이것이 정말 필요한가?"라고 스스로에게 물어보세요.
➡ _____

48 또한 쇼핑하러 가기 전에 쇼핑 목록을 만드세요.
➡ _____

49 만약 물건들이 할인 판매 중이라고 해도 목록에 없는 물건들은 사지 마세요.
➡ _____

50 그러면 즉석에서 물건을 사지 않게 될 거예요.
➡ _____

구석구석 지문 Test

※ 다음 우리말과 일치하도록 빈칸에 알맞은 말을 쓰시오.

After You Read C

1. _____ Money _____ and Dr. Money's _____

2. Jason's Worry: I _____, but I _____ _____ _____.

3. _____ _____, _____ my money _____ _____.

4. Dr. Money's Advice: _____ _____ _____ all of _____ _____.

5. _____ the money _____ days and _____ only the money you _____ _____ _____ _____.

1. 십대들의 돈과 관련된 걱정거리와 Dr. Money의 조언
2. Jason의 걱정거리: 저는 매주 용돈을 받지만, 절대로 충분하지 않아요.
3. 목요일쯤이면 용돈이 모두 사라져요.
4. Dr. Money의 조언: 일주일 용돈 전부를 가지고 다니지 마세요.
5. 용돈을 하루 단위로 나누고 하루에 필요한 돈만 들고 다니세요.

Language in Use A

1. The computer I _____ _____ _____ was very _____.

2. _____ is foolish _____ _____ _____ during the _____ _____.

3. My jeans are _____ _____, _____ I am going to _____ them _____ _____ _____ _____ _____.

1. 할인 중에 산 컴퓨터는 매우 값이 쌌다.
2. 우기에 캠핑을 가는 것은 어리석다.
3. 내 청바지가 너무 꽉 끼여서 나는 그것을 더 큰 사이즈로 교환할 것이다.

Think and Write

1. My money problem is _____ I _____ _____ _____ _____ _____.

2. One time, I _____ a smartphone case _____ _____ _____ _____.

3. _____, I _____ _____ that I _____ _____ _____ at home.

4. I don't know _____ _____ _____ _____ _____ on the spot.

1. 나의 돈과 관련된 고민은 즉석에서 물건을 산다는 것이다.
2. 한번은, 나는 스마트폰 케이스가 좋아 보여서 그것을 샀다.
3. 하지만, 집에 와서는 내가 이미 케이스를 세 개 갖고 있다는 것을 발견했다.
4. 나는 즉석에서 물건을 사는 것을 어떻게 멈출 수 있는지 모르겠다.

※ 다음 우리말을 영어로 쓰시오.

After You Read C

1. 십대들의 돈과 관련된 걱정거리와 Dr. Money의 조언

   ➡ _____

2. Jason의 걱정거리: 저는 매주 용돈을 받지만, 절대로 충분하지 않아요.

   ➡ _____

3. 목요일쯤이면 용돈이 모두 사라져요.

   ➡ _____

4. Dr. Money의 조언: 일주일 용돈 전부를 가지고 다니지 마세요.

   ➡ _____

5. 용돈을 하루 단위로 나누고 하루에 필요한 돈만 들고 다니세요.

   ➡ _____

Language in Use A

1. 할인 중에 산 컴퓨터는 매우 값이 쌌다.

   ➡ _____

2. 우기에 캠핑을 가는 것은 어리석다.

   ➡ _____

3. 내 청바지가 너무 꽉 끼여서 나는 그것을 더 큰 사이즈로 교환할 것이다.

   ➡ _____

Think and Write

1. 나의 돈과 관련된 고민은 즉석에서 물건을 산다는 것이다.

   ➡ _____

2. 한번은, 나는 스마트폰 케이스가 좋아 보여서 그것을 샀다.

   ➡ _____

3. 하지만, 집에 와서는 내가 이미 케이스를 세 개 갖고 있다는 것을 발견했다.

   ➡ _____

4. 나는 즉석에서 물건을 사는 것을 어떻게 멈출 수 있는지 모르겠다.

   ➡ _____

※ 다음 영어를 우리말로 쓰시오.

01 main	
02 hire	
03 invisible	
04 carry	
05 promote	
06 already	
07 crew	
08 recommendation	
09 expensive	
10 perfect	
11 manage	
12 several	
13 attention	
14 limit	
15 assistant	
16 hurt	
17 choose	
18 therefore	
19 especially	
20 tribe	
21 register	

22 activity	
23 direction	
24 experienced	
25 support	
26 tapper	
27 suggest	
28 particular	
29 breathe	
30 achieve	
31 harmony	
32 hidden	
33 allow	
34 windy	
35 in short	
36 most of all	
37 wear out	
38 have difficulty -ing	
39 sign up for	
40 on one's own	
41 keep track of	
42 in many ways	
43 depending on	

※ 다음 우리말을 영어로 쓰시오.

01 달성하다, 성취하다 _____

02 운반하다 _____

03 값비싼 _____

04 조화, 화합 _____

05 돕다, 지원하다 _____

06 주의, 주목 _____

07 숨쉬다 _____

08 그러므로 _____

09 보조자 _____

10 숨겨진 _____

11 응원하다 _____

12 제안하다 _____

13 경험 있는 _____

14 선택하다 _____

15 바람이 심한 _____

16 주된 _____

17 (눈에) 보이지 않는,
   볼 수 없는 _____

18 홍보하다 _____

19 부족, 종족 _____

20 이끌다 _____

21 쏘다 _____

22 이미 _____

23 한계 _____

24 특정한 _____

25 팀, 조 _____

26 추천 _____

27 등록하다 _____

28 몇몇의 _____

29 방향 _____

30 특히 _____

31 관리하다 _____

32 완벽한 _____

33 허용하다 _____

34 두드리는 사람 _____

35 ~에 따라 _____

36 끝나다 _____

37 간단히 말해서 _____

38 (낡아서) 떨어지다, 헤지다 _____

39 등록하다, 신청하다 _____

40 주목을 받다 _____

41 ~을 돌보다 _____

42 ~에 어려움을 겪다 _____

43 무엇보다도 _____

※ 다음 영영풀이에 알맞은 단어를 <보기>에서 골라 쓴 후, 우리말 뜻을 쓰시오.

1 _____ : to pay someone to work for you: _____

2 _____ : not able to be seen: _____

3 _____ : to make something more popular, well-known, etc.: _____

4 _____ : to succeed in doing or getting something you want: _____

5 _____ : to take air into your body and let it out again: _____

6 _____ : a group of people with a particular skill who work together: _____

7 _____ : to put someone's or something's name on an official list: _____

8 _____ : a person whose job is to help another person to do work: _____

9 _____ : to have something on your body as a piece of clothing, a decoration, etc.:
_____

10 _____ : to say that you agree with a person, group, or idea: _____

11 _____ : a group of people who have their own language and ways of living:
_____

12 _____ : to decide that a particular person or thing is the one that you want:
_____

13 _____ : a metal cup or other object that someone gets for winning a game or
race: _____

14 _____ : a set of clothes made of the same cloth, including a jacket and trousers
or a skirt: _____

15 _____ : the area beside a race track where cars are repaired or get more gas
during a race: _____

16 _____ : to use something a lot so that it no longer works, or can no longer be
used: _____

보기			
suit	pit	assistant	crew
tribe	wear out	hire	invisible
trophy	support	register	breathe
wear	choose	promote	achieve

※ 다음 우리말과 일치하도록 빈칸에 알맞은 말을 쓰시오.

해석

Listen and Talk A 1

B: How _____ do you _____ _____?

G: I play _____ a week, but I want to play _____ _____.

B: I _____ you join my basketball club. We play _____ _____ a week.

G: That sounds _____! It'll be fun _____ _____ with you.

B: 얼마나 자주 농구를 하니?
G: 일주일에 한 번 해. 그런데 더 자주 하고 싶어.
B: 네가 우리 농구 동아리에 들어오기를 제안해. 우리는 일주일에 세 번 농구를 해.
G: 좋은 생각이야! 같이 하면 재미있을 거야.

Listen and Talk A 2

B: I don't swim often. How _____ you, Kate? _____ _____ do you _____?

G: I swim _____ _____ _____ _____.

B: _____ often? _____, _____ 'll be fun _____ together today.

G: Yes, but before we swim, I _____ we _____ _____ exercises.

B: That's a good idea.

B: 난 수영을 자주 하지 않아. 넌 어떠니, Kate? 얼마나 자주 수영을 하러 가니?
G: 일주일에 네 번 수영을 해.
B: 그렇게 자주? 어쨌든 오늘 같이 수영을 하면 재미있을 거야.
G: 응, 그런데 우리가 수영하기 전에 스트레칭을 하는 것을 제안해.
B: 좋은 생각이다.

Listen and Talk A 3

B: Suji, _____ _____ do you _____ bowling _____?

G: _____ a week. I'm just a _____. I heard you're very good.

B: Well, I love bowling. Hmm. Your bowling ball looks _____ for you. I _____ you _____ a _____ _____.

G: OK. I'll look _____ a lighter _____, then.

B: 수지야, 너는 얼마나 자주 볼링 수업을 받니?
G: 일주일에 두 번 받아. 나는 초보야. 난 네가 볼링을 잘한다고 들었어.
B: 음, 난 볼링을 좋아해. 흠. 네 볼링공이 무거워 보인다. 더 가벼운 공을 쓰는 것을 제안해.
G: 알겠어. 그럼 더 가벼운 공을 찾아봐야겠다.

Listen and Talk A 4

B: Mina, _____ _____ do you come here _____ _____?

G: _____ day.

B: Can I run _____ you today?

G: Sure, but I _____ you _____ running shoes. Your shoes aren't _____ _____ _____.

B: 미나야, 넌 달리기를 하러 이곳에 얼마나 자주 오니?
G: 매일 와.
B: 오늘 너와 함께 달리기를 해도 될까?
G: 물론이야, 하지만 네가 운동화를 신는 것을 제안해. 네 신발은 달리기에 적합하지 않아.

Listen and Talk B

A: Minsu, _____ _____ do you _____?

B: I exercise _____ _____ _____.

A: I _____ you _____ more often.

B: OK. I'll _____.

A: 민수야, 너는 얼마나 자주 운동을 하니?
B: 나는 일주일에 한 번 운동을 해.
A: 더 자주 운동하기를 제안해.
B: 알겠어. 시도해 볼게.

Listen and Talk C

W: Hello. _____ _____ Sports World. May I help you?
B: Yes, I came _____ _____ _____ a swimming _____.
W: Is this your first time _____ _____ _____?
B: Yes, it is. I don't know _____ _____ _____

_____.
W: I see. _____ _____ do you want to _____ classes?
B: I want to _____ classes _____ _____ _____ _____. I'd like to _____ classes _____ weekdays and not _____ weekends.
W: Then, I suggest _____ you _____ the Beginner 2 class. This class meets _____ Tuesdays and Thursdays.
B: That _____ _____. I'd like to _____ _____ _____ _____ that class. How big is the class?
W: The class has _____ _____ _____ _____ 10 people.
B: That's _____.

Talk and Play

A: Jiho, _____ _____ do you _____?
B: I exercise _____ _____ _____ _____.
A: That's good.

Review 1

B: Mina, _____ _____ do you _____?
G: I swim _____ _____.
B: Can I _____ _____ _____ you this afternoon?
G: Sure, but I _____ you _____ a swimming cap. _____ a swimming cap, you _____ _____ in the pool.

Review 2

B: Somi, is your piano _____ _____ _____?
G: Yes, it is.
B: _____ _____ do you _____?
G: I practice _____ _____ _____.

Review 3

W: Hello. May I help you?
B: Yes, I came to _____ _____ a _____ _____.
W: I see. _____ _____ do you want to _____ _____?
B: I want to _____ classes _____ _____ _____ _____. I'd like to _____ classes _____ weekends.
W: Then, I _____ that you _____ the Beginner 1 class. This class meets _____ Saturdays and Sundays.
B: That sounds _____.

W: 안녕하세요. Sports World에 오신 것을 환영합니다. 무엇을 도와드릴 까요?
B: 네, 수영 수업을 등록하려고 왔어요.
W: 수영 수업을 받는 것이 이번이 처음 인가요?
B: 네. 저는 수영하는 법을 전혀 알지 못해요.
W: 알겠어요. 얼마나 자주 수업을 받고 싶으신가요?
B: 일주일에 두 번 수업을 듣길 원해요. 주말이 아니라 주중에 수업을 듣고 싶어요.
W: 그럼, 초급 2반을 들을 것을 권합니 다. 이 수업은 화요일과 목요일에 있 어요.
B: 좋아요. 그 수업으로 등록할게요. 그 수업은 몇 명이 듣나요?
W: 그 수업은 제한 인원이 열 명입니다.
B: 좋아요.

A: 지호야, 너는 얼마나 자주 운동을 하 니?
B: 나는 일주일에 세 번 운동을 해.
A: 좋다.

B: 미나야, 너는 얼마나 자주 수영을 하 니?
G: 나는 매일 수영을 해.
B: 오늘 오후에 너와 수영하러 가도 될 까?
G: 물론이지, 하지만 수영 모자를 챙기 는 것을 제안해. 수영 모자 없이 수 영장에 들어가는 것은 허락되지 않 아.

B: 소미야, 피아노 연습은 끝났니?
G: 응, 그래.
B: 얼마나 자주 연습을 하니?
G: 나는 일주일에 두 번 연습을 해.

W: 안녕하세요. 무엇을 도와드릴까요?
B: 네, 축구 수업을 등록하러 왔어요.
W: 알겠습니다. 얼마나 자주 수업을 수 강하기를 원하나요?
B: 일주일에 두 번 수강하고 싶어요. 주 말에 수업을 수강하는 게 좋아요.
W: 그럼, 초급 1반을 수강하기를 제안 드려요. 이 수업은 토요일과 일요일 에 있어요.
B: 좋아요.

※ 다음 우리말에 맞도록 대화를 영어로 쓰시오.

Listen and Talk A 1

B: _____

G: _____

B: _____

G: _____

B: 얼마나 자주 농구를 하니?
G: 일주일에 한 번 해. 그런데 더 자주 하고 싶어.
B: 네가 우리 농구 동아리에 들어오기를 제안해. 우리는 일주일에 세 번 농구를 해.
G: 좋은 생각이야! 같이 하면 재미있을 거야.

Listen and Talk A 2

B: _____

G: _____

B: _____

G: _____

B: _____

B: 난 수영을 자주 하지 않아. 넌 어떠니, Kate? 얼마나 자주 수영을 하러 가니?
G: 일주일에 네 번 수영을 해.
B: 그렇게 자주? 어쨌든 오늘 같이 수영을 하면 재미있을 거야.
G: 응, 그런데 우리가 수영하기 전에 스트레칭을 하는 것을 제안해.
B: 좋은 생각이다.

Listen and Talk A 3

B: _____

G: _____

B: _____

_____

G: _____

B: 수지야, 너는 얼마나 자주 볼링 수업을 받니?
G: 일주일에 두 번 받아. 나는 초보야. 난 네가 볼링을 잘한다고 들었어.
B: 음, 난 볼링을 좋아해. 흠. 네 볼링공이 무거워 보인다. 더 가벼운 공을 쓰는 것을 제안해.
G: 알겠어. 그럼 더 가벼운 공을 찾아봐야겠다.

Listen and Talk A 4

B: _____

G: _____

B: _____

G: _____

B: 미나야, 넌 달리기를 하러 이곳에 얼마나 자주 오니?
G: 매일 와.
B: 오늘 너와 함께 달리기를 해도 될까?
G: 물론이야, 하지만 네가 운동화를 신는 것을 제안해. 네 신발은 달리기에 적합하지 않아.

Listen and Talk B

A: _____

B: _____

A: _____

B: _____

A: 민수야, 너는 얼마나 자주 운동을 하니?
B: 나는 일주일에 한 번 운동을 해.
A: 더 자주 운동하기를 제안해.
B: 알겠어. 시도해 볼게.

Listen and Talk C

W: _____

B: _____

W: _____

B: _____

W: _____

B: _____

_____

W: _____

_____

B: _____

W: _____

B: _____

Talk and Play

A: _____

B: _____

A: _____

Review 1

B: _____

G: _____

B: _____

G: _____

_____

Review 2

B: _____

G: _____

B: _____

G: _____

Review 3

W: _____

B: _____

W: _____

B: _____

W: _____

_____

B: _____

W: 안녕하세요. Sports World에 오신 것을 환영합니다. 무엇을 도와드릴까요?

B: 네, 수영 수업을 등록하려고 왔어요.

W: 수영 수업을 받는 것이 이번이 처음인가요?

B: 네. 저는 수영하는 법을 전혀 알지 못해요.

W: 알겠어요. 얼마나 자주 수업을 받고 싶으신가요?

B: 일주일에 두 번 수업을 듣길 원해요. 주말이 아니라 주중에 수업을 듣고 싶어요.

W: 그럼, 초급 2반을 들을 것을 권합니다. 이 수업은 화요일과 목요일에 있어요.

B: 좋아요. 그 수업으로 등록할게요. 그 수업은 몇 명이 듣나요?

W: 그 수업은 제한 인원이 열 명입니다.

B: 좋아요.

A: 지호야, 너는 얼마나 자주 운동을 하니?

B: 나는 일주일에 세 번 운동을 해.

A: 좋다.

B: 미나야, 너는 얼마나 자주 수영을 하니?

G: 나는 매일 수영을 해.

B: 오늘 오후에 너와 수영하러 가도 될까?

G: 물론이지, 하지만 수영 모자를 챙기는 것을 제안해. 수영 모자 없이 수영장에 들어가는 것은 허락되지 않아.

B: 소미야, 피아노 연습은 끝났니?

G: 응, 그래.

B: 얼마나 자주 연습을 하니?

G: 나는 일주일에 두 번 연습을 해.

W: 안녕하세요. 무엇을 도와드릴까요?

B: 네, 축구 수업을 등록하러 왔어요.

W: 알겠습니다. 얼마나 자주 수업을 수강하기를 원하나요?

B: 일주일에 두 번 수강하고 싶어요. 주말에 수업을 수강하는 게 좋아요.

W: 그럼, 초급 1반을 수강하기를 제안드려요. 이 수업은 토요일과 일요일에 있어요.

B: 좋아요.

※ 다음 우리말과 일치하도록 빈칸에 알맞은 것을 골라 쓰시오.

1 _____ _____ People
　A. in　　　　　B. Hidden　　　C. Sports

2 In sports, _____ the players get a trophy or medal, they don't win _____ their _____.
　A. own　　　B. only　　　C. on　　　D. but

3 _____ are people _____ help the _____.
　A. who　　　B. there　　　C. players

4 These people are _____ _____ and don't _____ _____.
　A. attention　　B. often　　C. get　　D. hidden

5 _____, they are _____ _____ as the players.
　A. as　　　B. however　　C. important

6 _____ _____ some _____.
　A. are　　　B. here　　　C. examples

7 _____ a _____
　A. Marathon　　B. in　　　C. Pacers

8 Pacers _____ _____ other _____ and _____ them in a marathon.
　A. lead　　　B. with　　　C. run　　　D. runners

9 Pacers are _____ runners, and their job is to help _____ runners _____ their race _____.
　A. manage　　B. experienced　　C. better　　D. other

10 _____ _____ several pacers in a race.
　A. be　　　B. can　　　C. there

11 Each pacer _____ at different _____ and _____ the race in different _____.
　A. times　　　B. speeds　　C. runs　　D. finishes

12 _____ usually _____ flags or balloons _____ their _____ time.
　A. showing　　B. pacers　　C. finish　　D. have

13 Runners can _____ a pacer _____ _____ their _____ finish time.
　A. depending　　B. target　　C. on　　D. choose

14 For example, if a runner wants to _____ the race in four _____, the runner will _____ the four-hour _____.
　A. follow　　B. hours　　C. finish　　D. pacer

15 _____ the pacer keeps _____ of the time, the runner can achieve his or her goal of _____ the marathon in a _____ time more easily.
　A. particular　　B. since　　C. finishing　　D. track

16 _____ _____, pacers run but they don't run _____.
　A. short　　　B. to　　　C. in　　　D. win

17 They _____ _____ _____.
　A. for　　　B. run　　　C. others

18 _____ in _____ _____
　A. Crews　　　B. Racing　　C. Car　　D. Pit

19 You may only see the car and the driver _____ most car races, but _____ is a team _____ the _____.
　A. behind　　B. during　　C. driver　　D. there

1　스포츠 속 숨은 조력자들
2　스포츠에서 선수들만 트로피나 메달을 받지만, 그들은 혼자 힘으로 이긴 것이 아니다.
3　그 선수들을 돕는 사람들이 있다.
4　이 사람들은 종종 숨겨져 있고 주목을 받지 못한다.
5　하지만 그들은 선수들만큼 중요하다.
6　여기 몇 가지 예가 있다.
7　마라톤의 페이서들
8　페이서들은 마라톤에서 다른 선수들과 함께 달리며 그들을 이끈다.
9　페이서들은 경험이 많은 선수들이며 그들의 역할은 다른 선수들이 경기를 더 잘 운영하도록 돕는 것이다.
10　한 경기에는 여러 명의 페이서들이 있을 수 있다.
11　각각의 페이서는 다른 속도로 달리고 다른 시간대에 경기를 마친다.
12　페이서들은 주로 자신들의 완주 시간을 나타내는 깃발이나 풍선들을 가지고 있다.
13　선수들은 자신들의 목표 완주 시간에 따라 페이서를 선택할 수 있다.
14　예를 들어, 한 선수가 4시간 안에 경기를 마치고 싶다면, 그 선수는 4시간 페이서를 따라갈 것이다.
15　페이서가 시간을 계속해서 파악하기 때문에, 선수는 특정 시간에 마라톤을 완주하려는 자신의 목표를 더 쉽게 달성할 수 있다.
16　요컨대, 페이서들은 달리지만 우승을 하기 위해 달리는 것은 아니다.
17　그들은 다른 선수들을 위해 달린다.
18　자동차 경주의 피트 크루
19　여러분은 대부분의 자동차 경주에서 자동차와 레이서만 보겠지만 그 레이서 뒤에는 팀이 있다.

20 This team _____ a _____ _____.
　A. called　　　　B. crew　　　　C. pit　　　　D. is

21 A pit is a place _____ the side _____ the race _____, and drivers stop there _____ times during a race.
　A. several　　　B. track　　　C. on　　　D. of

22 The _____ _____ of the pit crew is to _____ the car and _____ the tires.
　A. check　　　B. job　　　C. change　　　D. main

23 _____ the tires is especially important _____ the tires _____ easily in a high speed race.
　A. out　　　B. changing　　　C. wear　　　D. because

24 A pit stop can be _____ _____ as 2 _____, and there are as many as 20 members on a _____.
　A. seconds　　　B. crew　　　C. short　　　D. as

25 Therefore, the pit crew _____ to work _____ _____.
　A. in　　　B. has　　　C. harmony　　　D. perfect

26 The driver may _____ all the _____, but as people say, "Races are _____ in the _____."
　A. attention　　　B. pits　　　C. get　　　D. won

27 Sherpas _____ _____ _____
　A. Climbing　　　B. in　　　C. Mountain

28 The word *Sherpa* _____ from the Sherpa _____, _____ lives in the _____ part of Nepal.
　A. tribe　　　B. eastern　　　C. which　　　D. comes

29 Sherpas have good _____ _____ and know their _____ the mountains well.
　A. around　　　B. climbing　　　C. way　　　D. skills

30 They also _____ _____ _____ high up in the mountains.
　A. little　　　B. have　　　C. breathing　　　D. difficulty

31 Therefore, mountain climbers started to _____ Sherpas _____ them _____ Mount Everest.
　A. help　　　B. hire　　　C. climb　　　D. to

32 Sherpas _____ mountain _____ the _____ of the mountain.
　A. climbers　　　B. top　　　C. to　　　D. lead

33 They _____ climbers _____ many _____.
　A. in　　　B. support　　　C. ways

34 _____ example, they _____ _____ tents and _____ climbers' bags.
　A. carry　　　B. put　　　C. for　　　D. up

35 Sherpas are often called the _____ people of Mount Everest _____ people often see a picture of only the _____ at the _____ of the mountain.
　A. because　　　B. invisible　　　C. top　　　D. climbers

20 이 팀은 피트 크루라고 불린다.

21 피트는 경주 트랙의 한쪽에 있는 공간으로 레이서들은 경주 도중에 그곳에서 여러 번 정지한다.

22 피트 크루가 하는 주요 역할은 자동차를 점검하고 타이어를 교체하는 것이다.

23 빠른 속도의 경주에서는 타이어가 쉽게 마모되기 때문에 타이어를 교체하는 것이 특히 중요하다.

24 피트에서의 정지는 짧게는 2초 정도이고 한 팀에는 많게는 20명에 이르는 구성원이 있다.

25 그러므로 피트 크루는 완벽한 조화를 이루며 일해야 한다.

26 레이서만 주목을 받을지 모르지만 사람들이 말하는 것처럼, "경주의 우승은 피트에서 이루어진다."

27 등반에서의 셰르파

28 'Sherpa'라는 단어는 셰르파족에서 유래되었는데, 셰르파족은 네팔의 동쪽 지역에 산다.

29 셰르파는 훌륭한 등반 기량을 갖고 있으며 산 지리를 잘 안다.

30 그들은 또한 산의 높은 곳에서 호흡하는 데 어려움이 거의 없다.

31 그래서 등산가들은 자신들이 에베레스트산을 등반하는 것을 돕는 셰르파를 고용하기 시작했다.

32 셰르파는 등산가들을 산 정상까지 이끈다.

33 그들은 여러 방면에서 등산가들을 지원한다.

34 예를 들면, 그들은 텐트를 치고 등산가들의 가방을 운반한다.

35 셰르파는 종종 에베레스트산의 보이지 않는 사람들로 불리는데, 왜냐하면 사람들이 산 정상에서 등산가들만 찍힌 사진을 자주 보기 때문이다.

※ 다음 우리말과 일치하도록 빈칸에 알맞은 것을 골라 쓰시오.

1 _____ People in Sports

2 In sports, _____ the players get a trophy or medal, but they don't _____ _____ _____ _____.

3 There are _____ _____ _____ the players.

4 These people are often _____ and don't _____ _____.

5 _____, they are _____ _____ the players.

6 _____ _____ some _____.

7 _____ in a Marathon

8 Pacers _____ _____ _____ and _____ them in a marathon.

9 Pacers are _____ runners, and their job is _____ _____ other runners _____ _____ _____ _____.

10 _____ _____ _____ several pacers in a race.

11 Each pacer runs _____ _____ _____ and _____ the race _____ _____ _____.

12 Pacers usually have flags or balloons _____ their finish time.

13 Runners _____ _____ a pacer _____ _____ their target finish time.

14 For example, if a runner wants to finish the race _____ _____ _____, the runner will _____ the _____-hour pacer.

15 Since the pacer _____ _____ _____ the time, the runner _____ _____ his or her goal of finishing the marathon in a particular time more _____.

16 _____ _____, pacers run but they don't run _____ _____.

17 They run _____ _____.

18 Pit Crews in _____

19 You may only see the car and the driver _____ most car races, but there is a team _____ _____ _____.

1	스포츠 속 숨은 조력자들
2	스포츠에서 선수들만 트로피나 메달을 받지만, 그들은 혼자 힘으로 이긴 것이 아니다.
3	그 선수들을 돕는 사람들이 있다.
4	이 사람들은 종종 숨겨져 있고 주목을 받지 못한다.
5	하지만 그들은 선수들만큼 중요하다.
6	여기 몇 가지 예가 있다.
7	마라톤의 페이서들
8	페이서들은 마라톤에서 다른 선수들과 함께 달리며 그들을 이끈다.
9	페이서들은 경험이 많은 선수들이며 그들의 역할은 다른 선수들이 경기를 더 잘 운영하도록 돕는 것이다.
10	한 경기에는 여러 명의 페이서들이 있을 수 있다.
11	각각의 페이서는 다른 속도로 달리고 다른 시간대에 경기를 마친다.
12	페이서들은 주로 자신들의 완주 시간을 나타내는 깃발이나 풍선들을 가지고 있다.
13	선수들은 자신들의 목표 완주 시간에 따라 페이서를 선택할 수 있다.
14	예를 들어, 한 선수가 4시간 안에 경기를 마치고 싶다면, 그 선수는 4시간 페이서를 따라갈 것이다.
15	페이서가 시간을 계속해서 파악하기 때문에, 선수는 특정 시간에 마라톤을 완주하려는 자신의 목표를 더 쉽게 달성할 수 있다.
16	요컨대, 페이서들은 달리지만 우승을 하기 위해 달리는 것은 아니다.
17	그들은 다른 선수들을 위해 달린다.
18	자동차 경주의 피트 크루
19	여러분은 대부분의 자동차 경주에서 자동차와 레이서만 보겠지만 그 레이서 뒤에는 팀이 있다.

20 This team _____ _____ a pit crew.

21 A pit is a place _____ _____ _____ _____ _____
_____ _____, and drivers stop there _____ _____
during a race.

22 The _____ _____ of the pit crew is _____ _____ the
car and change the tires.

23 _____ the tires _____ especially important because the tires
_____ _____ in a high speed race.

24 A pit stop can be _____ _____ _____ 2 _____, and
there are _____ _____ _____ 20 members on a crew.

25 _____, the pit crew has to work _____ _____ _____.

26 The driver may _____ _____ _____ _____ _____, but as
people say, "Races are won _____ _____ _____ _____."

27 Sherpas in _____ _____

28 The word *Sherpa* _____ _____ the Sherpa tribe, _____
lives in the _____ _____ of Nepal.

29 Sherpas have _____ _____ _____ _____ and know their way
around the mountains well.

30 They also _____ _____ _____ _____ _____ high up in the
mountains.

31 Therefore, mountain climbers started _____ _____ Sherpas
_____ _____ _____ _____ Mount Everest.

32 Sherpas _____ mountain climbers _____ the top of the
mountain.

33 They support climbers _____ _____ _____.

34 _____ example, they _____ _____ tents and _____
climbers' bags.

35 Sherpas are often called the _____ people of Mount Everest
because people often see a picture of only the climbers _____
_____ _____ the mountain.

20 이 팀은 피트 크루라고 불린다.

21 피트는 경주 트랙의 한쪽에 있는 공간으로 레이서들은 경주 도중에 그곳에서 여러 번 정지한다.

22 피트 크루가 하는 주요 역할은 자동차를 점검하고 타이어를 교체하는 것이다.

23 빠른 속도의 경주에서는 타이어가 쉽게 마모되기 때문에 타이어를 교체하는 것이 특히 중요하다.

24 피트에서의 정지는 짧게는 2초 정도이고 한 팀에는 많게는 20명에 이르는 구성원이 있다.

25 그러므로 피트 크루는 완벽한 조화를 이루며 일해야 한다.

26 레이서만 주목을 받을지 모르지만 사람들이 말하는 것처럼, "경주의 우승은 피트에서 이루어진다."

27 등반에서의 셰르파

28 'Sherpa'라는 단어는 셰르파족에서 유래되었는데, 셰르파족은 네팔의 동쪽 지역에 산다.

29 셰르파는 훌륭한 등반 기량을 갖고 있으며 산 지리를 잘 안다.

30 그들은 또한 산의 높은 곳에서 호흡하는 데 어려움이 거의 없다.

31 그래서 등산가들은 자신들이 에베레스트산을 등반하는 것을 돕는 셰르파를 고용하기 시작했다.

32 셰르파는 등산가들을 산 정상까지 이끈다.

33 그들은 여러 방면에서 등산가들을 지원한다.

34 예를 들면, 그들은 텐트를 치고 등산가들의 가방을 운반한다.

35 셰르파는 종종 에베레스트산의 보이지 않는 사람들로 불리는데, 왜냐하면 사람들이 산 정상에서 등산가들만 찍힌 사진을 자주 보기 때문이다.

※ 다음 문장을 우리말로 쓰시오.

1 Hidden People in Sports
➡ _____

2 In sports, only the players get a trophy or medal, but they don't win on their own.
➡ _____

3 There are people who help the players.
➡ _____

4 These people are often hidden and don't get attention.
➡ _____

5 However, they are as important as the players.
➡ _____

6 Here are some examples.
➡ _____

7 Pacers in a Marathon
➡ _____

8 Pacers run with other runners and lead them in a marathon.
➡ _____

9 Pacers are experienced runners, and their job is to help other runners manage their race better.
➡ _____

10 There can be several pacers in a race.
➡ _____

11 Each pacer runs at different speeds and finishes the race in different times.
➡ _____

12 Pacers usually have flags or balloons showing their finish time.
➡ _____

13 Runners can choose a pacer depending on their target finish time.
➡ _____

14 For example, if a runner wants to finish the race in four hours, the runner will follow the four-hour pacer.
➡ _____

15 Since the pacer keeps track of the time, the runner can achieve his or her goal of finishing the marathon in a particular time more easily.
➡ _____

16 In short, pacers run but they don't run to win.
➡ _____

17 They run for others.
➡ _____

18 ▶ Pit Crews in Car Racing

➡ _____

19 ▶ You may only see the car and the driver during most car races, but there is a team behind the driver.

➡ _____

20 ▶ This team is called a pit crew.

➡ _____

21 ▶ A pit is a place on the side of the race track, and drivers stop there several times during a race.

➡ _____

22 ▶ The main job of the pit crew is to check the car and change the tires.

➡ _____

23 ▶ Changing the tires is especially important because the tires wear out easily in a high speed race.

➡ _____

24 ▶ A pit stop can be as short as 2 seconds, and there are as many as 20 members on a crew.

➡ _____

25 ▶ Therefore, the pit crew has to work in perfect harmony.

➡ _____

26 ▶ The driver may get all the attention, but as people say, "Races are won in the pits."

➡ _____

27 ▶ Sherpas in Mountain Climbing

➡ _____

28 ▶ The word *Sherpa* comes from the Sherpa tribe, which lives in the eastern part of Nepal.

➡ _____

29 ▶ Sherpas have good climbing skills and know their way around the mountains well.

➡ _____

30 ▶ They also have little difficulty breathing high up in the mountains.

➡ _____

31 ▶ Therefore, mountain climbers started to hire Sherpas to help them climb Mount Everest.

➡ _____

32 ▶ Sherpas lead mountain climbers to the top of the mountain.

➡ _____

33 ▶ They support climbers in many ways.

➡ _____

34 ▶ For example, they put up tents and carry climbers' bags.

➡ _____

35 ▶ Sherpas are often called the invisible people of Mount Everest because people often see a picture of only the climbers at the top of the mountain.

➡ _____

_____

※ 다음 괄호 안의 단어들을 우리말에 맞도록 바르게 배열하시오.

1 (People / Hidden / Sports / in)
➡ _____

2 (sports, / in / the / only / get / players / a / or / trophy / medal, / they / but / win / don't / their / on / own.)
➡ _____

3 (are / there / who / people / help / players. / the)
➡ _____

4 (people / these / often / are / hidden / and / get / don't / attention.)
➡ _____

5 (they / however, / are / important / as / the / as / players.)
➡ _____

6 (are / here / examples. / some)
➡ _____

7 (in / Pacers / Marathon / a)
➡ _____

8 (run / pacers / other / with / and / runners / lead / in / them / marathon. / a)
➡ _____

9 (are / pacers / runners, / experienced / and / job / their / to / is / other / help / manage / runners / their / better. / race)
➡ _____

10 (can / there / several / be / in / pacers / race. / a)
➡ _____

11 (pacer / each / at / runs / speeds / different / and / the / finishes / race / different / in / times.)
➡ _____

12 (usually / pacers / flags / have / or / showing / balloons / finish / their / time.)
➡ _____

13 (can / runners / a / choose / pacer / on / depending / target / their / time. / finish)
➡ _____

14 (example, / for / a / if / wants / runner / finish / to / race / the / in / hours, / four / runner / the / follow / will / four-hour / the / pacer.)
➡ _____

15 (the / since / keeps / pacer / of / track / time, / the / runner / the / achieve / can / her / or / his / of / goal / the / finishing / in / marathon / a / time / particular / more / easily.)
➡ _____

16 (short, / in / run / pacers / they / but / don't / to / run / win.)
➡ _____

17 (run / they / others. / for)
➡ _____

18 (Crews / Pit / Car / in / Racing)
➡ _____

19 (may / you / see / only / car / the / and / driver / the / most / during / races, / car / there / but / is / team / a / the / behind / driver.)
➡ _____

1 스포츠 속 숨은 조력자들
2 스포츠에서 선수들만 트로피나 메달을 받지만, 그들은 혼자 힘으로 이긴 것이 아니다.
3 그 선수들을 돕는 사람들이 있다.
4 이 사람들은 종종 숨겨져 있고 주목을 받지 못한다.
5 하지만 그들은 선수들만큼 중요하다.
6 여기 몇 가지 예가 있다.
7 마라톤의 페이서들
8 페이서들은 마라톤에서 다른 선수들과 함께 달리며 그들을 이끈다.
9 페이서들은 경험이 많은 선수들이며 그들의 역할은 다른 선수들이 경기를 더 잘 운영하도록 돕는 것이다.
10 한 경기에는 여러 명의 페이서들이 있을 수 있다.
11 각각의 페이서는 다른 속도로 달리고 다른 시간대에 경기를 마친다.
12 페이서들은 주로 자신들의 완주 시간을 나타내는 깃발이나 풍선들을 가지고 있다.
13 선수들은 자신들의 목표 완주 시간에 따라 페이서를 선택할 수 있다.
14 예를 들어, 한 선수가 4시간 안에 경기를 마치고 싶다면, 그 선수는 4시간 페이서를 따라갈 것이다.
15 페이서가 시간을 계속해서 파악하기 때문에, 선수는 특정 시간에 마라톤을 완주하려는 자신의 목표를 더 쉽게 달성할 수 있다.
16 요컨대, 페이서들은 달리지만 우승을 하기 위해 달리는 것은 아니다.
17 그들은 다른 선수들을 위해 달린다.
18 자동차 경주의 피트 크루
19 여러분은 대부분의 자동차 경주에서 자동차와 레이서만 보겠지만 그 레이서 뒤에는 팀이 있다.

20 (team / this / called / is / pit / a / crew.)
➡ _____

21 (pit / a / is / place / a / the / on / side / the / of / track, / the / race / drivers / and / there / stop / several / during / times / race. / a)
➡ _____

22 (main / the / job / of / pit / the / is / crew / check / to / car / the / and / the / change / tires.)
➡ _____

23 (the / changing / tires / especially / is / because / important / tires / the / out / wear / easily / a / in / speed / high / race.)
➡ _____

24 (pit / a / stop / be / can / short / as / 2 / as / seconds, / there / and / as / are / many / 20 / as / members / a / on / crew.)
➡ _____

25 (the / therefore, / pit / has / crew / work / to / perfect / in / harmony.)
➡ _____

26 (driver / the / get / may / all / attention, / the / as / but / say, / people / are / "races / won / the / in / pits.")
➡ _____

27 (in / Sherpas / Climbing / Mountain)
➡ _____

28 (word / the / 'Sherpa' / from / comes / Sherpa / the / tribe, / lives / which / the / in / part / eastern / Nepal. / of)
➡ _____

29 (have / Sherpas / good / skills / climbing / and / their / know / around / way / mountains / the / well.)
➡ _____

30 (also / they / little / have / breathing / difficulty / up / high / the / in / mountains.)
➡ _____

31 (mountain / therefore, / started / climbers / hire / to / to / Sherpas / them / help / climb / Everest. / Mount)
➡ _____

32 (lead / Sherpas / climbers / mountain / the / to / of / top / mountain. / the)
➡ _____

33 (support / they / in / climbers / ways. / many)
➡ _____

34 (example, / for / put / they / tents / up / and / carry / bags. / climbers')
➡ _____

35 (are / Sherpas / called / often / invisible / the / of / people / Everest / Mount / people / because / see / often / picture / a / only / of / climbers / the / the / at / of / top / mountain. / the)
➡ _____

---

20 이 팀은 피트 크루라고 불린다.

21 피트는 경주 트랙의 한쪽에 있는 공간으로 레이서들은 경주 도중에 그곳에서 여러 번 정지한다.

22 피트 크루가 하는 주요 역할은 자동차를 점검하고 타이어를 교체하는 것이다.

23 빠른 속도의 경주에서는 타이어가 쉽게 마모되기 때문에 타이어를 교체하는 것이 특히 중요하다.

24 피트에서의 정지는 짧게는 2초 정도이고 한 팀에는 많게는 20명에 이르는 구성원이 있다.

25 그러므로 피트 크루는 완벽한 조화를 이루며 일해야 한다.

26 레이서만 주목을 받을지 모르지만 사람들이 말하는 것처럼, "경주의 우승은 피트에서 이루어진다."

27 등반에서의 셰르파

28 'Sherpa'라는 단어는 셰르파족에서 유래되었는데, 셰르파족은 네팔의 동쪽 지역에 산다.

29 셰르파는 훌륭한 등반 기량을 갖고 있으며 산 지리를 잘 안다.

30 그들은 또한 산의 높은 곳에서 호흡하는 데 어려움이 거의 없다.

31 그래서 등산가들은 자신들이 에베레스트산을 등반하는 것을 돕는 셰르파를 고용하기 시작했다.

32 셰르파는 등산가들을 산 정상까지 이끈다.

33 그들은 여러 방면에서 등산가들을 지원한다.

34 예를 들면, 그들은 텐트를 치고 등산가들의 가방을 운반한다.

35 셰르파는 종종 에베레스트산의 보이지 않는 사람들로 불리는데, 왜냐하면 사람들이 산 정상에서 등산가들만 찍힌 사진을 자주 보기 때문이다.

※ 다음 우리말을 영어로 쓰시오.

1 스포츠 속 숨은 조력자들

➡ _____

2 스포츠에서 선수들만 트로피나 메달을 받지만, 그들은 혼자 힘으로 이긴 것이 아니다.

➡ _____

3 그 선수들을 돕는 사람들이 있다.

➡ _____

4 이 사람들은 종종 숨겨져 있고 주목을 받지 못한다.

➡ _____

5 하지만 그들은 선수들만큼 중요하다.

➡ _____

6 여기 몇 가지 예가 있다.

➡ _____

7 마라톤의 페이서들

➡ _____

8 페이서들은 마라톤에서 다른 선수들과 함께 달리며 그들을 이끈다.

➡ _____

9 페이서들은 경험이 많은 선수들이며 그들의 역할은 다른 선수들이 경기를 더 잘 운영하도록 돕는 것이다.

➡ _____

10 한 경기에는 여러 명의 페이서들이 있을 수 있다.

➡ _____

11 각각의 페이서는 다른 속도로 달리고 다른 시간대에 경기를 마친다.

➡ _____

12 페이서들은 주로 자신들의 완주 시간을 나타내는 깃발이나 풍선들을 가지고 있다.

➡ _____

13 선수들은 자신들의 목표 완주 시간에 따라 페이서를 선택할 수 있다.

➡ _____

14 예를 들어, 한 선수가 4시간 안에 경기를 마치고 싶다면, 그 선수는 4시간 페이서를 따라갈 것이다.

➡ _____

15 페이서가 시간을 계속해서 파악하기 때문에, 선수는 특정 시간에 마라톤을 완주하려는 자신의 목표를 더 쉽게 달성할 수 있다.

➡ _____

_____

16 요컨대, 페이서들은 달리지만 우승을 하기 위해 달리는 것은 아니다.

➡ _____

17 그들은 다른 선수들을 위해 달린다.

➡ _____

18 자동차 경주의 피트 크루

➡ _____

19 여러분은 대부분의 자동차 경주에서 자동차와 레이서만 보겠지만 그 레이서 뒤에는 팀이 있다.

➡ _____

20 이 팀은 피트 크루라고 불린다.

➡ _____

21 피트는 경주 트랙의 한쪽에 있는 공간으로 레이서들은 경주 도중에 그곳에서 여러 번 정지한다.

➡ _____

22 피트 크루가 하는 주요 역할은 자동차를 점검하고 타이어를 교체하는 것이다.

➡ _____

23 빠른 속도의 경주에서는 타이어가 쉽게 마모되기 때문에 타이어를 교체하는 것이 특히 중요하다.

➡ _____

24 피트에서의 정지는 짧게는 2초 정도이고 한 팀에는 많게는 20명에 이르는 구성원이 있다.

➡ _____

25 그러므로 피트 크루는 완벽한 조화를 이루며 일해야 한다.

➡ _____

26 레이서만 주목을 받을지 모르지만 사람들이 말하는 것처럼, "경주의 우승은 피트에서 이루어진다."

➡ _____

27 등반에서의 셰르파

➡ _____

28 'Sherpa'라는 단어는 셰르파족에서 유래되었는데, 셰르파족은 네팔의 동쪽 지역에 산다.

➡ _____

29 셰르파는 훌륭한 등반 기량을 갖고 있으며 산 지리를 잘 안다.

➡ _____

30 그들은 또한 산의 높은 곳에서 호흡하는 데 어려움이 거의 없다.

➡ _____

31 그래서 등산가들은 자신들이 에베레스트산을 등반하는 것을 돕는 셰르파를 고용하기 시작했다.

➡ _____

32 셰르파는 등산가들을 산 정상까지 이끈다.

➡ _____

33 그들은 여러 방면에서 등산가들을 지원한다.

➡ _____

34 예를 들면, 그들은 텐트를 치고 등산가들의 가방을 운반한다.

➡ _____

35 셰르파는 종종 에베레스트산의 보이지 않는 사람들로 불리는데, 왜냐하면 사람들이 산 정상에서 등산가들만 찍힌 사진을 자주 보기 때문이다.

➡ _____

_____

※ 다음 우리말과 일치하도록 빈칸에 알맞은 말을 쓰시오.

After You Read B

1. Host: _____ _____ _____ _____ about your job?

2. Pacer: Pacers have flags or balloons _____ _____ _____
   _____ .

3. Pit Crew: A pit stop _____ _____ _____ _____
   _____ _____ .

4. So the pit crew _____ _____ _____ _____
   _____ .

5. Sherpa: Sherpas like me _____ _____ _____
   _____ _____ in the mountains.

1. 사회자: 여러분의 직업에 관해 어떤 흥미로운 것이 있나요?
2. 페이서: 페이서는 자신들의 완주 시간을 나타내는 깃발이나 풍선들을 가지고 있어요.
3. 피트 크루: 피트에서의 정지는 짧게는 2초 정도입니다.
4. 그래서 피트 크루는 완벽한 조화를 이루며 일해야 해요.
5. 셰르파: 저와 같은 셰르파는 산의 높은 곳에서 호흡하는 데 어려움이 거의 없어요.

Around the World

1. In swimming, a tapper uses a long pole _____ _____ _____
   _____ _____ .

2. In a race, a guide runner _____ _____ _____ _____
   and _____ him or her _____ _____ _____ _____ .

3. _____ _____ _____ , _____ _____ _____ tells his
   or her team players which _____ _____ _____ .

1. 수영에서, tapper는 시각 장애인 수영 선수가 수영하는 것을 돕기 위해 장대를 사용한다.
2. 달리기에서, guide runner는 시각 장애인 선수와 함께 달리며 그들이 트랙에서 벗어나지 않도록 돕는다.
3. 시각 장애인 축구에서, shooting assistant는 자신의 팀 선수들에게 슛하는 방향을 말해 준다.

Think and Write

1. _____ in _____ .

2. _____ people _____ _____ _____ that cheerleaders are
   _____ _____ _____ a football team, they _____ _____
   _____ _____ a football game.

3. _____ _____ at a game, they _____ _____ _____ .

4. They _____ _____ their team and fans.

5. _____ _____ _____ _____ _____ , cheerleaders _____
   _____ _____ and _____ .

6. They also _____ _____ _____ _____ _____ _____
   and _____ .

7. _____ _____ _____ , they need to _____ _____ _____
   _____ _____ .

1. 미식축구 경기에서의 치어리더
2. 사람들이 보통 치어리더는 미식축구팀의 일원이라고 생각하지 않을지라도 그들은 축구 경기에서 중요한 역할을 한다.
3. 경기에서 응원을 함으로써 그들은 공동체 정신을 만들어낸다.
4. 그들은 또한 팀과 팬들을 격려한다.
5. 자신의 역할을 잘 하기 위해, 치어리더들은 몸을 건강하게 관리하고 강해야 한다.
6. 그들은 또한 점프하는 것과 춤추는 것을 잘 해야 한다.
7. 무엇보다도, 그들은 선수들만큼이나 열심히 일해야 한다.

구석구석 지문 Test

※ 다음 우리말을 영어로 쓰시오.

After You Read B

1. 사회자: 여러분의 직업에 관해 어떤 흥미로운 것이 있나요?
➡ _____

2. 페이서: 페이서는 자신들의 완주 시간을 나타내는 깃발이나 풍선들을 가지고 있어요.
➡ _____

3. 피트 크루: 피트에서의 정지는 짧게는 2초 정도입니다.
➡ _____

4. 그래서 피트 크루는 완벽한 조화를 이루며 일해야 해요.
➡ _____

5. 셰르파: 저와 같은 셰르파는 산의 높은 곳에서 호흡하는 데 어려움이 거의 없어요.
➡ _____

Around the World

1. 수영에서, tapper는 시각 장애인 수영 선수가 수영하는 것을 돕기 위해 장대를 사용한다.
➡ _____

2. 달리기에서, guide runner는 시각 장애인 선수와 함께 달리며 그들이 트랙에서 벗어나지 않도록 돕는다.
➡ _____

3. 시각 장애인 축구에서, shooting assistant는 자신의 팀 선수들에게 슛하는 방향을 말해 준다.
➡ _____

Think and Write

1. 미식축구 경기에서의 치어리더
➡ _____

2. 사람들이 보통 치어리더는 미식축구팀의 일원이라고 생각하지 않을지라도 그들은 축구 경기에서 중요한 역할을 한다.
➡ _____

3. 경기에서 응원을 함으로써 그들은 공동체 정신을 만들어낸다.
➡ _____

4. 그들은 또한 팀과 팬들을 격려한다.
➡ _____

5. 자신의 역할을 잘 하기 위해, 치어리더들은 몸을 건강하게 관리하고 강해야 한다.
➡ _____

6. 그들은 또한 점프하는 것과 춤추는 것을 잘 해야 한다.
➡ _____

7. 무엇보다도, 그들은 선수들만큼이나 열심히 일해야 한다.
➡ _____

MEMO

MEMO

영어 기출 문제집

적중100

1학기

정답 및 해설

동아 | 윤정미

중 3

적중100

영어 기출 문제집

1학기

정답 및 해설

동아 | 윤정미

적중100

중 3

Stories of English Words and Expressions

시험대비 실력평가
p.08

01 ⑤　　02 universe　　03 ⑤　　04 ①

05 ④　　06 ①

01 동의어 관계이다. source: 근원, origin: 기원, determine: 결정하다, decide: 결심하다

02 '항성과 행성을 포함한 모든 공간'은 'universe(우주, 은하계)'가 적절하다. 그는 우주 기원의 새로운 개념을 발표했다.

03 ① present: 현재의. 우리의 현재 상황은 어렵지만, 우리는 최선을 다할 것이다. ② suggest: 제안하다. 선생님은 우리가 매일 신문을 읽어야 한다고 제안하셨다. ③ justice: 정의. 만약 당신이 좋은 판사가 되기를 원한다면 남을 공정하게 판단하시오. ④ civilization: 문명. 잉카 제국은 매우 발달된 문명이었다. ⑤ myth: 신화. 여느 대단한 신화나 전설처럼 여전히 한 가지 의문점이 남아 있다. legend: 전설

04 origin: 기원, 유래 / 햄버거의 유래는 분명하지 않다.

05 ① originate from: ~에서 비롯되다, 그 영화의 제목은 라틴어 표현에서 유래되었다. ② keep in touch: 연락하다, 나는 너와 계속 연락을 하고 싶지만 방법을 모르겠어. ③ introduce: 소개하다, 새로운 사람들을 소개해 줄 수 있습니다. ④ produce: 생산하다, destroy: 파괴하다, 저희는 그 모델을 더 이상 생산하지 않습니다. ⑤ call ~ after …: …을 본떠 ~의 이름을 부르다, 그들은 첫딸 이름을 아기의 할머니 이름을 따서 지었다.

06 cup of tea: [부정어와 함께; one's ~] 기호[취미]에 맞는 사람[물건], 공포영화는 정말 내 취향이 아니다. break a leg: 행운을 빌다, 그 배우는 나에게 행운을 빈다고 말했다.

서술형 시험대비
p.09

01 (1) flood　(2) slave　(3) suggest　(4) borrow

02 (1) Italian　(2) suggestion

03 (1) weather　(2) pulling　(3) picks　(4) passing

04 (1) The teacher was angered by the student's rudeness.

(2) Have you ever experienced cultural differences?

---

(3) If you want to turn on the computer, press this red button.

(4) He passed the exam for entering a law school.

01 (1) flood: 홍수, 평상시 마른 땅을 뒤덮는 많은 물 (2) slave: 노예, 돈을 받지 않고 다른 사람에게 소유되어 그들을 위하여 일하는 사람 (3) suggest: 제안하다, 무엇을 해야 하는지를 누군가에게 말하다 (4) borrow: 빌리다, 누군가에게 속한 것을 사용하고 나중에 되돌려 주어야만 하다

02 (1) '나라 이름 – 형용사/언어'의 관계이다. China 중국 – Chinese 중국의; 중국어, Italy: 이탈리아 – Italian: 이탈리아의; 이탈리아어 (2) '동사 – 명사' 관계이다. decide: 결심하다 – decision: 결심, suggest 제안하다 – suggestion 제안

03 (1) under the weather: 몸이 안 좋은 (2) pull one's leg: 놀리다 (3) pick up: ~을 익히게 되다 (4) pass through: 거쳐 지나가다

04 (1) anger: 화나게 하다, 수동태가 적절하므로 was를 추가한다. (2) experience: 경험하다, 현재완료가 적절하므로 have를 추가한다. (3) press: 누르다, on을 추가한다. turn on: 켜다 (4) law: 법, law를 추가한다. law school: 법학 대학원

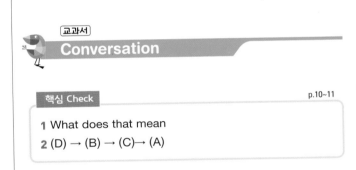

교과서 Conversation

핵심 Check
p.10~11

1 What does that mean

2 (D) → (B) → (C) → (A)

교과서 대화문 익히기

Check(√) True or False
p.12~13

1 F　2 T　3 T　4 F　5 T　6 F　7 T　8 F

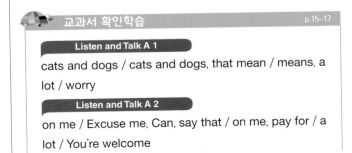

교과서 확인학습
p.15~17

Listen and Talk A 1

cats and dogs / cats and dogs, that mean / means, a lot / worry

Listen and Talk A 2

on me / Excuse me, Can, say that / on me, pay for / a lot / You're welcome

Listen and Talk A 3

delicious / Would, like some / not, tea / Not, tea / don't like something / see

Listen and Talk A 4

under the weather / Excuse me, can, say that again / under the weather, don't feel well / Why don't you, get, get / should

Listen and Talk B 1

make a long face / Excuse me, can you please say that again / make a long face / What does that mean / feel sad

Listen and Talk B 2

Break a leg / Excuse me, can you please say that again / Break a leg / What does that mean / Good luck

Listen and Talk B 3

under the weather / Excuse me, can you please say that again / under the weather / What does that mean

Listen and Talk C

had a great time / My pleasure, come visit / love to, like to invite / it, that, come / longer, keep my fingers crossed / Excuse me, can you, say that again / keep my fingers crossed, wish you good luck / Have, trip / keep in touch

Review 1

keep my fingers crossed / can you please say that again / keep my fingers crossed, wish you good luck

Review 2

feel under the weather / can you please say that again / feel under the weather / What does that mean / don't feel well / Why don't you buy / will

Review 3

cats and dogs / Can you say that again / cats and dogs / What does that mean / a lot

Review 4

is on me / What does that mean / pay for

시험대비 기본평가   p.18

01 It's raining cats and dogs.   02 ④

03 ③   04 Can you say that again?

01 'It's raining cats and dogs.'는 '비가 아주 많이 내린다.'라는 뜻이다.

02 'What does that mean?'은 '그게 무슨 뜻이니?'라는 뜻으로 상대방이 한 말의 의미를 설명해 달라고 요청할 때 쓰는 표현이

다.

03 'That's alright.'은 상대방이 'I'm sorry.'로 미안함을 표한 것에 대한 답으로 쓰는 표현이다.

04 'Can you say that again?'은 반복해서 말해 줄 것을 요청할 때 쓰는 표현이다.

시험대비 실력평가   p.19~20

01 ④   02 ②

03 I don't like something.

04 What does that mean?

05 ⑤   06 ⑤   07 Don't feel sad.

08 ③   09 ④

10 can you please say that again   11 ②

12 I wish you good luck.   13 ⑤

01 무슨 뜻인지 묻는 말에 했던 말을 반복하는 것은 어색하다. A와 B를 서로 바꿔야 한다.

02 다음에 나오는 말들로 보아 B는 스파게티를 안 좋아하므로 ② 번이 가장 적절하다.

03 뒤에 이어서 소녀가 'You don't like spaghetti.'라고 하고 있으므로 좋아하지 않는다고 했음을 알 수 있다.

04 What does that mean?: 상대방이 한 말의 의미를 설명해 달라고 요청할 때 쓰는 표현이다.

05 소녀가 'Oh, I see.'라고 하고 있으므로 이해했음을 알 수 있다.

06 빈칸 다음에서 앞에서 한 말을 다시 하고 있으므로 빈칸에는 다시 한 번 반복해서 말해 줄 것을 요청하는 말이 자연스럽다.

07 Don't make a long face. = Don't feel sad.: 슬퍼하지 마.

08 반복해서 설명해 줄 것을 요청하는 주어진 문장에 이어, (C)에서 다시 한 번 말해 주고, (B)에서 한 말의 의미를 설명해 달라고 요청하고, (A)에서 설명해 주고, (D)에서 '약을 좀 사라'고 제안한 후, 그렇게 하겠다는 말로 마무리한다.

09 'You can say that again.'은 동의할 때 쓰는 말로 적절하지 않다.

10 이어지는 말로 보아 빈칸 (B)에는 다시 한 번 반복해서 말해줄 것을 요청하는 질문이 적절하다.

11 '즐거운 여행이 되길 바란다'는 말에 고맙다며 '연락하겠다.'라고 하는 말이 적절하다.

12 I wish you good luck.은 행운을 비는 표현이다.

13 밑줄 친 문장은 다시 말해 줄 것을 요청할 때 쓰는 표현이다.

서술형 시험대비   p.21

01 (D) → (B) → (C) → (A)

02 Please come visit me again

01 축구 시합에 올 수 없어서 너무 안타깝다는 문장에 이어서, 유감이라며 행운을 빈다는 (D)가 나오고, 다시 말해줄 것을 요청하는 (B)가 나오고, 다시 말해주는 (C)가 나오고, 고맙다며 즐거운 여행이 되길 바라는 (A)에 이어, 고맙다며 연락하겠다고 하는 순서가 적절하다.

02 'come visit'는 'come and visit' 또는 'come to visit'으로도 쓸 수 있다.

03 Lucy는 '더 오래 머물 수 없어서 유감이야.'라고 하고 있고 마지막에 '즐거운 여행이 되길 바랄게.'라고 하고 있으므로 헤어지면서 하는 대화임을 알 수 있다.

04 'I feel under the weather.'의 뜻인 'I don't feel well.'을 쓰면 된다.

05 소녀는 'I think I have a cold.'라고 말하고 있다.

06 소년이 '비행기 타기 전에 약을 좀 사는 게 어때?'라고 하는 것으로 보아 공항에 있다는 것을 추측할 수 있다.

07 '~ is on me'는 '내가 내겠다.'라는 의미이다.

08 'pay for'는 '~에 대한 값을 지불하다'라는 뜻이다.

교과서
Grammar

핵심 Check
p.22~23

1 (1) which   (2) which
2 (1) that   (2) that

시험대비 기본평가
p.24

01 (1) that → which   (2) it → 삭제, 또는 which → and
   (3) which → who   (4) and → 생략, 또는 which → it
02 ③   03 ②
04 It is thought that the origin of the first hamburger is not clear.

01 (1) 콤마가 있는 계속적 용법의 관계대명사 자리이므로 that이 아닌 which가 적절하다. (2) 관계대명사가 있을 때는 관계대명사가 대신 받는 주어 또는 목적어 자리는 생략된다. 그러므로 it을 생략하는 게 적절하다. 단, which 대신 접속사 and를 쓸 경우에는 it을 생략하지 않는다. (3) 인간을 창조한 신들이 선행사이므로 관계대명사는 who가 적절하다. (4) 접속사 and가 있을 때에는 which로 바꾸지 않고, 대명사 it을 그대로 쓰는 것이 적절하다. and를 생략하고 관계대명사절을 쓰는 것도 좋다.

02 ③번을 포함 모두 가주어-진주어 구문의 It으로 시작했다. 그러나 다른 것은 진주어절을 이끄는 접속사 that이지만, ③은 명사 book을 수식하는 지시형용사 that이다. 동명사 reading이 진주어로 쓰였다.

03 계속적 용법의 관계대명사로서, 선행사는 작품명인 Sunflowers이다. which가 적절하다.

04 원래 문장에서의 that절이 think의 목적어로 쓰였으므로, 주어로 바꿔 수동태로 만들면 That the origin of the first hamburger is not clear is thought.가 된다. 진주어로 하는 것이 조건이므로, 가주어 It으로 시작하면, 정답과 같이 되는데, 이 때 일반인 주어 people을 수동태에서 by people로 표시할 필요는 없다.

시험대비 실력평가
p.25~27

01 ⓐ have → has ⓑ who → which,
   ⓒ which → and 또는 such food 생략,
   ⓔ which → who
02 ②
03 it is true that Mat cheated on the exam
04 ④   05 ①   06 ⑤   07 ④
08 My friends know Jasmine, who has no math problems that can't be solved.
09 ⑤   10 ⑤
11 It is important that they (should) learn many words of foreign origin.   12 ②
13 I want to visit the British Museum, which is in London.
14 ④   15 ①
16 It is surprising that the pizza was made by Jane, who is only 7.
17 ②, ③, ⑤

01 ⓐ 선행사가 the Louvre이므로 관계대명사 뒤의 동사는 단수 취급 ⓑ 선행사가 사람이 아니므로 which가 적절. ⓒ 관계대명사 뒤에는 불완전한 절이다. 목적어를 생략하거나, which를 접속사 and로 수정해야 한다. ⓔ 사람이 선행사이다.

02 ②번의 that은 It ~ that 강조구문으로 쓰였다. 나머지는 모두 가주어 It과 진주어 명사절의 접속사 that이다.

03 동사의 시제 cheated에 유의하여, 가주어 it과 that절을 활용해서 글자 수에 맞게 영작한다.

04 내용상 기술자에게 노트북의 수리를 맡겼고, '그 기술자가 노트북을 수리한 것'이 '비용이 들게 하다'라는 의미의 동사 cost의

주어가 되는 선행사이므로, 관계대명사 which가 적절하다.

05 영작하면, 'It is interesting that the idea of using the word *robot* didn't come from the author himself.'이다.

06 ⑤번은 'It ~ that' 강조구문이다. 나머지는 모두 가주어 It과 진주어 명사절을 이끄는 접속사 that이 쓰였다.

07 ④번은 가주어 It과 진주어 명사절을 이끄는 접속사 that이 쓰였다. 나머지는 모두 'It ~ that' 강조구문이다.

08 계속적 관계대명사 who까지는 어렵지 않은데 has no math problems that can't be solved에 유의해야 한다.

09 내용상 '올림픽이 서울에서 개최된' 1988년을 선행사로 받는 관계대명사이므로, 관계대명사 앞에 in이 있어야 한다. Seoul 앞의 in과는 무관하다. which를 in which 또는 관계부사 when으로 바꿔야 한다.

10 빈칸은 모두 관계사가 들어가는 자리이다. 선행사는 각각 (A) a girl, (B) a button, (C) 1517이다. 1517은 연도이고, 뒤에 완전한 절이므로 관계부사 when 또는 in which가 적절하다.

11 명사절 접속사 that과 주어 they를 활용하여 영작한다. 내용상 당위의 should가 필요한데, 생략 가능하기 때문에 쓰지 않아도 된다.

12 ①, ③은 앞 문장 전체가 선행사이므로, ④번은 불필요한 of를 삭제하고, 계속적 용법의 관계대명사 which가 적절하다. ⑤번은 동사의 수의 일치가 틀렸다. ① that → which, ③ who → which, ④ of which → which, ⑤ come → comes

13 문맥상 방문을 원하는 곳과 위치에 대한 설명을 해야 하므로, 대영박물관 뒤에 which is in London을 쓴다.

14 ④번을 제외한 모든 문장에는 진주어 명사절을 이끄는 접속사 that이 쓰였고, 다른 단어로 대체 불가능하다. ④에는 'It ~ that' 강조구문이 쓰였고, 강조되는 명사의 성격에 따라 that을 who/which로, 부사(구/절)가 강조될 때는 when/where로 대체 가능하다. ④는 where로 대체할 수 있다.

15 옳은 문장은 ⑤ 1개이다. ⓐ that → which 또는 and it, ⓑ were → was, ⓒ which → that ⓓ who → which, ⓔ and who → who 또는 and he

16 진주어 접속사 that과 '계속적' 용법의 관계대명사 who를 사용하여, 문맥에 맞게 배열한다.

17 ② 앞 문장 전체가 선행사이므로, 관계대명사는 that이 아닌 which가 적절하다. ③ 사람이 선행사이므로 who를 써야 한다. ⑤ 가주어-진주어 구문이라면 that 뒤가 완전한 절이 되어야 한다. 강조구문이 될 수도 없는 잘못된 문장이다.

서술형 시험대비   p.28~29

01 amazing that an old lady who can't remember anything sings along

02 (1) Mom said, "I feel under the weather," which means "I don't feel well."

(2) Emma is a coffee trader, who buys and sells coffee.

(3) I learned the expression, "This is on me," which refers to "I'll pay for this."

03 (1) of → for   (2) for → of   (3) what → that
(4) of → for   (5) excited → exciting

04 It is interesting that some animals such as beavers can use tools.

05 (1) which → it[that] 또는 but 삭제
(2) which → and 또는 such food 삭제
(3) who → which
(4) that → which
(5) it → and it, 또는 it → which

06 It is true that many English words came from different peoples.

07 (1) Robot comes from roboti, which means 'slave workers' in Czech.

(2) Most people in the temple stop working every three hours, who pray to their god.

(3) Hamburger comes from Hamburg, which is the second-largest city in Germany.

(4) Amy uses shampoo every day to wash her dog, which[who] doesn't like it.

(5) Wendy received a massage from her aunt, but it didn't make her feel better.

(6) The castle looked quite modern, though[but] it was built in the 8th century.

(7) Maria loves Spanish food, which actually is not Spanish but Mayan.

01 '어떤 것도 기억 못하는 할머니가 자신의 어린 시절 노래를 따라 부르는 것은 놀랍다'는 내용이다. 가주어-진주어 구문을 활용하여, 주어진 단어들을 적절히 배열한다.

02 (1), (3)과 (2)의 차이는 '선행사가 사람인지 아닌지'이다. (2)는 선행사가 사람이다. *refer to:~을 지칭하다, 언급하다

03 (1), (2), (4) to부정사구가 진주어로 쓰인 가주어-진주어 구문이다. 일반적으로 '의미상 주어'는 to부정사 앞에 'for+목적격'으로 쓰지만, 사람의 성품이나 성질에 관한 형용사가 있을 경우 'of+목적격'으로 써야 한다. (3) what 대신 가주어-진주어 구문의 접속사 that을 써야 한다. (5) 주어가 사람이 아니라 that절이므로 excited가 아닌, exciting을 써야 한다.

04 가주어-진주어 형식이므로 It is interesting으로 시작해서 that절을 이끄는 것이 핵심이 되는 영작 문제이다. some animals such as beavers의 어순과 글자 수에 유의한다.

05 (1) 앞 문장 전체가 선행사이므로 접속사 but을 삭제하거나, 앞 문장 전체를 받는 대명사로 바꾸는 것이 적절하다. (2) 관계대명사 which를 쓰면, such food를 없애야 한다. 아니면, which를 접속사 and로 바꿔도 어법상 맞다. (3) 선행사가 요가 동작이므로

which가 적절하다. (4) 앞 문장 전체가 선행사이고, 콤마가 있으므로 that을 which로 해야 한다. (5) 접속사가 없으므로 and를 넣어 주거나 it을 관계대명사 which로 바꿔야 한다.

06 가주어-진주어 형태로 적절하게 배열하되, peoples의 형태에 유의하도록 한다. people은 a people, peoples와 같은 형태로 쓰면 국민, 민족의 의미가 있다.

07 접속사와 대명사는 계속적 용법의 관계대명사로 바꿀 수 있다. (4)의 dog은 관점에 따라 which, who 둘 다 가능하므로 어느 것을 써도 틀리지 않으며, (6)의 접속사 though도 내용상 but으로 써도 괜찮다.

Reading

확인문제　p.30

1 T　2 F　3 T　4 F　5 T

확인문제　p.31

1 T　2 F　3 T　4 F　5 T　6 F

교과서 확인학습 A　p.32~33

01 Foreign Origin
02 borrowed words, other cultures
03 with interesting stories
04 from, to press　05 was used
06 with a head massage　07 a few times, entered
08 present, washing the hair
09 Shortly after that, to be also used
10 was written　11 look like
12 are designed, are produced
13 the idea of using, himself
14 from, for　15 However, in Czech
16 to use　17 was made into
18 originates from
19 creation myth, gods, created
20 angered, so, caused　21 Spanish contact with
22 passing through, picked up, for it
23 In English, uses, by
24 originally, second-largest
25 in German　26 is not clear
27 it is believed that, between, and
28 placed, Hamburg-style, two slices of bread, such food

교과서 확인학습 B　p.34~35

1 English Words of Foreign Origin
2 English has often borrowed words from other cultures or languages.
3 Here are some examples with interesting stories.
4 The word *shampoo* comes from the Hindi word *chāmpo*, which means "to press."
5 In India, the word was used for a head massage.
6 British traders in India experienced a bath with a head massage and introduced it to Britain in the 18th century.
7 The meaning of the word *shampoo* changed a few times after it first entered English around 1762.
8 In the 19th century, *shampoo* got its present meaning of "washing the hair."
9 Shortly after that, the word began to be also used for a special soap for the hair.
10 The word *robot* comes from the play *R.U.R.*, which was written in 1920 by a Czech writer Karel Čapek.
11 In the play, robots are machines that look like humans.
12 They are designed to work for humans and are produced in a factory.
13 It is interesting that the idea of using the word *robot* didn't come from Karel Čapek himself.
14 He originally called the machines in his play *labori* from the Latin word for "work."
15 However, his brother suggested *roboti*, which means "slave workers" in Czech.
16 Karel Čapek liked the idea and decided to use the word *roboti*.
17 In 1938, the play was made into a science fiction show on television in Britain.
18 The word *hurricane* comes from the Spanish word *huracán*, which originates from the name of a Mayan god.
19 In the Mayan creation myth, Huracán is the weather god of wind, storm, and fire, and he is one of the three gods who created humans.
20 However, the first humans angered the gods, so Huracán caused a great flood.
21 The first Spanish contact with the Mayan civilization was in 1517.
22 Spanish explorers who were passing through the Caribbean experienced a hurricane and picked up the word for it from the people in the area.

23 In English, one of the early uses of *hurricane* was in a play by Shakespeare in 1608.
24 The word *hamburger* originally comes from Hamburg, Germany's second-largest city.
25 *Hamburger* means "people or things from Hamburg" in German.
26 The origin of the first hamburger is not clear.
27 However, it is believed that the hamburger was invented in a small town in Texas, USA, sometime between 1885 and 1904.
28 A cook placed a Hamburg-style steak between two slices of bread, and people started to call such food a hamburger.

시험대비 실력평가
p.36~39

01 ⑤　　02 and it　　03 ①　　04 ④
05 (A) Hamburg　(B) *hamburger*　(C) Hamburg
06 robots are machines that look like humans
07 ⑤　　08 They were called *labori*.　09 ②
10 (A) weather　(B) great flood
11 the Caribbean　　12 ②, ⑤
13 *chāmpo*　14 ③　　15 ②　　16 ①
17 ④　　18 It's the name of a Mayan god.
19 (A) so　(B) were　(C) was　20 ⑤
21 Germany's second-largest city　22 ①

01 ⓐ from: (출처, 기원) ~에서 온, ⓑ introduce A to B: B에게 A를 소개하다

02 which는 *chāmpo*를 선행사로 하는 관계대명사로 계속적 용법으로 쓰였다. 계속적 용법의 관계대명사는 '접속사+대명사'로 바꿔 쓸 수 있다.

03 영어가 다른 문화나 언어에게 '빌려준' 많은 단어를 가지고 있는 것이 아니라, 영어가 종종 다른 문화나 언어에서 단어를 '빌려왔다'고 되어 있다. ② originate in/from: ~에서 유래하다

04 ④ two slices of bread: 빵 두 조각, ② lump: (보통 특정한 형태가 없는) 덩어리, a lump of sugar(각설탕 한 개), ③ (초콜릿·비누 등 막대기같이 생긴 것을 가리켜) 바[막대/개], a bar of chocolate/soap(초콜릿/비누 한 개)

05 '함부르크'는 독일에서 두 번째로 큰 도시의 이름이고, *hamburger*라는 단어는 독일어로 '함부르크' 출신의 사람 또는 사물을 의미한다.

06 look like: …처럼 보이다

07 ⓑ와 ⑤: 가주어, ① 가목적어, ② [사정·상황을 막연히 가리키는] 비인칭 주어, ③ 문장의 어떤 부분을 강조할 때 쓰는 대명사, ④ 그것(앞에 이미 언급되었거나 현재 이야기되고 있는 사

물·동물을 가리킴)

08 *labori*라고 불렸다.

09 ③번의 the gods는 ①번에서 언급한 the three gods를 가리키며, 그 사이의 '매년 허리케인이 카리브 제도 근처의 많은 지역에 해를 끼친다.'는 ②번 문장은 전체 글의 흐름에서 벗어난다.

10 마야의 창조 신화에 따르면, '날씨'의 신이며 인간을 창조한 세 명의 신들 중 한 명인 Huracán은 최초의 인간들이 신들을 화나게 했기 때문에 '거대한 홍수'를 일으켰다.

11 '카리브 제도'를 가리킨다.

12 ⓐ와 ②, ⑤: 경험 용법(ever, never, once, twice, how many times, before, often 등과 함께 쓰임,), ① 결과 용법, ③ 계속 용법, ④ 완료 용법

13 the word는 '*chāmpo*'를 가리킨다.

14 '이 글은 다른 문화나 언어에서 유래된 영어 단어 중 *shampoo*라는 단어의 기원과 의미 변화에 관한 내용이므로, 제목으로는 ③번 '*shampoo*라는 단어에 대한 재미있는 이야기를 소개해 드리겠습니다.'가 적절하다.

15 ⓐ word for ~: ~에 해당하는 단어, ~을 의미하는 단어, ⓑ in: 언어, 재료 등을 나타냄, in Czech: 체코어로

16 (A)와 ①: 동격 관계, ② [성질·상태] ~의, ~을 지닌, ③ [재료] ~으로 (만든), ~으로 (된), ④ [분리·박탈] ~을, ⑤ [기원·출처] ~으로부터, ~의

17 *labori*라는 단어가 얼마나 오래 사용되었는지는 알 수 없다. ① In the play *R.U.R.* ② It indicated a machine that looked like a human. indicate: 가리키다, 지칭하다 ③ A Czech writer Karel Čapek used it. ⑤ It means "work" in Latin.

18 스페인어 단어 *huracán*의 기원은 마야 신의 이름이다.

19 (A) 최초의 인간들이 신들을 '화나게 해서' Huracán은 거대한 홍수를 일으켰다고 해야 하므로 so가 적절하다. (B) 선행사가 Spanish explorers이므로 were가 적절하다. (C) 'one of the+복수 명사'에서 주어가 단수(one)이므로 동사는 was가 적절하다.

20 ⑤는 'a hurricane'을 가리킨다.

21 second-largest: 두 번째로 큰

22 이 글은 '*hamburger*라는 단어와 햄버거라는 음식이 만들어지게 된 기원'을 소개하는 글이므로, 주제로는 ①번 '*hamburger*라는 단어와 최초의 햄버거의 기원'이 적절하다.

서술형 시험대비
p.40~41

01 Spanish　　02 one of the early uses of hurricane
03 (A) Huracán　(B) *huracán*　(C) *hurricane*
04 (A) first hamburger　(B) Hamburg-style steak
05 (A) borrowed　(B) massage　(C) times

06 did not change at all → changed a few times

07 (A) to press (B) head massage

08 which a Czech writer Karel Čapek wrote in 1920

09 using the word *robot*

10 (A) *labori* (B) *roboti* (C) science fiction show

01 Spanish: 스페인의(형용사); 스페인어(명사)

02 one of the+복수 명사: ~ 중의 하나

03 (1) 마야어에서: 마야의 창조 신화에서 마야의 신 'Huracán'
은 날씨의 신이다. (2) 스페인어에서: 스페인어 단어 'huracán'
은 스페인 탐험가들이 카리브 제도를 지나는 동안 그들이 겪었
던 허리케인을 의미하는 단어를 그 지역 사람들으로부터 듣게 되
었다. (3) 영어에서: 'hurricane'이라는 단어는 huracán이라는
단어에서 왔고, 1608년 셰익스피어에 의해 그의 희곡에서 사용
되었다.

04 1885년에서 1904년 사이의 언젠가 미국 텍사스에 있는 작은
마을에서 한 요리사가 빵 두 조각 사이에 '함부르크 스타일의 스
테이크'를 넣어 '최초의 햄버거'를 발명했다.

05 (A) 다른 문화나 언어에서 단어를 '빌려왔다'고 해야 하므
로 borrowed가 적절하다. borrow: 빌리다, lend: 빌려주
다, (B) 머리 '마사지'라고 해야 하므로 massage가 적절하다.
message: 메시지[메일/문자], (C) '몇 번' 바뀌었다고 해야 하
므로 times가 적절하다. a few times: 몇 번, a few hours:
몇 시간

06 *shampoo*라는 단어의 의미는 그 단어가 1762년쯤 영어에 처
음으로 들어온 이후 '몇 번 바뀌었다.'

07 힌디어 *chāmpo*는 '누르다'를 의미하고, 인도에서는 그 단어를
'머리 마사지'라는 의미로 썼다.

08 계속적 용법의 관계대명사는 목적격이라도 생략할 수 없다.

09 'robot'이라는 단어를 사용하는 것'을 가리킨다. 동격 관계의 전
치사 of 다음에 나오는 'using the word *robot*'을 가리킨다.

10 (1) 1920년, "*R.U.R.*"이라는 연극에서 체코의 작가 Karel
Čapek이 인간처럼 생긴 기계를 '*labori*'라고 불렀다. (2)
Karel의 형이 *labori* 대신 '*roboti*'를 사용할 것을 제안했다.
(3) 1938년에 "*R.U.R.*"이라는 연극은 영국 TV에서 '공상 과
학물'로 만들어졌다.

영역별 핵심문제 p.43~47

01 ① 02 picked up 03 trader / originally

04 (l)aw / (o)rigin / (1) law (2) origin

05 (A) Vietnamese (B) French (C) Irish 06 ⑤

07 Will you have some of my spaghetti? /
   Do you want (to have) some of my spaghetti?

08 ③ 09 It's raining a lot.

10 Because he has an umbrella in his backpack.

11 ④ 12 The girl will pay for the juice.

13 ④ 14 ④ 15 ① 16 ④

17 ③ 18 ① 19 ⑤

20 My father made a family motto, which would
remind us the love between family members that
had never been thought of before.

21 ④ 22 was used 23 ③ 24 ②

25 (A) interesting (B) to use (C) into

26 ③ 27 ④

01 ① 넌 그런 아이디어가 언제 생각났니? ② 이 훌륭한 전통은 어
디에서 유래됐을까? ③ 요가는 인도에서 유래했다. ④ 많은 모
래 폭풍은 몽골에서 유래된다. ⑤ 스팸 메일의 발원지가 어느
국가인가?

02 '의도하지 않고 새로운 기술을 배우거나 버릇을 시작하다'라는
의미로 'pick up(~을 익히게 되다)'이 적절하다.

03 (1) 주어로 명사가 나오는 것이 적절하다. 동사에 er을 붙여 명
사가 된 어휘인데, 동사가 e로 끝나므로 r만 붙인다. trader: 상
인, 거래자. 그 상인은 제조업자로부터 직접 제품을 구매했다.
(2) 문장 구성상 부사가 적절하다. originally: 원래, 본래 / 명
사 origin에 al을 붙여 형용사가 되고 거기에 ly를 붙여 부사가
된 어휘이다. 내 가족은 원래 멕시코에서 왔다.

04 (1) law: 법, 사회나 정부가 범죄 등을 다루기 위해 개발한 규칙
의 체계. 누구나 법 앞에 평등하다. (2) origin: 기원, 유래, 무
엇인가의 시작, 근거 또는 근원. 토성 고리의 기원은 아직도 알
려지지 않았다. Saturn: 토성

05 Vietnam - Vietnamese, France - French, Ireland - Irish
각 나라와 그 나라의 형용사형이나 언어, 사람으로 쓰이는 어휘
이다.

06 모든 것이 맛있어 보인다는 말에 이어, 그렇다면 스파게티를 좀
먹겠는지 묻고(D), 괜찮다며 스파게티는 'not my cup of tea'
라고 하자(B), 그게 무슨 뜻인지 묻고(C), 의미를 설명해 주고
(A), 알겠다고 답하며 주어진 문장으로 이어지는 것이 적절하
다.

07 Would you like ~? = Will you have ~? = Do you want
(to have) ~?

08 약을 좀 사는 게 어떠냐는 말에 '너는 그렇게 해야 한다.'고 대답
하는 것은 어색하다. 'I guess I should.'가 적절하다.

09 'It's raining cats and dogs.'는 'It's raining a lot.'과 같은
의미이다.

10 소년이 소녀에게 '걱정 마.'라고 한 이유는 배낭에 우산이 있기
때문이다.

11 다시 한 번 말해 달라는 말에, 다시 한 번 말해 주고 나서 그 의
미를 설명하는 것이 자연스러우므로 ④번이 적절하다.

12 첫 문장에서 소녀가 'This juice is on me, Suho.'라고 하고 있
다.

13 소녀가 'This juice is on me, Suho.'라고 말하고 있는 것으로

보아 주스를 마셨음을 짐작할 수 있다.

14 ① that → who ② what → which[that] ③ which → who ⑤ what → which[that]

15 의문사절은 that절처럼 가주어-진주어 구문의 주어로 쓸 수 있다. ①번의 that은 불필요하므로, 삭제해야 한다.

16 ① 선행사가 있으므로 what 대신 that 또는 which가 적절하다 ② it 불필요 ③ which 뒤에 동사 is 필요 ⑤ and 불필요

17 ① and 불필요 ② it 불필요 ④ 내용상 which를 명사절을 이끄는 접속사 that으로 고치는 것이 적절하다 ⑤ knows는 단수동사이다. 주어가 all of whom이므로 복수동사가 적절하다.

18 ①번의 that은 'It ~ that' 강조구문의 that이다. 나머지는 모두 가주어-진주어 구문에서 진주어 역할을 하는 명사절 접속사 that으로 사용되었다.

19 <보기>의 which는 '계속적 용법'의 관계대명사로 사용되었다. ⑤번의 which는 의문형용사로서 '어느'라는 뜻이다. 나머지는 모두 관계대명사로 사용되었다.

20 본문에 나온 표현만으로 계속적, 제한적 관계대명사를 모두 사용해야 하기 때문에, 보충 설명이 필요한 두 번째 문장을 계속적 용법의 'which'로 연결하고, 수동태 형태의 세 번째 문장을 제한적 용법의 'that'으로 연결하는 것이 적절하다. *family motto: 가훈

21 buy and sell → buys and sells

22 인도에서 그 단어는 머리 마사지라는 의미로 '쓰였다'고 해야 하므로 수동태로 쓰는 것이 적절하다.

23 ③ Shortly는 '곧, 얼마 안 있어'라는 뜻이다.

24 이 글은 shampoo라는 단어의 기원과 의미 변화에 관한 내용이므로, 주제로는 ②번 'shampoo라는 단어의 기원과 의미'가 적절하다.

25 (A) 감정을 나타내는 동사는 감정을 유발할 때 현재분사를 쓰는 것이 적절하므로 interesting이 적절하다. (B) decide는 목적어로 to부정사를 취하므로 to use가 적절하다. (C) 공상 과학물에 의해 만들어진 것이 아니라, '공상 과학물로 만들어지게 된', 즉 '공상 과학물로 된' 것이므로 into가 적절하다. be made into ~: ~이 …으로 만들어지다

26 ⓐ와 ③: 강조의 의미, ①, ⑤: 관용어구, by oneself: 홀로 (alone), for oneself: 혼자 힘으로, ②, ④: 재귀적 용법(주어와 목적어가 같은 경우)

27 The word *roboti* means "slave workers" in Czech.

단원별 예상문제
p.48~51

01 ②　　　　　　　　　　02 ③
03 experience(d) / experience
04 (1) (s)lice　(2) slaves　(3) flood
05 Why don't you buy　06 get　07 ④
08 I'm in trouble.　09 We ate a lot.

10 ④　　　　11 (1) ⓑ (2) ⓐ (3) ⓑ (4) ⓐ (5) ⓑ
12 ⑤
13 It was foolish of the donkey to deceive its master.
14 빵 두 조각 사이에 함부르크 스타일의 스테이크를 넣은 음식
15 ④　　　　　　　16 (A) Hamburg　(B) Hamburg-style
17 ⓐ are designed　ⓑ are produced
18 (A) ②, ③, ⑤　(B) ①, ④　19 (A) *labori*　(B) *roboti*
20 ①　　　　　　　21 ②, ⑤
22 a bath with a head massage　　　23 ②
24 (A) between two slices of bread
　　(B) a card game

01 ②번은 반의어 관계이다. 나머지는 모두 동의어 관계이다. include: 포함하다, exclude: 제외하다 ① trader: 상인, 거래자, merchant: 상인 ③ present: 현재의, current: 현재의 ④ suggest: 제안하다, propose: 제안하다 ⑤ design: 설계하다, devise: 고안하다

02 ① be in hot water: 곤경에 처하다, 그는 차를 훔쳐서 법적 곤경에 처했다. ② pig out: 돼지 같이 먹다, 내가 좋아하는 요리들을 엄마가 만들어 줘서 엄청 먹었어. ③ a piece of cake: 식은 죽 먹기, 그 코스가 점수 따기 쉽다는 얘길 들었어. ④ keep fingers crossed: 행운을 빌다, 새로 하는 사업이 잘 되길 빌어. ⑤ see eye to eye: 의견을 같이하다, 그들은 서로 뜻이 맞지 않는다.

03 experience: 경험하다(동); 경험(명). 우리는 홍수 때문에 힘든 시기를 경험했다. 헤밍웨이는 후에 이탈리아에서의 그의 경험에 대해 썼다.

04 (1) slice: 얇게 썬 조각, 한 조각 (2) slave: 노예 (3) flood: 홍수

05 'Why don't you ~?'는 '권유'하는 표현으로 'How about ~?', 'What about ~?', 'What do you say to ~?' 등으로 바꿔 쓸 수 있다.

06 get on: 타다, get: 얻다, 입수하다, 사다

07 소녀가 비행기에 탄 후, 무엇을 할 것인지는 알 수 없다.

08 'I'm in hot water.'는 '나 지금 곤경에 빠졌어.'라는 의미로 'I'm in trouble.'을 의미한다고 할 수 있다.

09 'We pigged out.'은 '엄청 많이 먹었어요.'라는 의미로 'We ate a lot.'을 의미한다고 할 수 있다.

10 관계대명사는 접속사와 대명사 역할이므로, 뒤에 불완전한 절이 온다. ④번의 it을 삭제하는 것이 적절하다.

11 (1), (3), (5)는 'It ~ that' 강조 구문이고 (2), (4)는 접속사 that이 이끄는 진주어 명사절이 쓰였다.

12 ⑤번의 선행사는 fire가 아니라 '앞 문장 전체'이다. Jim은 불을 두려워하지 않았고, 그것(Jim이 불을 두려워하지 않음)이 그가 소방관이 되는 것을 가능하게 했다.

9

13 가주어-진주어 형태로 배열할 때, to부정사가 진주어가 된다. 의미상 주어가 당나귀이므로 전치사 for를 넣기 쉬운데, foolish로 보아 of를 추가하는 것이 적절하다.

14 그런 음식은 '한 요리사가 빵 두 조각 사이에 함부르크 스타일의 스테이크를 넣은 음식'을 가리킨다.

15 최초의 햄버거의 기원은 분명하지 않다.

16 *hamburger*는 독일어로 '함부르크' 출신의 사람 또는 사물을 의미하는데, 이 음식은 빵 두 조각 사이에 '함부르크 스타일'의 스테이크를 넣어 만들었기 때문이다.

17 robots는 설계되거나 생산되는 것이므로 수동태(ⓐ are designed, ⓑ are produced)로 쓰는 것이 적절하다.

18 (A)와 ②, ③, ⑤: 관계대명사, (B)와 ①, ④: 접속사

19 "*R.U.R.*"이라는 연극에서 인간처럼 생긴 기계들이 원래 *labori*라고 불렸지만, *roboti*로 변경되었다.

20 주어진 문장의 the word에 주목한다. ①번 앞 문장의 *chāmpo*를 가리키므로 ①번이 적절하다.

21 ⓐ와 ②, ⑤: ~에서 유래하다, come from = derive from = be derived from도 같은 뜻이다. ④ come up with: ~을 생각해 내다

22 '머리 마사지를 함께하는 목욕'을 가리킨다.

23 after: ~을 따라서

24 단어 *sandwich*는 샌드위치 백작 4세에게서 유래했는데, 그는 먹는 동안에 '카드 게임'을 하기 위하여 '빵 두 조각 사이에' 고기를 끼워서 먹는 것을 즐겼기 때문이다.

서술형 실전문제 p.52~53

01 Excuse me
02 She invites him to London.
03 He is seeing off Lucy.
04 which means she wishes you good luck
05 it is believed that the hamburger was invented in a small town in Texas, USA.
06 entered into → entered
07 the word *chāmpo*
08 (A) a head massage (B) washing the hair
   (C) a special soap for the hair
09 *roboti* → *labori*, *labori* → *roboti*
10 (A) Latin (B) slave workers

01 '누군가를 짜증나게 할지도 모를 어떤 것을 하거나 말하기 전에 사용되는' 말은 'Excuse me.'이다.

02 'I'd like to invite you to visit me in London.(난 런던으로 널 초대하고 싶어.)'이라고 Lucy는 지호를 런던으로 초대하고 있다.

03 지호는 Lucy를 배웅하고 있다. see off: ~를 배웅[전송]하다

---

04 계속적 용법의 관계대명사 which로 시작하여, 선행사에 맞게 단수동사 means와, 화법에 맞춰서 she wishes you good luck을 알맞게 배열한다.

05 가주어-진주어 표현과 우리말의 '믿어진다'에 알맞게 It is believed로 시작하여, 기본 어순에 적절하게 배열한다.

06 enter(~에 들어가다[오다])는 타동사이기 때문에, 전치사 없이 바로 목적어를 쓰는 것이 적절하다. enter into: (논의·처리 등을) 시작하다

07 인도에서 사람들은 '*chāmpo*라는 단어'를 머리 마사지라는 의미로 썼다.

08 (1) 18세기에, 인도에서 '머리 마사지'(*chāmpo*)를 함께하는 목욕을 경험했던 영국 상인들이 그것을 영국에 소개했다. (2) 19세기에, *shampoo*는 '머리 감기'라는 현재의 의미를 갖게 되었다. (3) 그 후 얼마 지나지 않아, 그 단어는 '머리에 사용하는 특별한 비누'에도 쓰이기 시작했다.

09 "*R.U.R.*"라는 연극에서 Karel Čapek은 인간처럼 생긴 기계들을 '*labori*'라고 불렀지만, 그의 형은 그것들을 '*roboti*'로 부를 것을 제안했다.

10 *labori*는 '라틴어'로 일을 의미하고, *roboti*는 체코어로 '노예 근로자들'을 의미한다.

창의사고력 서술형 문제 p.54

|모범답안|

01 (1) Do you know what the expression "He hit the ceiling again" means? It means "He was angry again."
   (2) Do you know what the expression "He pulled my leg" means? It means "He made fun of me."
   (3) Do you know what the expression "It's a piece of cake" means? It means "It's very easy."

02 (A) the 4th Earl of Sandwich
   (B) between two slices of bread
   (C) play a card game (D) eating
   (E) a sandwich

단원별 모의고사 p.55~60

01 borrow   02 century   03 ⑤   04 (c)ause
05 (p)ress   06 civilization   07 ①
08 weather   09 ④
10 He suggests to her that she buy some medicine.
11 Have a nice trip.
12 He asks Lucy to come visit him again.

13 She asks Jiho to visit her in London.
14 (1) The fox tried to eat the grapes, which were too high.
   (2) The grapes were so high for the fox, who considered them sour.
15 ①
16 (1) I watched the movie *Frozen 2*, which is the second episode of *Frozen*.
   (2) It was surprising that Taeyeon sang its Korean version OST.
17 ⑤
18 (1) The octopus artist has many hands, which helps her draw at once.
   (2) One of the musical geniuses is Mozart, who wrote a symphony at the age of eight.
19 British traders　20 ③
21 (A) washing the hair　(B) a special soap
22 ④　23 ③　24 ②　25 ③
26 ⓑ exclude → include　27 origin　28 ②
29 (A) Mayan　(B) a hurricane　(C) picked up
30 Dictionary　31 originates from

01 special: 특별한 – general: 일반적인, lend: 빌려주다 – borrow: 빌리다

02 '백년의 기간'은 'century(세기, 100년)'가 적절하다. 그 성은 8세기 중반에 지어졌다.

03 law: 법, expression: 표현, 그녀를 사랑하지 말라는 법은 없다. 그는 그녀에게 사랑의 표시로 장미꽃을 보냈다. rare: 드문, row: 열, 줄, raw: 날 것의, 가공하지 않은, low: 낮은, invention: 발명, creation: 창조, depression: 불경기, 불황, impression: (사람·사물로부터 받는) 인상[느낌]

04 cause: 초래하다 – 어떤 일이 일어나도록 만들다

05 press: 누르다 – 어떤 것을 강하게 밀다

06 civilization: 문명 – 잘 정돈되고 발전된 사회 / 동양 사회는 서양 문명을 받아들이지 않았다.

07 do yoga: 요가를 하다. 나는 일주일에 두 번 요가를 한다. pick up: ~을 익히게 되다. 나는 이 책에서 몇몇 유용한 영어 표현을 익혔다.

08 '특정한 시간에 한 지역의 대기의 상태'를 나타내는 말은 '날씨'이다.

09 dose를 get이나 buy로 고치는 것이 적절하다. dose: 투약하다, 복용시키다

10 소년은 소녀에게 가게에서 약을 살 것을 제안하고 있다. suggest에 이끌리는 that절에서는 '(should+)동사원형'을 사용하는 것에 주의한다.

11 지호가 Lucy를 배웅하고 있는 것이므로 '즐거운 여행이 되길 바랄게.'라고 하는 것이 적절하다.

12 지호는 Lucy에게 다음에 또 와 달라고 하고 있다.

13 Lucy는 지호에게 런던으로 초대하고 싶다고 하고 있다.

14 접속사와 대명사를 사용해서 다시 쓰면, (1) The fox tried to eat the grapes, but they were too high. (2) The grapes were so high for the fox, and it considered them sour. 가 된다. but they = which, and he = who로 쓰였다.

15 주어진 문장은 '계속적' 용법의 관계대명사이다. ③, ④번은 전치사의 목적어 역할(한정적 용법), ②, ⑤번은 의문사로 쓰인 which이다.

16 내용을 정확히 이해하고, 조건에 맞게 질문에 답하도록 한다. (1) 관계대명사의 계속적 용법을 활용한다. (2) 주어진 조건에 its와 the Korean version OST의 사용과 가주어-진주어 형식을 반드시 사용하도록 했음에 유의하여 영작한다.

17 ⑤번만 강조구문이고, 나머지는 모두 접속사 that이다.

18 관계대명사 계속적 용법의 영작이다. (1) which 뒤의 동사의 수의 일치 helps에 유의, (2) who 뒤의 동사의 시제 일치 wrote에 유의하여 주어진 단어들을 적절히 배열한다.

19 인도에서 머리 마사지를 함께하는 목욕을 경험한 '영국 상인'들이 그것을 18세기에 영국에 소개했다.

20 ⓐ와 ③: 약 ~, ~쯤(부사), ① 사방에(서)(부사), ② (건너편에[에서/으로]) 돌아(전치사), ④ 이리저리, 여기저기(부사), ⑤ ~ 둘레에, ~ 주위에(전치사)

21 *shampoo*라는 단어의 원래 의미는 '누르다'였지만, 19세기 이후, 그것은 '머리 감기' 뿐만 아니라 머리에 사용하는 '특별한 비누'에도 쓰여 왔다.

22 ④번 다음 문장의 However에 주목한다. 주어진 문장의 내용과 상반되는 내용을 뒤에 이끌고 있으므로 ④번이 적절하다.

23 ⓐ와 ③, ⑤: 부사적 용법, ①, ②, ④: 명사적 용법

24 이 글은 *hurricane*이라는 단어의 기원에 관한 내용이므로, 제목으로는 ②번 '*hurricane*이라는 단어의 기원'이 적절하다.

25 ③ Huracán은 '지진'이 아니라 '홍수'를 일으켰다.

26 judge(판사)와 justice(정의)와 같은 단어들을 예로 들 수 있다(포함한다)고 해야 하기 때문에, include로 고치는 것이 적절하다. include: 포함하다, exclude: 제외[배제]하다

27 위 글의 내용은 다른 언어에서 '유래된' 몇 영어 단어에 대한 것이다.

28 앞에 나오는 내용과 상반되는 내용이 뒤에 이어지므로 However가 가장 적절하다. ① 게다가, 더욱이, ③ 그러므로, ⑤ 비슷하게, 유사하게, 마찬가지로

29 (1) '마야의' 창조 신화에서, 날씨의 신인 Huracán은 최초의 인간들이 그들의 창조주인 신들을 화나게 했기 때문에 거대한 홍수를 일으켰다. (2) 1517년에 스페인 탐험가들이 카리브 제도를 지나는 동안 '허리케인'을 겪었고 그 지역 사람들로부터 그것을 의미하는 단어를 '듣게 되었다'(pick up: 정보를 듣게/알게 되다/배우다).

30 '사전'이 적절하다.

31 originate from: ~에서 비롯되다

Lesson 4

Be a Smart Spender

시험대비 실력평가
p.64

01 ⑤   02 budget   03 ②   04 ①
05 ④   06 ③

01 반의어 관계이다. easy: 쉬운, difficult: 어려운, true: 진실인, false 거짓인

02 '개인이나 회사가 쓸 수 있는 금액'은 'budget(예산)'이 적절하다. 그 예산의 적은 일부만이 책에 쓰인다.

03 ① on the spot: 즉각, 즉석에서. 그는 차를 보고 즉석에서 사기로 결정했다. ② change one's mind: 마음을 바꾸다. 그가 마음을 바꿀 가능성은 전혀 없다. ③ take care of: 돌보다, 처리하다. 제가 처리해야 할 일이 몇 가지 있어요. ④ have difficulty (in) -ing: ~하는 데 어려움을 겪다. 이번 주까지 생산을 완료해야 한다는 당신의 의견을 이해하기가 어렵습니다. ⑤ get a refund: 환불받다. 나는 이 티켓을 환불받으려고 노력 중이다.

04 receipt: 영수증. 내가 뭔가를 20일 전에 샀는데, 영수증이 없어.

05 ① result: 결과. 그 투표 결과는 오늘 밤에 발표될 것이다. ② refund: 환불. 그 점원은 내 돈을 환불해줄 것이다. ③ loose: 헐렁한. 이 바지는 나에게 조금 헐렁하다. ④ Efforts: 노력. 평화를 지키려던 노력들은 실패했다. ⑤ donate: 기부하다. 그는 아프리카에 있는 학교에 돈을 기부했다.

06 on sale: 할인 중인, 판매되는. 그 셔츠는 40퍼센트까지 할인 판매중이다. take effort: 노력을 필요로 하다. 그것은 시간과 노력이 필요할 것입니다. expansion: 팽창, 신장, hide: 숨기다

서술형 시험대비
p.65

01 (1) correct (2) effort (3) remaining (4) majority
02 (1) loose (2) advice
03 (1) effort (2) (t)ight (3) (r)eceived (4) exchange
04 (1) Mike has difficulty using his new camera.
   (2) I have saved my allowance to buy a hat.
   (3) Justin played the guitar on the spot.
   (4) It is easy to check your bank balance on the Internet.

01 (1) correct: 바로 잡다. 무엇인가를 제대로 되도록 하거나 원래의 방식대로 작동하게 만들다 (2) effort: 노력, 어떤 것을 이루려고 애쓸 때 하는 힘든 일 (3) remaining: 남아 있는, 일부가 제거되거나 사용되거나 분실된 후에 남아 있는 (4) majority: 대다수. 한 그룹 내의 대부분의 사람이나 물건

02 (1) '반의어'의 관계이다. same: 같은, different: 다른, loose: 느슨한, tight: 꽉 조이는[딱 붙는] (2) '동사 - 명사' 관계이다. donate: 기부하다 – donation: 기부, advise: 충고하다 – advice: 충고

03 (1) make an effort: 노력하다 (2) tight: 빠듯한 (3) receive: 받다 (4) exchange: 교환하다

04 (1) have difficulty (in) -ing: ~ 하는 데 어려움을 겪다. 'have difficulty (in)' 다음에 동명사가 적절하므로 using을 추가한다. (2) allowance: 용돈. 'pocket money'도 '용돈'이라는 뜻이지만 한 단어이므로 allowance를 추가한다. (3) on the spot 즉각, 즉석에서. spot을 추가한다. (4) balance: 잔액. 가주어 it을 추가한다.

교과서 Conversation

핵심 Check
p.66~67

1 ④   2 I'd like to get a refund for this bag.
3 ③

교과서 대화문 익히기

Check(√) True or False
p.68~69

1 T 2 F 3 T 4 F 5 T 6 F 7 F 8 T

교과서 확인학습
p.71~73

Listen and Talk A 1
help you / refund / wrong / get, back / take care of

Listen and Talk A 2
need some help / return / Let's see, receipt / Here it is, it / it's possible

Listen and Talk A 3
looking for, special / exchange / would you like / Here you are

Listen and Talk A 4

What, do for you / for / What, would, like / I'd like, one / Here you are

Listen and Talk B 1

May I help you / I'd like to / What, it for / it for

Listen and Talk B 2

May I / get a refund for / receipt / do, Here it is

Listen and Talk C

May I help you / get a refund for / receipt / don't, it as / it's, to get / I see, exchange, for something else / can, would you like to get / want to get / Let me see, take it

Listen and Talk D

look good on, if, exchange it for / up to

Talk and Play

Excuse me, exchange, for / anything wrong
Excuse me, get a refund for / anything wrong

Review 1

May I help you / I'd like to return / anything wrong with / have, back / Here's your money

Review 2

Can I help you / I'd like to exchange / would you like to exchange it for / have it in / Here you are

Review 3

get a refund for / afraid you can't / exchange, for / can

Review 4

get a refund for / receipt / do, Here it is

시험대비 기본평가 p.74

01 ③ 02 Can I have my money back?

03 ③ 04 May I help you?

01 이어지는 대화에서 돈을 되돌려 받고 있으므로 환불을 요청하는 표현이 적절하다.

02 'get one's money back'은 '돈을 돌려받다'라는 뜻이다.

03 '어떤 것의 대가를 지불했음을 보여주는 종이 조각'은 'receipt(영수증)'이다.

04 'Do you need some help?'는 'May I help you?'로 바꿔 쓸 수 있다.

시험대비 실력평가 p.75~76

01 ④ 02 ③

03 can I exchange it for something else?

04 it's not possible to get a refund

05 ⑤ 06 ②, ④ 07 ① 08 ②

09 ③ 10 ④ 11 ⑤

12 He wants to exchange the black umbrella for a yellow one[umbrella].

13 umbrella

01 영수증이 있는지 묻는 말에 교환하고 싶다고 말하는 것은 어색하다. A와 B를 서로 바꿔야 한다.

02 다음에 나오는 말들로 보아 상점에서 일어난 대화로 M이 점원으로 보이므로 ③번이 가장 적절하다.

03 뒤에서 G가 모자를 가방과 교환하고 있으므로 교환을 요청하는 표현이 적절하다. exchange A for B: A를 B로 바꾸다

04 get a refund: 환불받다

05 대화의 마지막 부분에서 M이 'you can just take it(this blue bag).'라고 하고 있다.

06 'Here it is.'와 'Here you are.'는 모두 '여기 있습니다.'라는 의미이다.

07 (a)에는 의문문이므로 anything, (b)에는 'Are you ~?'로 묻고 있으므로 'I'm not', (c)에는 change는 '바꾸다'라는 뜻이고, exchange는 '교환하다'라는 뜻이므로 exchange가 적절하다.

08 상점에서 손님을 응대하는 주어진 글에 이어, (B)에서 교환하고 싶다고 말하며 작다고 이유를 말하자, (C)에서 어떤 사이즈로 교환하고 싶은지 묻고, (A)에서 사이즈를 말하며 빨간색으로 바꿀 수 있는지 묻고, (D)에서 그렇다며 물건을 건네줄 때 쓰는 'Here you are.'로 마무리한다.

09 A가 'What would you like to exchange ~?'라고 묻고 있으므로 교환하고 싶다는 말을 했음을 추론할 수 있다.

10 exchange A for B: A를 B로 바꾸다

11 밑줄 친 문장은 환불을 요청할 때 쓰는 표현이다.

12 소년은 'Can I exchange ~?'라고 말하고 있다.

13 one은 부정대명사로 앞에 나온 'umbrella'를 대신해서 쓰이고 있다.

서술형 시험대비 p.77

01 (D) → (C) → (A) → (B)

02 Is it possible for me to get a refund for this cap?

03 It's because she doesn't have the receipt since she received it as a gift.

04 She finally gets a blue bag.

05 If you don't have the receipt, then, it's not possible to get a refund.

06 Here you are.

07 It's because the T-shirt is too small.

08 Are you looking for anything special?

09 refund

13

01 영수증이 없으면, 환불은 가능하지 않다는 문장에 이어서, 알았다며 교환은 가능한지 묻는 (D)가 나오고, 가능하다며 어떤 것을 원하는지 묻는 (C)가 나오고, 원하는 것을 말하는 (A)가 나오고, 가격이 같으니까 가져가서도 된다는 (B)에 이어, 고맙다고 말하는 순서가 적절하다.

02 밑줄 친 (a)는 환불을 요청하는 표현이다. it을 가주어로 하여 가능한지를 묻는 표현으로 쓸 수 있다.

03 소녀는 모자를 선물로 받았기 때문에 영수증이 없다.

04 마지막 부분에서 'so you can just take it(blue bag)'이라고 하고 있다.

05 it을 가주어로 쓴다.

06 'Here you are.'는 '여기 있습니다.'라는 뜻이다.

07 소년은 셔츠가 너무 작아서 교환하고 싶다고 말하고 있다.

08 look for: 찾다 anything은 형용사가 뒤에서 수식하므로 anything special로 써야 하는 것에 주의한다.

09 '반환되는 돈의 총액'은 'refund(환불금)'이다.

【교과서】
Grammar

핵심 Check   p.78~79

1 (1) since   (2) for
2 (1) Let's decide what to eat for lunch.
     (2) She doesn't know how to ride a bike.

시험대비 기본평가   p.80

01 (1) where to go   (2) which book to choose
     (3) what to buy for her
     (4) how I should[can] get to
02 (1) Marie has been playing computer games for
       four hours.
     (2) Susan and her friends have been watching a
       drama for two hours.
03 how to use / how I can[should] use   04 ②

---

01 '의문사+to부정사'는 '의문사+주어+should[can/could]+동사원형'의 형태로 바꿔 쓸 수 있다.

02 (1) 주어가 3인칭 단수이므로 have been은 has been으로, 현재완료진행시제이므로 play는 playing으로 쓰는 것에 유의한다. (2) have been watching에 유의하여 배열한다.

03 '의문사+to부정사'는 '의문사+주어+should[can/could]+동사원형'의 형태로 바꿔 쓸 수 있다. '~를 사용하는 법'은 'how to use'이며, 절로 바꾸면 'how 주어 can[should] use'가 된

04 현재완료진행시제는 '동작'을 대상으로 한다. '상태'를 나타내는 know, have 등의 동사는 쓸 수 없다. have been knowing → have known

---

시험대비 실력평가   p.81~83

01 ③   02 has been solving the puzzle since
03 (1) when to visit the palace
     (2) which color to use
04 ①   05 that → what 또는 which   06 ②
07 ③   08 ③   09 ②   10 ②
11 ⓓ when → where   12 ⑤
13 ③   14 ⑤
15 (1) has been traveling (2) has been learning
     (3) has been taking (4) has been listening
     (5) have been painting
16 ⑤
17 (1) who[whom] to invite (2) when to visit
     (3) when to stop (4) who[whom] to meet
     (5) which way to choose (6) what dress to wear

---

01 '과거형+현재진행형'은 현재완료진행시제로 표현한다. 'has been composing'이 적절하다.

02 과거에 시작된 일이 현재에도 진행되고 있을 때, 현재완료진행시제로 표현한다. 동사는 'has been solving'이, 전치사는 '~이래로'를 나타내는 since가 적절하다.

03 '의문사+주어+should[can/could]+동사원형'의 형태는 '의문사+to부정사'로 바꿔 쓸 수 있다. 의문문이 '의문사+to부정사 구'로 바뀌었으므로 주절에 맞게 물음표는 쓰지 않는다. (2) 문장에서의 which는 의문형용사로 사용되었다.

04 (1) 어느 것을 사야 할지 (2) 어떻게 고칠지 (3) 어디에서 숙박해야 할지 등에 적절한 의문사를 찾는다.

05 그의 아내를 위해 무엇을 살지 물어보는 것이므로 의문대명사 what 또는 which가 적절하다.

06 '의문사+to부정사'는 '의문사+주어+should[can/could]+동사원형'의 형태로 바꿔 쓸 수 있다.

07 주어진 단어를 활용하여 영작하면, Let her know when to start the meeting.이 된다.

08 ① visiting → visited ② see → seen ④ since → for ⑤ '먹어 본 적이 있다'라는 경험을 표현하는 글은 완료진행형으로 쓸 수 없다. has been eating → has eaten

09 의문대명사 which와 to부정사가 결합해서 명사구를 만들 때, which는 내용상 to부정사의 목적어 역할을 한다. 그러므로 the oven은 불필요하다. which를 의문부사 how나 when 등으로 바꾸는 것이 적절하다.

10 ① '아침부터 앉아 있었다'는 내용이므로 'has sat' 또는 'has

---

been sitting'이 적절하다. ③ '가지고 있다'는 상태를 나타내는 동사 have는 현재완료진행형으로 쓸 수 없다. ④ 직업을 잃는 것도 상태이므로 현재완료진행형으로 쓸 수 없다. ⑤ 'have been making' 또는 'have made'가 적절하다.

11 'Peter의 사무실이 어떻겠는가?'라는 A의 대답으로 미뤄 보아, 흐름상 ④는 '어디에서 과자를 만들지 모르겠다'는 내용이다. when을 where로 바꾸는 것이 적절하다.

12 <보기>는 현재완료시제의 용법들 중 '경험'이며, ① 결과 ② 완료 ③ 계속 ④ 결과로 사용되었다. ⑤는 '시장으로 두 번 선출되었다'는 내용으로 <보기>와 같은 '경험' 용법이다.

13 a. what should → what she should b. why to come은 쓸 수 없다. d. where to going → where to go

14 현재완료시제의 '계속' 용법, 또는 현재완료진행시제가 적절하다.

15 (1) 청소년 원정대의 여행 (2) 외국어 학습 (3) 약 복용 (4) 라디오 청취 (5) 벽화 그리기 등 각각의 내용에 적절하게 동사를 선택하여, 주어의 수에 맞게 has/have 등을 활용하여 현재완료진행시제를 쓴다. *expedition: 원정대

16 현재완료진행시제는 과거에 시작한 일이 현재까지 진행되고 있음을 의미하며, ⑤는 '15분 전까지'라는 명백한 과거시제 표현이기 때문에 부적절하다.

17 'whom to'는 'who to'로도 쓸 수 있다. 우리말에 맞게 적절한 의문사와 to부정사를 쓰도록 한다.

서술형 시험대비
p.84~85

01 (1) The runners have been working out in the gym for over eight hours.
 (2) Grace has been chewing a gum after lunch for 30 minutes.
 (3) Patrick has been composing online since he first bought a computer.

02 which, how to drink

03 (1) has been writing an email for 5 hours
 (2) has been learning Chinese for 2 years
 (3) has been practicing playing the cello for 4 months

04 (1) Mason told me how to use my laptop.
 (2) Can you teach me how to play the piano?

05 (1) decide which novel to read
 (2) tell us when to visit your office
 (3) know where to park my car
 (4) teach her how to play the violin

06 (1) look after his mom three years ago / looking after
 (2) watch birds an hour ago / watching birds

07 Aiden has been doing his daughter's homework for five hours.

08 (A) which club to join   (B) where to apply
   (C) when you will apply

01 현재완료진행시제에 맞게 각 단어를 적절히 활용한다.

02 둘 중 어느 것을 마실지는 'which to drink'이고, 어떻게 마실지는 'how to drink'이다. and로 연결해서 빈칸의 개수를 맞게 하려면 'which and how to drink'가 적절하다.

03 전치사 for를 꼭 사용해야 하기 때문에, 기간 계산에 유의한다. (1) 아침 7시에서 정오까지이므로 '5시간 동안' (2) 2017년 5월부터 2019년 5월이므로 '2년 동안' (3) 4달 전에 시작했으므로 '4개월 간'이 적절하다. 또한, practice는 동명사를 목적어로 취하므로 playing 형태에도 유의해야 한다.

04 '노트북을 사용하는 방법'은 'how to use my laptop'이다. '피아노를 어떻게 연주하는지'도 '피아노 연주 방법'과 같다. 'how to play the piano'를 쓴다.

05 (1) '두 가지 소설을 모두 읽고 싶은데, 어느 소설을 읽을지 결정할 수 없다' (2) '몇 시에 당신의 사무실을 방문해야 할지 모르므로 말해 달라' (3) '어디에 주차할지 모르겠다' (4) '바이올린 연주 방법을 가르쳐 달라' 등의 내용에 맞게 의문사와 동사들을 활용하여 영작한다.

06 현재완료진행시제는 '과거에 시작된 일'을 '현재에도 계속 하고 있는 것'이므로, '과거 시작 시점'과 '현재 상태'의 두 문장으로 나눌 수 있다. 시작 시점에 ago가 함께 쓰이는 것에 유의한다.

07 5시간 전에 집에 도착한 딸 Emma가, 집에 도착하자마자 아버지에게 숙제를 부탁했고, Emma 대신 숙제를 시작한 아버지 'Aiden이 5시간 동안 딸의 숙제를 하고 있는 중'이므로, 현재완료진행시제를 활용하여 영작한다.

08 (A) 클럽을 선택하는 것이므로 의문형용사 which와 to부정사를 사용해서 which club to join (B) 의문부사 where를 사용 (C) 'when to apply'라고 하면, 빈칸 개수도 안 맞고 will을 쓸 수 없다. when you will apply가 적절하다.

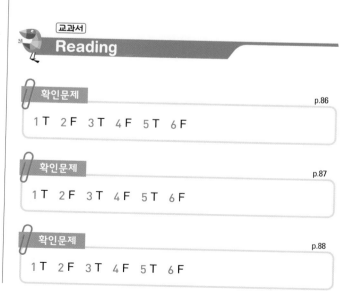

교과서 Reading

확인문제
p.86

1 T 2 F 3 T 4 F 5 T 6 F

확인문제
p.87

1 T 2 F 3 T 4 F 5 T 6 F

확인문제
p.88

1 T 2 F 3 T 4 F 5 T 6 F

01 Ask

02 Times

03 Spending Habits

04 How smart

05 a survey

06 smart with

07 As, while

08 biggest money worry

09 As, enough allowance, have difficulty saving

10 Lastly, spent, on

11 the majority, smart with

12 Managing, becoming

13 money worries

14 talk with

15 I'm

16 weekly allowance, enough

17 is gone

18 how to solve

19 I'm

20 spending diary

21 used up, at the beginning

22 my tip

23 carry around

24 Divide, into

25 carry, for each day

26 Hello

27 I'm

28 have difficulty saving

29 I've been saving, for the last two months

30 However, still don't

31 what to do

32 Let's see

33 In the last few

34 you've been spending

35 have a tighter budget

36 the 50%-40%-10% rule

37 donate the remaining

38 By following, manage, better

39 faster to buy

40 I'm

41 on sale

42 although

43 already have

44 things you need

45 In your case, don't even need

46 Here's

47 ask yourself

48 go shopping

49 on the list

50 on the spot

1 Ask Dr. Money

2 The Green Middle School Times

3 Teens' Spending Habits

4 How smart are you with your money?

5 These are the results of a survey of 100 students at Green Middle School.

6 We first asked students "Are you smart with your money?"

7 As Graph 1 shows, 70% answered "No" while 30% answered "Yes."

8 We then asked the students who answered "No" what their biggest money worry is.

9 As Graph 2 shows, 60% think they don't have enough allowance while 28% think they have difficulty saving money.

10 Lastly, 12% said they spent money on things they didn't need.

11 Our survey shows that the majority of students think they are not smart with their money.

12 Managing money is not easy, and becoming a smart spender takes effort.

13 Do you have any money worries?

14 Let's talk with Dr. Money.

15 I'm Jason.

16 I get a weekly allowance, but I never have enough.

17 By Thursday, all of my money is gone.

18 I don't know how to solve this problem.

19 Hi, I'm Dr. Money.

20 Let's look at your spending diary.

21 You used up most of your money at the beginning of the week.

22 Here's my tip.

23 Don't carry around all of your weekly allowance.

24 Divide the money into days.

25 Then carry only the money you need for each day.

26 Hello, Dr. Money.

27 I'm Steve.

28 I have difficulty saving money.

29 For example, I've been saving to go to my favorite singer's concert for the last two months.

30 However, I still don't have enough money.

31 I don't know what to do.

32 Let's see.

33 In the last few weeks, you spent 80% of your allowance and only saved 20%.

34 I think you've been spending too much.

35 To save money, you need to have a tighter budget.

36 For example, you can follow the 50%-40%-10% rule.

37 Save 50%, spend 40%, and donate the remaining 10% to charity.

38 By following the rule, you can manage your money better.

39 Then you can save money faster to buy the ticket.

40 I'm Minji.

41 I like to buy things on sale.

42 If something's on sale, I buy it although I don't need it.

43 Last week, I bought two T-shirts on sale, but I already have many.

44 Buying things on sale is good if you buy things you need.

45 In your case, the problem is that you buy things you don't even need.

46 Here's some advice.

47 Before you buy something, ask yourself, "Do I really need this?"

48 Also, before you go shopping, make a shopping list.

49 Don't buy items that aren't on the list even if they're on sale.

50 Then you won't buy things on the spot.

시험대비 실력평가
p.95~99

01 ⑤　　　　02 ②　　　　03 Seventy(70)

04 ①

05 50%를 저축하고, 40%를 쓰고, 남아 있는 10%를 자선 단체에 기부하는 것

06 (A) 20　(B) 50　　　07 ④　　　08 ②

09 ②　　　10 ②　　　11 ③　　　12 five

13 ④　　　14 ②　　　15 ③

16 (A) 80　(B) 40　　　17 ①, ③, ⑤

18 items that aren't on the list

19 (A) on sale　(B) a shopping list

20 (A) is gone　(B) most　(C) Divide

21 By Thursday, all of my money is gone.

22 ③　　　　23 the negative

24 60% thinks → 60% think

　　28% thinks → 28% think

25 ④　　　　　　26 ④

27 ⓐ 100 students at Green Middle School

　　ⓑ the students who answered "No"

28 three-fifths

01 ⓐ with: [관계·입장] ~에 관해서[대해서], ~에 있어서는, ~의 경우는, ⓑ spend+돈+on: ~에 돈을 쓰다

02 ② 위 글은 '(신문·잡지의) 글, 기사'이다. ① 수필, ③ 요약, 개요, ④ (책·연극·영화 등에 대한) 논평[비평], 감상문, ⑤ 독후감

03 학생 100명에게 설문 조사한 중에 70%가 "아니요"라고 답했기 때문에, '70명'에 해당한다.

04 ① 앞의 내용의 예가 나오고 있으므로 For example이 가장 적절하다. ② 게다가, 더욱이, ③ 그러므로, ⑤ 즉[말하자면]

05 다음에 이어지는 문장의 내용을 쓰는 것이 적절하다.

06 Dr. Money는 Steve에게 용돈의 '20%'에서 '50%'로 저축률을 늘리라고 충고한다.

07 ④번 다음 문장의 내용은 Dr. Money의 조언을 구체적으로 설

명하는 것이므로 ④번이 적절하다.

08 이 글은 '목요일쯤이면 용돈의 대부분을 다 쓰고 용돈이 절대로 충분하지 않다고 말하고 있는 Jason에게 용돈을 하루 단위로 나누라는 조언을 하는 내용'의 글이므로, 제목으로는 ②번 '용돈이 절대로 충분하지 않다고요? 용돈을 하루 단위로 나누세요.'가 적절하다. ① broke: 빈털터리의

09 '화요일'이 아니라 '목요일쯤'이면 용돈이 모두 사라진다.

10 (A)의 then asked가 (B)의 first asked보다 뒤에 나와야 하고, (C)의 60%가 (A)의 the students 중의 60%를 가리키므로 (A) 다음에 (C)가 와야 한다. 그러므로 (B)-(A)-(C)의 순서가 적절하다.

11 ⓐ와 ③: ~와 같이, ~처럼(접속사), ① ~이므로, ~인 까닭에 (접속사), ② ~처럼(전치사), ④ ~하고 있을 때(접속사), ⑤ 보통 as ... as ~로 형용사·부사 앞에서] ~와 같은 정도로 (as ... as ~에서, 앞의 as가 지시부사, 뒤의 as는 접속사)

12 충분한 용돈을 받지 못한다고 생각하는 학생들의 퍼센트(60%)가 필요하지 않은 것에 돈을 소비했다고 말한 학생들의 퍼센트(12%)보다 '5배' 더 크다. five times: 5배

13 '더 빠듯한 예산'을 세우는 것이 필요하다고 하는 것이 적절하다. ① loose: 느슨한, ② deposit: (은행에의) 예금, 예금액

14 위 글은 '용돈의 80%를 사용하고 20%만을 저축해 온 Steve에게 돈을 모으기 위해서 더 빠듯한 예산을 세워 50%를 저축하고, 40%를 쓰고, 남아 있는 10%를 자선 단체에 기부하라고 조언하는 내용'의 글이므로, 주제로는 ②번 '돈을 모으기 위해서, 50%-40%-10%의 규칙을 따르기'가 적절하다.

15 이 글은 '돈을 모으기 위해서, 더 빠듯한 예산을 세우는 것이 필요하다'는 내용의 글이므로, 어울리는 속담으로는 '티끌 모아 태산'이 적절하다. ③을 제외한 나머지: 티끌 모아 태산, ③ 소탐대실; 한 푼 아끼려다 열 냥 잃는다, 적은 금액을 절약하려다 그 때문에 큰돈을 잃는 것은 어리석다는 것을 뜻하는 속담.

16 Dr. Money는 Steve에게 용돈의 '80%'에서 '40%'로 소비를 줄이라고 충고한다.

17 ⓐ와 ①, ③, ⑤: 재귀적 용법(주어와 목적어가 같음), ②, ④: 강조 용법(주어, 목적어, 보어와 동격일 때, 생략 가능)

18 '목록에 없는 물건들'을 가리킨다.

19 (A) 민지의 돈에 대한 고민: 어떤 물건이 '할인 판매를 하면' 저는 그것이 필요하지 않더라도 사요. 지난주에는 할인 판매하는 티셔츠 두 장을 샀지만 이미 많이 가지고 있었어요. (B) 🅰의 조언: 쇼핑하러 가기 전에 '쇼핑 목록'을 만드세요. 목록에 없는 물건들은 사지 마세요.

20 (A) disappear는 수동태로 쓸 수 없으므로 is gone이 적절하다. (B) 용돈의 '대부분'이라고 해야 하므로 most가 적절하다. almost: 거의 (C) 용돈을 하루 단위로 '나누라'고 해야 하므로 Divide가 적절하다. add: (수·양을) 합하다[더하다]

21 바로 앞 문장의 내용인 '목요일쯤이면 용돈이 모두 사라져요.'를 가리킨다.

17

22 Jason은 이 문제를 해결할 방법을 모르겠다고 했으므로, '무엇을 해야 할지 알지만 실천하지 않는 것이 문제'라는 ③번이 옳지 않다.

23 answer in the negative: '아니오'라고 대답하다, 부정[거절]하다, answer in the affirmative: 긍정하다(say yes)

24 60%와 28% 뒤에 of the students who answered "No"가 각각 생략되어 있으므로, 60%와 28%를 복수 취급하는 것이 적절하다.

25 "아니요"라고 대답한 학생들 중의 '28%'가 자신들이 돈을 모으는 것에 어려움이 있다고 생각한다고 했으므로, 'More than one third'를 'Less than 30%'로 고치는 것이 적절하다. ③ three-fifths: 5분의 3

26 ④번의 save는 '구하다'는 뜻이 아니라, '(돈을) 모으다, 저축하다'라는 뜻임, rescue: 구출하다, 구조하다, ① outcome: 결과, ② whereas: 반면에(두 가지 사실을 비교·대조할 때 씀), ③ 용돈, ⑤ finally: (여러 개를 언급할 때) 마지막으로

27 ⓐ는 'Green 중학교 학생 100명', ⓑ '"아니요"라고 대답한 학생들'을 가리킨다.

28 60% = three-fifths: 5분의 3

서술형 시험대비　　　　　　p.100~101

01 (A) As　(B) who　(C) Lastly

02 trouble[a hard time/a problem]

03 Forty-two 또는 42

04 (A) smart　(B) money worries

05 I should[can]

06 Then carry only the money you need for each day

07 (A) never have enough　(B) Divide

08 To save money, you need to have a tighter budget. 또는 You need to have a tighter budget to save money.

09 ① 2,000원　② 5,000원　③ 8,000원
　　④ 4,000원　⑤ 0원　⑥ 1,000원

10 (A) ask herself　(B) make a shopping

11 (A) should not　(B) even if　(C) if

01 (A) 그래프 1이 '보여 주듯이'라고 해야 하므로 As가 적절하다. as: ~와 같이, ~처럼(접속사), since: ~부터[이후], ~ 때문에, (B) 선행사(사람)가 있으므로 관계대명사 who를 쓰는 것이 적절하다. (C) '마지막으로'라고 해야 하므로 Lastly가 적절하다. at last: 마침내, lastly: 마지막으로

02 have difficulty/trouble/a hard time/a problem ~ing: ~ 하는 데 어려움을 겪다

03 "아니요"라고 대답한 학생들(70명)의 60%가 충분한 용돈을 받지 못한다고 생각하는 것이므로, 70명×0.6 = 42명

---

04 Green 중학교 학생 100명 중 70명은 '현명한' 방법으로 돈을 쓰지 못하고, 충분한 용돈을 받지 못하는 것, 돈을 모으는 것에 어려움이 있는 것, 필요하지 않은 것에 돈을 소비하는 것과 같은 '돈에 대한 고민들'을 가지고 있다.

05 의문사+to부정사 = 의문사+주어+should[can]+동사원형

06 the money와 you need 사이에 목적격 관계대명사가 생략되어 있음.

07 Jason의 돈에 대한 고민: 저는 매주 용돈을 받지만, '절대로 충분하지 않아요.' 목요일쯤이면 용돈이 모두 사라져요. Dr. Money의 조언: 일주일 용돈 전부를 가지고 다지지 마세요. 용돈을 하루 단위로 '나누세요.' 그리고 하루에 필요한 돈만 들고 다니세요.

08 have a tighter budget: 더 빠듯한 예산을 세우다

09 ① 용돈의 20%, ② 용돈의 50%, ③ 용돈의 80%, ④ 용돈의 40%, ⑤ 0%, ⑥ 용돈의 10%

10 (A) 무언가를 사기 전: "이것이 정말 필요한가?"라고 '스스로에게 물어보아야' 한다. (B) 쇼핑하러 가기 전: '쇼핑 목록을 만들어야' 한다.

11 '비록' 물건들이 할인 판매 중이라고 해도 '만약' 그것이 쇼핑 목록에 없다면 사지 '말아야 한다.'고 해야 하므로 (A) should not (B) even if (C) if가 적절하다.

영역별 핵심문제　　　　　　p.103~107

01 ①

02 (c)harity / (e)xchange / (1) charity　(2) exchange

03 on sale　04 spender / allowance

05 (A) (d)ifficulty　(B) (f)oolish　(C) (t)ight　06 ④

07 I'd like to get a refund for this baseball glove.

08 Here you are., Here it is.　　　　09 ②

10 Excuse me.

11 Because he doesn't like the color.

12 Is there anything wrong with it?

13 ⑤　　　　　　　　　　14 ③

15 has been studying wild animals in Africa for 11 years

16 ④

17 (A) has been trying to be　(B) since　18 ③, ④

19 (1) has been taking pictures of himself
　　(2) has been watching birds

20 ①　　　　21 ⑤　　　　22 ③

23 ①, ②, ⑤　24 Twenty-eight(28)　　　25 ④

26 ③　　　　27 Divide the money into days.

28 once　　　　　　29 shopping

30 something that is on sale

31 Here are some tips.

32 Because she buys things she doesn't even need.

01 ①번은 '잔액'이라는 의미로 쓰였고 <보기>와 나머지는 모두 '균형'이라는 뜻으로 쓰였다. <보기> 우리의 내부를 자세히 들여다보면 완벽한 균형을 찾을 수 있다. ① 인터넷으로 예금 잔액 조회가 가능하다. ② 일과 놀이에 있어 균형을 유지할 필요가 있다. ③ 운동선수는 훌륭한 균형 감각이 필요하다. ④ 그 순간에 그가 균형을 잃고 넘어졌다. ⑤ 그 강타의 충격으로 Jack이 휘청거리며 균형을 잃었다.

02 (1) charity: 자선 단체. 가난하거나 아픈 사람에게 돈, 물품 또는 도움을 주는 단체. 그는 세상을 떠난 아내를 추모하여 그 자선 단체를 설립했다. (2) exchange: 교환. 누군가에게 무엇인가를 주고 그들로부터 다른 어떤 것을 받는 행위. 포로 교환은 오늘 오전에 이뤄졌다.

03 '특히 상점이나 가게에서 살 수 있는'이라는 의미로 'on sale(할인 중인, 판매되는)'이 적절하다.

04 (1) 보어로 형용사의 수식을 받는 명사가 나오는 것이 적절하다. 동사에 er을 붙여 명사가 된 어휘이다. spender: 돈을 쓰는 사람. 다음에 크게 한 턱 내세요. (2) 문장 구성상 목적어로 관사가 앞에 있으므로 명사가 적절하다. allowance: 용돈. 동사 allow에 -ance를 붙여 명사가 된 어휘이다. 나는 부모님에게서 용돈을 받는다.

05 (A) have difficulty (in) -ing ~하는 데 어려움을 겪다 (B) foolish: 어리석은 (C) tight: 꽉 조이는[딱 붙는], 빠듯한

06 (D)의 무엇을 도와줄지 묻는 말에 이어, (B)에서 야구 글러브를 환불받고 싶다고 말하고, (A)에서 무슨 문제가 있는지 묻고, (C)에서 아니라며 마음이 바뀌었다고 한 후, 알았다며 돈을 돌려주는 주어진 문장으로 이어지는 것이 적절하다.

07 return 대신에 'get a refund for'를 쓸 수 있다.

08 Here's your money. = Here you are. = Here it is.

09 'I'm afraid'는 유감스러운 내용을 말할 때 예의상 덧붙이는 표현이므로 그 다음에 긍정의 내용이 나오는 것은 어울리지 않는다. 'I'm afraid you can't.'가 적절하다.

10 '(1) 누군가를 불쾌하게 할지도 모르는 것을 하거나 말하기 전에, 또는 누군가의 주의를 끌기 위해, (2) 잠시 동안 장소를 떠날 때' 사용되는 표현은 'Excuse me.(실례합니다.)'이다.

11 소년은 '색이 마음에 들지 않아요.'라고 하고 있다.

12 'Is there'로 '있다'는 것을 나타내고 'anything wrong'으로 '잘못된 것 = 문제'를 나타낸다. wrong이 뒤에서 anything을 수식하는 것에 유의한다.

13 소년이 티셔츠를 바지로 교환하려는 것으로 보아 두 사람은 상점에서 대화를 나누고 있음을 짐작할 수 있다.

14 ① why+to부정사 형태는 쓸 수 없다. ② when 뒤에 주어가 나오면 to부정사를 쓸 필요가 없다. 문맥상 when도 좋지 않다. when they를 what으로 바꾸는 것이 적절하다. ④ starting → start. ⑤ using → use *photocopier: 복사기

15 과거의 시작 시점부터 현재까지 지속되는 것은 현재완료진행시

제로 표현하며, 기간은 전치사 for를 이용한다.

16 언제 시작할지 알려달라는 말이므로, 'when to start'를 'when I should start'로, 'let me know'를 'tell me'로 전환한 문장이 가장 적절하다.

17 배우가 된 이후로 지금까지 최고의 여배우가 되기 위해 노력해 오고 있다는 말로 보아 'try to be' 표현을 활용하여, 현재완료진행시제로 쓴다. '~한 이래로'는 since가 적절하다.

18 ③ 자동사 fall은 have been fell로 쓸 수 없으므로 'I have fallen'으로 쓰면 적절하다. ④ 강당이 덥게 느껴지는 '상태'이므로, 진행형은 부적절하다. 'has felt' 또는 feels가 적절하다.

19 주어진 문장들에 공통으로 '~ 이후로, ~ 동안'의 표현이 있으므로, 현재완료진행시제를 쓰는 것이 적절하다. be동사를 시제와 인칭에 맞게 'has been V-ing'로 쓴다. (1) 준수는 점심시간 이후로 한 시간 동안 꽃밭에서 자기 사진을 찍고 있다. (2) 영수는 세 시 이후로 30분 동안 새들을 관찰하고 있다.

20 영작하면, 'Let her know when to leave.'이다.

21 대화의 답이 노란색 제품이 훨씬 더 냄새가 좋다고 했으므로, 선택의문사 which가 쓰인 ⑤번이 적절하다. ①은 모양에 관한 질문이므로 부적절하고, ②도 향수 냄새를 맡는 법을 묻고 있으므로, 답이 될 수 없다.

22 현재완료진행시제는 과거에 시작한 일이 현재까지 진행되고 있음을 의미하며, '동작의 진행'을 나타내기 때문에 상태 표현 동사에 사용할 수 없다. ③ own은 '소유하고 있다'라는 뜻으로, 진행형으로 쓰지 않는다. *relative: 친척

23 ⓐ와 ①, ②, ⑤: 동명사, ③, ④: 현재분사

24 '28%'의 학생들이 자신들이 돈을 모으는 것에 어려움이 있다고 생각한다.

25 평균적으로, 학생들이 1주일에 용돈을 얼마나 받는지는 알 수 없다. on average: 평균적으로 ① 30 students are smart spenders. ② 70 students aren't smart with their money. ③ They think they are not smart with their money. ⑤ No, it takes effort to become a smart spender.

26 ⓐ by+때: '~쯤에는', '~까지는'(완료), ⓑ at the beginning of the week: 주의 초반에

27 divide A into B: A를 B로 나누다

28 Jason은 매주 용돈을 받으므로, 일주일에 '한번'이라고 하는 것이 적절하다.

29 go ~ing: ~하러 가다

30 '할인 판매를 하는 물건'을 가리킨다.

31 tip은 셀 수 있는 명사이므로 some 다음에 복수 형태로 써야 하고, Here 다음의 동사도 are로 바꾸는 것이 적절하다.

32 조언의 내용 중 'In your case, the problem is that ~'에서, 민지의 문제점이 '필요하지 않은 물건도 사는 것'임을 알 수 있고, 그런 이유로 민지는 비록 할인 판매하는 물건을 사지만 현명한 소비자가 아니다.

01 ②　　　02 ④　　　03 back / back

04 (1) (A)lthough　(2) (n)ative　(3) (r)ecently

05 ④　　　06 If I cannot get a refund for this hat

07 if 또는 whether

08 Because her sister says that the color doesn't look good on her.

09 ②　　　　　　　　10 ③

11 To return the smartphone case.

12 ③　　　13 ⑤　　　14 ①, ④

15 ⓐ risen → rising　ⓑ what → how
　　ⓒ which → how　ⓓ since → for
　　ⓔ has been having → has had

16 allowance　　　　　17 ⑤

18 More than → Less than　19 ②　　　20 ②, ⑤

21 ③　　　22 to buy → buying　　　23 ②

---

01 ②번은 반의어 관계이다. 나머지는 모두 동의어 관계이다. divide: 나누다, combine: ~을 결합시키다 ① recently: 최근에, lately: 최근에 ③ pocket money: 용돈, allowance: 용돈 ④ result: 결과, outcome: 결과 ⑤ paper money: 지폐, bill: 지폐

02 ① medicine: 의약품. 우리는 의사들이 여러분의 건강을 유지할 수 있도록 해주는 데 기여하는 의약품을 제조합니다. ② work: 작동하다. 그 기계는 스스로 작동한다. ③ case: 사례. 그것은 미국에서의 첫 광우병 발병 사례였다. ④ carry around: 가지고 다니다. 동전이 너무 많으면 갖고 다니기가 아주 무거워요. ⑤ be gone: 사라지다. 그들이 간 뒤에 돈이 없어진 것을 알았다.

03 • have money back: 돈을 돌려받다. 그것이 실패하면 돈은 돌려받을 수 있다. • get back: (특히 자기 집이나 머무르고 있는 곳으로) 돌아오다[가다]. 너 지난밤에 몇 시에 돌아왔니?

04 (1) although: 비록 ~일지라도 (2) native: 토착민, 현지인 (3) recently: 최근에

05 빈칸 다음에 '죄송하지만 안 됩니다.'라고 하고 있고, 대화의 뒷부분에서 '그렇다면 이 모자를 저기에 있는 장갑과 교환할 수 있을까요?'라는 말로 보아 '환불'을 요청했음을 추론할 수 있다.

06 이 대화에서 Then(그렇다면)은 '환불이 안 된다면'이라는 뜻이다.

07 'I wonder.'와 'Should I exchange it for a different color?'라는 두 문장을 간접의문문으로 연결한 것으로 의문사가 없으므로 if나 whether를 이용하여 연결해야 한다.

08 소녀는 '여동생이 색깔이 그녀에게 잘 어울리지 않는다'고 해서 다른 색으로 교환할지 고민이라고 하고 있다.

09 스마트폰 케이스를 환불받고 싶다는 말에, '잠시만요.(가만있자.)'라고 한 후, 영수증을 가지고 있는지 묻는 것이 자연스러우

10 소년이 왜 반품하려고 하는지는 알 수 없다.

11 소년은 smartphone case를 반품하기 위해 상점을 방문하고 있다.

12 각각 (A) '어디에서 묵을지' (B) '어떻게 갈지' (C) '무엇을 할지' 등의 내용이므로, 그에 적절한 의문사를 선택한다.

13 모든 지문에 현재완료진행시제가 쓰였다. ⑤번 문장은 시제 자체에는 문제가 없으나, 'during the summer vacation'이 '명백한 과거 시점'을 지칭하므로, '과거에 시작된 일이 지금도 진행되고 있다'는 의미의 현재완료진행시제로 표현할 수 없다. during을 since로 바꾸면, '지난 여름방학 이후로 Trump의 아들들이 포커 게임을 해오고 있는 중이다'가 된다.

14 의문사의 종류가 다른 두 개를 찾는 문제이다. '의문사+to부정사' 표현에서는 주로 의문대명사와 의문부사가 쓰이는데, 내용상 ①, ④번에는 의문대명사 which 또는 what을 써야 하고, 나머지는 모두 의문부사가 적절하다. ② how to play ③ where[when] to beg for money ⑤ when, where 모두 가능.

15 ⓐ 기름 가격이 2년간 꾸준히 상승해오고 있다. 능동의 현재완료진행이므로 risen을 rising으로 고친다. ⓑ '깊은 바다에서 어떻게 수영할지'이므로 how ⓒ '젓가락을 써 본 적이 없으므로 면을 어떻게 먹을지'가 적절하다. ⓓ 랩 가사같은 소리를 '15분간' 외치고 있으므로 since를 for로 고친다. (단, '15분전부터'라는 말도 가능하기 때문에, 그럴 경우 뒤에 ago를 추가하면 되는데, 골라서 고치는 문제이므로 since를 수정) ⓔ '소유'를 나타내는 have는 진행형을 쓸 수 없다. 현재완료시제로도 충분히 표현 가능.

16 allowance: 용돈, (특정 목적을 위한) 비용, 어떤 사람에게 필요한 물건들을 사는 것을 돕기 위해 대체로 규칙적으로 주어지는 돈

17 (A)와 ⑤: [반대·비교·대조를 나타내어] 그런데, 한편(으로는), ①, ②, ③: ~하는 동안, 하는 사이, ④: ~하는 한

18 필요하지 않은 것에 돈을 소비했다고 말한 학생들은 '돈에 관하여 현명하지 않다'고 말한 70명 중의 12%로 8.4명에 해당하기 때문에, '10명 미만'으로 고치는 것이 적절하다.

19 ②번 다음 문장의 For example에 주목한다. 주어진 문장의 a tighter budget의 예에 해당하므로 ②번이 적절하다.

20 (A)와 ②, ⑤: 계속 용법, ① 경험 용법, ③ 결과 용법, ④ 완료 용법

21 Steve가 용돈의 80%를 무엇에 썼는지는 대답할 수 없다. ① To go to his favorite singer's concert. ② No. ④ He needs to have a tighter budget. ⑤ She advises him to follow the 50%-40%-10% rule.

22 즉석에서 물건을 사는 것을 그만두는 방법을 모른다고 해야 하

므로 buying으로 고치는 것이 적절하다. stop+~ing: ~을 그만두다, stop+to부정사: ~하기 위해 멈추다

23 위 글은 자신의 '소비' 습관의 문제점에 관한 조언을 구하는 글이다.

01 received　　02 She takes the blue bag.

03 Because the price of the blue bag is the same as that of the cap.

04 (1) What has Brian been watching since nine o'clock?

　　(2) She has been teaching French in a middle school in Incheon for five years.

05 (1) what he should do next

　　(2) how she can get to the subway station

　　(3) where he should park his luxury car

　　(4) how she could move the toy

06 minority → majority　　　07 It

08 Twelve(12)　　09 I still don't have enough money

10 saving → spending

11 (A) saving money　(B)50%-40%-10%

01 '누군가가 어떤 것을 당신에게 주거나 보내준 후에 그것을 갖다'는 'receive'이다.

02 소녀는 모자 대신에 파란색 가방을 가져간다.

03 소녀는 모자와 파란색 가방의 가격이 같기 때문에 파란색 가방을 가져갈 수 있다. that을 사용하라고 했으므로 'that of the cap'으로 표현해야 함에 주의한다.

04 현재완료진행형을 적절히 사용한다. (1) 의문문이므로 의문사 what을 문두에 놓고, has와 주어 Brian을 도치하는 점에 유의한다.(2) 인천의 한 중학교: a middle school in Incheon

05 '의문사+to부정사'는 '의문사+주어+should[can/could]+동사원형'의 형태로 바꿔 쓸 수 있다. can의 경우, 시제에 맞게 can과 could를 구분하며, (2)는 현재, (4)는 과거이다.

06 '대다수'의 학생들이 자신들이 돈에 관련하여 현명하지 못하다고 생각한다. minority: 소수

07 가주어 'It'을 쓰는 것이 적절하다.

08 '12%'의 학생들이 필요하지 않은 것에 돈을 소비한다.

09 still을 보충하면 된다. still은 부정의 조동사 앞에 쓴다.

10 용돈의 80%를 사용하고 20%만을 저축했기 때문에, '돈을 너무 많이 써 왔다고 생각한다.'로 고치는 것이 적절하다.

11 Steve의 돈에 대한 고민: 저는 좋아하는 가수의 콘서트에 가기 위한 '돈을 모으기'가 어려워요. 저는 더 많은 돈을 모을 필요가 있어요. Dr. Money의 조언: 더 빠듯한 예산을 세우는 것이 필요해요. '50%-40%-10%'의 규칙을 따르세요. 50%를 저축하고, 40%를 쓰고, 남아 있는 10%를 자선 단체에 기부하세요.

|모범답안|

01 (1) Is it possible to get a refund for

　　(2) Is it OK to get a refund for

02 (1) Alex has been teaching his students how to solve the cube puzzle for five years.

　　(2) Alex has been teaching English to the middle school students for 15 years.

　　(3) Alex has been teaching Esther to solve the cube puzzle for a year.

　　(4) Esther has been learning English from Alex for a year.

03 (A) money prob　(B) on the spot　(C) nice

　　(D) had three cases

01 (o)utcome　　　　　02 advice

03 allowance 또는 pocket money　　04 ④

05 difficulty　06 on the spot　　07 ⑤

08 ③　　　09 ④　　　10 as

11 The price is the same, so you can just take it.

12 (1) how to handle　(2) has been biting

　　(3) which foot to put out

13 ④

14 (1) has been watching the films directed by Bong for four

　　(2) has been working at a store owned by Butler for

15 (1) Wilson has been learning how to fix the photocopier since this morning.

　　(2) Susan's friends have been carrying those heavy bags for three hours.

16 ②

17 Jack has been working at the department store since last month.

18 ①　　　　19 isn't → aren't

20 what their biggest money worry is

21 No, they aren't.

22 ⑤　　　23 ②　　　24 ④번 → remaining

25 ⑤

26 (A) although　(B) advice　(C) even if

27 on the spot　　　　28 ③

01 동의어 관계이다. lastly: 마지막으로 – finally: 마지막으로, result 결과 – outcome 결과

02 '누군가에게 무엇을 해야 할지 말해 주는 의견'은 'advice(충고)'가 적절하다. 부모님의 충고를 들어라.

03 allowance: 용돈. 부모에 의해 아이에게 규칙적으로 주어지는 아이가 쓸 수 있는 돈. 그녀는 용돈을 모아 노트북을 샀다.

04 on sale: 할인 중인, 판매되는. 아이스크림이 반값에 팔리고 있다. remaining: 남아 있는. Jack은 남은 주스를 마셨다.

05 have difficulty (in) -ing: ~하는 데 어려움을 겪다. 나는 영어로 의사소통하는 데 어려움을 겪었다.

06 on the spot: 즉각, 즉석에서. 그는 그 차를 보고 즉석에서 사기로 결정했다.

07 빈칸 다음에 '그렇다면 이 모자를 저기에 있는 장갑으로 교환할 수 있을까요?'라고 하고 있으므로, 환불 요청에 대해 거절했음을 추론할 수 있다.

08 ⓒ의 change를 exchange로 고치는 것이 적절하다.

09 교환을 요청하는 말에, 가능하다며 어떤 것을 원하는지 묻는 것이 자연스러우므로 ④번이 적절하다.

10 as는 전치사로 '~로서'의 의미이다. as a gift: 선물로

11 so는 여기서 결과를 나타내는 접속사이다.

12 (1) 어떻게 처리할지 'how to handle', (2) 5분 전부터 물어뜯고 있는 것은 현재완료진행시제로 표현한다. (3) 어느 발을 내밀지 'which foot to put out' *governor: 통치자, 원님

13 ④ 의문대명사 what은 to부정사 뒤에 목적어를 쓰지 않는다. what이 목적어 역할을 하기 때문이다. how로 고치는 것이 적절하다.

14 조건을 충족시키면서 10 단어를 넘지 않도록 하고, 명사를 뒤에서 꾸미는 분사의 어법에도 유의한다. (1) 지난 토요일에 시청을 시작해서 오늘이 화요일이므로 기간은 4일이다. (2) 글자 수에 유의하여 마지막에 for가 오도록 영작한다.

15 (1) 어떻게 수리하는지: how to fix, 오늘 아침부터: since this morning (2) 저 무거운 가방들: those heavy bags

16 <보기>는 현재완료의 용법 중 '계속'이며, 과거에 시작된 일이 현재에도 지속되고 있음을 나타낸다. ②는 '건물 내부의 모든 방들에 대한 점검을 끝냈다'는 내용으로, '완료' 용법이며, 나머지는 모두 '계속' 용법이다.

17 '지난달 이후로'는 since last month를 쓴다.

18 ①번 다음 문장의 some advice에 주목한다. 주어진 문장의 the problem에 대한 조언이므로 ①번이 적절하다.

19 주격 관계대명사 that의 선행사가 items이기 때문에, aren't로 고치는 것이 적절하다.

20 asked의 직접목적어가 되도록, 간접의문문의 순서로 쓰는 것이 적절하다.

21 설문 조사에 따르면, 대다수의 학생들은 현명한 소비자가 아니다.

22 필요하지 않은 것에 돈을 소비한 학생들의 퍼센트(12%)는 충분한 용돈을 받지 못한다고 생각하는 학생들의 퍼센트(60%)의 '5분의 1'이다. ① 3분의 1, ② 3분의 2, ③ 4분의 1, ④ 4분의 3, ⑤ 5분의 1

23 앞에 나오는 내용과 상반되는 내용이 뒤에 이어지므로

24 ④ remaining 남아 있는, ① have difficulty -ing: ~하는 데 어려움이 있다, ② '현재완료진행시제'로 써서 과거부터 현재까지 돈을 저축해 오고 있다는 의미를 나타냄. ③ '현재완료진행시제'로 써서 과거부터 현재까지 돈을 너무 많이 써 오고 있다는 의미를 나타냄. ⑤ by ~ing: ~함으로써

25 50%-40%-10%의 규칙은 50%를 '저축하고', 40%를 '쓰고', 남아 있는 10%를 자선 단체에 기부하는 것을 의미한다.

26 (A) 뒤에 '주어+동사'가 있으므로 although가 적절하다. 'although+주어+동사', 'in spite of' 뒤에는 '주어+동사'가 올 수 없다. (B) advice: 셀 수 없는 명사이다. (C) '비록 물건들이 할인 판매 중이라고 해도'라고 해야 하므로 even if가 적절하다. even if: ~라고 할지라도, as if: 마치 ~인 것처럼

27 on the spot: 즉각, 즉석에서

28 민지가 필요한 물건을 산다면 할인 판매하는 물건을 사는 것은 좋지만, 필요하지 않은 물건도 사기 때문에 현명한 소비자가 아니다.

Lesson 5

The Team Behind the Team

01 ①	02 invisible	03 ②	04 ④
05 ③	06 ⑤		

01 동의어 관계이다. impolite: 무례한, rude: 버릇없는, 무례한, achieve: 달성하다, accomplish: 성취하다 accompany: ~에 동반하다

02 '볼 수 없는'은 'invisible'이 적절하다. 많은 별은 눈에 보이지 않는다.

03 ① be good for: ~에 좋다. 때때로 비판을 좀 받는 것이 좋을 수도 있다. ② keep track of: ~을 파악하다. 아이들이 드나드는 것을 계속 파악하기는 어렵다. ③ in short: 간단히 말해서. 간단히 말해서, 아이들에게 벌을 주는 가장 좋은 방법에 대하여 많은 의견의 불일치가 있다. ④ get attention: 주목을 받다. 여러분이 특이한 일을 한다면 주목 받을 것이고 예술가는 주목 받기를 원한다. ⑤ depending on: ~에 따라. 차 종류에 따라서 임대료가 달라집니까?

04 register: 등록하다. 몇 명의 학생이 영어 수업에 등록했나요?

05 ① give a speech: 연설하다. 나는 왜 그들이 그가 연설하기를 원했는지 이해할 수가 없어. ② cheer: 응원하다. 나는 언제나 나의 지역 팀을 응원해. ③ limit: 한계. 내 인내심도 한계에 다다랐다. ④ target: 목표. 누구를 목표 시장으로 삼고 있는가? ⑤ tribe: 부족, 종족. 그들은 12세기에 하나의 부족으로 시작했다.

06 support: 돕다, 지원하다. 많은 학생들이 교복을 바꾸는 계획을 지지한다. promote: 홍보하다. 그 밴드는 새 앨범 홍보를 위해 순회 공연을 떠났다.

01 (1) support (2) achieve (3) hire (4) register

02 (1) independent (2) breath

03 (1) wear (2) (s)everal (3) (a)chieve
   (4) (r)ecommendation

04 (1) I followed the map, keeping track of our position.
   (2) My personality changes depending on the person.
   (3) The house was hidden from sight behind some trees.
   (4) He managed to fix the problem on his own.

---

01 (1) support: 돕다, 지원하다. 어떤 사람, 그룹 또는 생각에 동의한다고 말하다 (2) achieve: 달성하다, 성취하다. 원하는 것을 하거나 얻는 것에 성공하다 (3) hire: 고용하다. 당신을 위해 일을 하도록 누군가에게 돈을 지불하다 (4) register: 등록하다. 공식적인 명단에 이름을 올리다

02 (1) '반의어'의 관계이다. possible: 가능한, impossible: 불가능한, dependent: 의존하는, independent: 독립적인 (2) '동사 - 명사'의 관계이다. achieve: 달성하다, achievement: 성취, breathe: 숨쉬다, breath: 호흡

03 (1) wear out: (낡아서) 떨어지다, 헤지다 (2) several: 몇몇의 (3) achieve: 달성하다, 성취하다 (4) recommendation: 추천

04 (1) keep track of: ~을 파악하다. track을 추가한다. (2) depending on: ~에 따라. on을 추가한다. (3) hidden: 숨겨진. 수동태가 되어야 하므로 was를 추가한다. (4) on one's own: 혼자서. own을 추가한다.

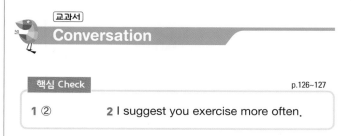

교과서
Conversation

1 ②   2 I suggest you exercise more often.

교과서 대화문 익히기

1 T   2 F   3 T   4 T

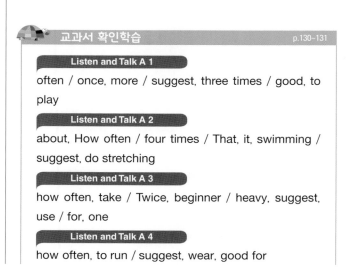

교과서 확인학습

Listen and Talk A 1

often / once, more / suggest, three times / good, to play

Listen and Talk A 2

about, How often / four times / That, it, swimming / suggest, do stretching

Listen and Talk A 3

how often, take / Twice, beginner / heavy, suggest, use / for, one

Listen and Talk A 4

how often, to run / suggest, wear, good for

Listen and Talk B

how often / a / suggest / try

Listen and Talk C

to register for / taking / how to swim at all / How often, take / take, twice a week, take, on, on / that, take, on / sounds good, sign up for / a limit of

Talk and Play

how often / three times a week

Review 1

how often / go swimming / suggest, bring, Without / aren't allowed

Review 2

over / How often / twice a week

Review 3

register for / How often, take / take, twice a week, take, on / suggest, take, on / good

---

시험대비 기본평가   p.132

01 ③

02 I suggest we do stretching exercises

03 ③   04 Twice a week

01 이어지는 대화에서 일주일에 한 번 한다고 하고 있으므로 얼마나 자주 하는지 묻는 표현이 적절하다.

02 상대방에게 제안하거나 권유할 때는 'I suggest (that)+주어+(should)+동사원형' 구문으로 말한다.

03 '제안하다'는 'suggest'이다.

04 twice는 '2회, 두 번; 2배로'라는 뜻이다.

시험대비 실력평가   p.133~134

01 ①   02 ②

03 I suggest that you take

04 I don't know how to swim at all.

05 ⑤   06 ②   07 ②, ④   08 ①

09 ④   10 ③   11 ⑤   12 ⑤

13 He will take the class twice a week.

01 빈도를 묻는 질문에 '많이 했다'고 답하는 것은 어색하다. 'I exercise twice a week.' 등으로 답하는 것이 적절하다.

02 weekdays나 weekends 앞에는 전치사 on이 쓰인다.

03 상대방에게 제안하거나 권유할 때는 'I suggest (that)+주어+(should)+동사원형' 구문으로 말한다.

04 not ~ at all = never: 결코 ~ 아닌

05 등록하고 싶다고 했지만 이미 등록한 것은 아니다.

06 얼마나 자주 하는지 빈도를 묻는 (B)에 이어, (C)에서 매일 한

다고 빈도에 대한 답을 하고, (A)에서 덜 하기를 제안하고, (D)에서 시도해 보겠다는 말로 마무리하는 것이 자연스럽다.

07 'OK. I'll try.'와 'I'll give it a try.'는 모두 '시도해 보겠다.'라는 의미이다.

08 (a)에는 대답으로 twice가 나오고 있으므로 빈도를 묻는 often이 적절하다. (b)에는 'per'의 의미로 쓰인 a가 적절하다. (c)에는 suggest가 '제안하다'라는 뜻으로 사용될 때 '주어+suggest+(that)+주어+(should)+동사원형 ~'의 구문으로 나타내므로 should가 생략된 read가 적절하다.

09 be over: 끝나다. 여기에 쓰인 over는 '부사'로 '끝나, 지나'라는 뜻이며 '부사'가 아닌 '형용사'로 볼 수도 있다.

10 빈도를 묻는 질문에 대한 답이므로 'always, usually, often, sometimes, never' 등과 같은 빈도부사를 사용하여 답하거나, 구체적인 빈도를 나타내는 '횟수+a+특정 기간(day/week/month/year 등)'으로 답하는 것이 적절하다.

11 밑줄 친 문장은 빈도를 물어 볼 때 쓰는 표현이다.

12 ⑤번 다음 문장의 'This class'가 주어진 문장의 'the Beginner 1 class'를 가리키므로 ⑤번이 적절하다.

13 소년은 '일주일에 두 번 수강하고 싶어요.'라고 하고 있다.

서술형 시험대비   p.135

01 (D) → (C) → (A) → (B)

02 I'd like to take classes on weekdays and not on weekends.

03 The class can have up to 10 people.

04 The writer suggests joining the club, Fun Wheels.

05 It's fun to ride bikes together.

06 (1) Sure   (2) Of course

07 I suggest you bring a swimming cap

01 (C)의 That이 (D)의 내용을 가리키므로 (D) 다음에 (C)가 이어지고, (A)는 (C)의 질문에 대한 답이므로 (C) 다음에 (A)가 나오고, (B)의 That이 (A)의 내용을 가리키므로 (A) 다음에 (B)가 나오는 순서가 적절하다.

02 I'd like to: ~하고 싶다, take classes: 수업을 듣다, on weekdays: 주중에 on weekends: 주말에, B and not A: A가 아니라 B

03 up to: (특정한 수·정도 등)까지

05 가주어 It과 진주어로 'to ride bikes together'를 쓴다.

06 이어지는 내용으로 보아 긍정의 대답인 'Sure'나 'Of course'가 적절하다.

07 상대방에게 어떤 일이나, 행동을 제안하거나 권유할 때는 동사 'suggest(제안하다)'를 사용하여 'I suggest (that)+주어+(should)+동사원형 ~'의 구문으로 나타낼 수 있으며, 이때 that과 should는 생략할 수 있다.

1 (1) wearing (2) broken

2 (1) Today is as windy as yesterday.
(2) The lamp is not so tall as the stool.

시험대비 기본평가
p.138

01 (1) more expensive → expensive
(2) earliest → early (3) than → as
(4) them → those

02 ⑤ **03** ④

04 (1) The girl waving across the street is Sarah.
(2) The storm approaching our country has a strong force.

01 (1) as ~ as를 이용한 표현에서는 비교급을 쓸 수 없다. (2) as ~ as 사이에는 형용사/부사의 원급만 가능하다. 비교급/최상급은 부적절하다. (3) as ~ as에 than은 부적절하다. than은 비교급 뒤에 사용한다. (4) 원급 비교에서 비교 대상을 일치시켜야 한다. the villagers in other towns를 대명사로 받을 때, those in other towns를 쓰는 것이 적절하다.

02 벌레들이 가득한 방은 '능동'이 아닌 '수동'이다. crowded가 적절하다.

03 not so[as] ~ as 구문은 원급을 써야 한다.

04 명사 주어를 뒤에서 수식하는 현재분사를 활용하여, 주어진 단어를 알맞게 배열한다. (1) wave를 waving으로, (2) approach를 approaching으로 어형을 바꾸는 것에 유의한다.

시험대비 실력평가
p.139~141

01 ④ **02** taking → taken **03** ③
04 ③ **05** ② **06** ④ **07** ④
08 ⑤ **09** ①, ③
10 (1) sung → singing (2) using → used
(3) ran → running
11 ②, ③, ④ **12** ⑤
13 (1) made by my ancestors is
(2) were some flies buzzing around
14 men wearing black sunglasses got on
15 ④ **16** ② **17** ④ **18** ②

01 'as ~ as'의 부정은 not을 앞에 쓰며, 그 경우 not 바로 뒤의 as는 so로 쓸 수 있다.

02 런던에서 촬영된 사진들이므로 과거분사가 적절하다.

03 John이 더 무겁기 때문에 'Sam만큼 무게가 나가지 않다(Sam보다 가볍다)'는 것은 표의 내용과 일치하지 않는다.

04 (1) 강의에 참석한 청중(능동) (2) 컴퓨터 게임에 쓰인 시간(수동) (3) 흥미진진한 콘서트(능동)이므로 정답은 ③

05 '그 지팡이는 그 뱀만큼 길다.' ① harder → hard ③ faster → fast ④ tallest → tall ⑤ heavier → heavy

06 ④는 forgot의 목적어로 쓰인 '동명사'이고, 나머지는 모두 명사를 앞 또는 뒤에서 수식하는 '현재분사'이다.

07 My backpack과 Sujin's backpack(= Sujin's)을 'as 원급 as'로 비교하는 문장이다.

08 'not as ~ as'는 비교급의 의미와 같게 사용되지만, not이 없는 'as ~ as'는 비교의 의미가 없다.

09 ① 영화가 감동적이었다. touched → touching ③ 축구 경기가 가장 흥미진진했다. excited → exciting

10 (1) 노래를 부르는 소녀(진행) (2) 사용된 조개껍질(수동) (3) 달리는 선수들(진행)

11 ② '내가 만난 사람들'로서 '관계대명사 목적격'이 생략된 '주어+동사'의 관계이므로 meeting → met ③ '도둑맞은 그림들이 다른 나라에서 발견되었다'는 뜻으로 앞부분의 동사 got을 삭제하고, 과거분사의 수식을 활용한다. ④ '넓은 수영장에서 빠르게 수영하고 있는 소년'이므로, The boy swimming fast in a wide pool로 고치는 것이 적절하다.

12 아기 펭귄 5마리가 어른 둘만큼 먹는다는 문장이므로 내용상 '많이'라는 의미의 부사가 필요하다. as와 as 사이에는 원급을 써야 하므로 much가 적절하다.

13 분사가 명사의 뒤에서 수식하는 것을 적절히 활용한다. (1) made by my ancestors가 The table을 수식(수동), (2) buzzing around the jam이 some flies를 수식(진행)

14 분사가 명사를 뒤에서 꾸며주는 것을 활용한다. 능동이므로 wearing을 사용하고, 과거시제이므로 get을 got으로 고치는 것에 유의한다.

15 ⓐ, ⓔ는 '동명사', ⓑ, ⓒ, ⓓ는 '현재분사'이다.

16 ②는 '가능한 한 많은 물을 마시는 것이 좋다'이므로, '수'를 나타내는 many가 아닌, '양'을 뜻하는 much가 적절하다.

17 'ⓐ producing → produced(생산된) ⓑ calling → called(~라고 불린) ⓒ walked → walking(걷고 있는) ⓔ taken → taking(찍는)

18 Alicia는 그녀의 학급에서 가장 힘이 센 학생이다. = 다른 어떤 학생도 그녀의 학급에서 Alicia만큼 힘이 세지 않다.

01 (1) is as old as Key   (2) is not so old as Key

    (3) is as tall as Dave   (4) is not so tall as Key

    (5) is so heavy as Sean   (6) is so tall as Key

02 (A) holding   (B) looking

03 (1) can speak English as freely as her teacher

    (2) sang as well as the singer

    (3) does the dishes as often as my mom

    (4) was not so interesting as the original novel

04 (1) the flowers planted in my garden

    (2) girls standing near the post office

    (3) written by Mark Twain is exciting

    (4) gentlemen dancing to the disco music

05 (1) could not write as neatly as his mother cut

    (2) didn't lose as much weight as he thought

06 (A) written   (B) known   (C) covering

    (D) making   (E) appearing

07 (1) a lady wearing a colorful skirt

    (2) are the illegally copied books

    (3) an airplane flying between the clouds

    (4) made by the master craftsman is so
      expensive

    (5) careful not to wake up the sleeping baby

08 sleeping, wearing

01 (1) Dave는 Key와 같은 나이이다. (2) Sean은 Key만큼의 나이가 아니다. (3) Sean은 Dave만큼 키가 크다. (4) Dave는 Key만큼 키가 크지 않다. (5) 누구도 Sean만큼 몸무게가 나가지 않는다. (6) 누구도 Key만큼 키가 크지 않다.

02 진행의 분사가 명사의 뒤에서 수식하는 것을 활용한다.

03 (1) 부사 freely에 유의. (3) 3인칭 현재 does에 유의. (4) 과거시제 was, 현재분사형 형용사 interesting에 유의.

04 명사를 뒤에서 꾸미는 분사 활용 (1) Daisy는 나의 정원에 '심어진 꽃들'(수동)을 보고 있었다. (2) 우체국 가까이에 '서 있는 소녀들'(진행)은 그들의 선생님을 기다리고 있다. (3) Mark Twain에 의해 '쓰여진 책'(수동)은 '흥미로웠다'. (4) 그 디스코 음악에 맞춰 '춤을 추는 신사들'(진행)은 누구입니까?

05 (1) neatly: 반듯하게, 깔끔하게 (2) lose weight: 살이 빠지다, 체중이 줄다

06 (A) 쓰여진 영화 (B) ~로서 알려진 (C) 덮고 있는 (D) (영화를 더욱 미스터리하게) 만드는 (E) 등장하는

07 (1) 화려한 스커트를 입은 숙녀 (2) 불법 복제된 책들 (3) 구름들 사이로 날아가는 비행기 (4) 그 명장에 의해 만들어진 바이올린 (5) 잠자는 아기

08 Minho는 아버지가 퇴근하고 집에 오시자마자 양복을 입은 채로 소파에서 주무시는 것을 발견했다.

Reading

확인문제   p.144

1 T   2 F   3 T   4 F   5 T   6 F

확인문제   p.145

1 T   2 F   3 T   4 F   5 T   6 F

교과서 확인학습 A   p.146~147

01 Hidden   02 on their own

03 who   04 hidden, get attention

05 as important as   06 Here are

07 Pacers   08 run with, lead

09 experienced, manage their race better

10 There can be

11 at different speeds, in different times

12 showing   13 depending on

14 in four hours, four   15 keeps track of, easily

16 to win   17 for others

18 Car Racing   19 during, behind the driver

20 is called

21 on the side of the race track

22 to check   23 Changing, is, wear out

24 as short as, as many as

25 in perfect harmony

26 get all the attention, in the pits

28 comes from   29 good climbing skills

30 have little difficulty breathing

31 to help them climb   32 lead, to

33 in many ways   34 put up

35 invisible, at the top of

교과서 확인학습 B   p.148~149

1 Hidden People in Sports

2 In sports, only the players get a trophy or medal, but they don't win on their own.

3 There are people who help the players.

4 These people are often hidden and don't get attention.

5 However, they are as important as the players.

6 Here are some examples.

7 Pacers in a Marathon

8 Pacers run with other runners and lead them in a marathon.

9 Pacers are experienced runners, and their job is to help other runners manage their race better.

10 There can be several pacers in a race.

11 Each pacer runs at different speeds and finishes the race in different times.

12 Pacers usually have flags or balloons showing their finish time.

13 Runners can choose a pacer depending on their target finish time.

14 For example, if a runner wants to finish the race in four hours, the runner will follow the four-hour pacer.

15 Since the pacer keeps track of the time, the runner can achieve his or her goal of finishing the marathon in a particular time more easily.

16 In short, pacers run but they don't run to win.

17 They run for others.

18 Pit Crews in Car Racing

19 You may only see the car and the driver during most car races, but there is a team behind the driver.

20 This team is called a pit crew.

21 A pit is a place on the side of the race track, and drivers stop there several times during a race.

22 The main job of the pit crew is to check the car and change the tires.

23 Changing the tires is especially important because the tires wear out easily in a high speed race.

24 A pit stop can be as short as 2 seconds, and there are as many as 20 members on a crew.

25 Therefore, the pit crew has to work in perfect harmony.

26 The driver may get all the attention, but as people say, "Races are won in the pits."

27 Sherpas in Mountain Climbing

28 The word *Sherpa* comes from the Sherpa tribe, which lives in the eastern part of Nepal.

29 Sherpas have good climbing skills and know their way around the mountains well.

30 They also have little difficulty breathing high up in the mountains.

31 Therefore, mountain climbers started to hire Sherpas to help them climb Mount Everest.

32 Sherpas lead mountain climbers to the top of the mountain.

33 They support climbers in many ways.

34 For example, they put up tents and carry climbers' bags.

35 Sherpas are often called the invisible people of Mount Everest because people often see a picture of only the climbers at the top of the mountain.

시험대비 실력평가 p.150~153

01 ①   02 ②, ③   03 ①   04 ②

05 ③, ⑤   06 ④   07 ②

08 (A) check   (B) change   09 ②

10 A pit stop can be as short as 2 seconds, and there are as many as 20 members on a crew.

11 ④   12 ③   13 ⑤   14 ①

15 ②   16 (A) climbers   17 hidden

18 win → don't win

19 people who help the players   20 ③

21 (a) checking   (b) changing

22 shorter → short, much → many

23 (A) eastern   (B) little   (C) invisible

24 mountain climbers started to hire Sherpas to help them climb Mount Everest

25 ④

01 ⓐ at different speeds: 다른 속도로, ⓑ in different times: 다른 시간대에

02 (A)와 ②, ③: 명사적 용법, ①, ⑤: 부사적 용법, ④: 형용사적 용법

03 페이서들은 마라톤에서 다른 선수들을 '이끈다.'

04 앞에 나오는 내용과 상반되는 내용이 뒤에 이어지므로 However가 가장 적절하다. ① 즉[말하자면], ③ 비슷하게, ④ 그 결과, ⑤ 게다가, 더욱이

05 on one's own: 혼자서, 혼자 힘으로(= alone, by oneself), ① 외로운, 쓸쓸한, ② 이성을 잃고, 어찌할 바를 모르고, ④ on behalf of: ~을 대신하여, ~을 대표하여, ~을 위해서

06 종종 숨겨져 있고 주목을 받지 못하지만 선수들만큼 중요한, 선수들을 돕는 사람들이 있다고 말하면서, 여기 몇 가지 예가 있다고 했으므로, 뒤에 올 내용으로는 '스포츠 속 숨은 조력자들'이 적절하다. ⑤ noticeable: 눈에 띄는, 주목할 만한

07 빠른 속도의 경주에서는 타이어가 쉽게 마모되기 때문에 타이어를 교체하는 것이 특히 중요한데 '피트'에서 피트 크루가 자동차를 점검하고 타이어를 교체해 주기 때문에, "경주의 우승은 '피트'에서 이루어진다."고 하는 것이 적절하다. ⑤ 응원석

08 자동차를 '점검하고' 타이어를 '교체하기' 위해서이다.

09 ⓐ와 ②, ⑤: 동명사, ①, ③, ④: 현재분사

10 as+형용사/부사의 원급+as: '~만큼 …한/하게'(동등 비교)

11 앞의 내용을 요약해서 설명하고 있으므로 In short가 가장 적절하다. in short: 요컨대, 요약하면, ② 게다가, ⑤ 다른 한편으로는

12 ③번 다음 문장의 For example에 주목한다. 주어진 문장의 예에 해당하므로 ③번이 적절하다.

13 이 글은 '마라톤에서 페이서들이 하는 역할'에 대한 글이므로, 주제로는 ⑤번 '마라톤에서 페이서들의 역할'이 적절하다.

14 have difficulty/trouble -ing: '~하는 데 어려움이 있다'

15 put up: (천막 따위를) 치다, 세우다

16 왜냐하면 그것은 사람들이 자주 보는 산 정상에 있는 '등산가들'만 찍힌 사진이기 때문이다.

17 이 사람들은 종종 숨겨져 있다고 해야 하므로 과거분사로 써서 수동태를 만드는 것이 적절하다.

18 스포츠에서 선수들만 트로피나 메달을 받지만, 그들은 '혼자 힘으로 이기는 것이 아니다'라고 해야 하므로, win을 don't win으로 고치는 것이 적절하다.

19 '선수들을 돕는 사람들'을 가리킨다.

20 피트에서의 정지는 짧게는 2초 정도인데 한 팀에는 많게는 20명에 이르는 구성원이 있으므로, 피트 크루는 '완벽한 조화를 이루며' 일해야 한다고 하는 것이 적절하다. ② 차례로, 이어서, ④ 가끔[이따금], ⑤ 조금씩, 천천히

21 보어로 쓰인 to부정사를 동명사로 바꾸는 것이 적절하다.

22 '동등 비교'는 as+'형용사/부사의 원급'+as로 써야 하고, '20명에 이르는 구성원'이라고 해야 하므로, 양을 나타내는 much가 아니라 수를 나타내는 many로 고치는 것이 적절하다.

23 (A) part를 수식하는 형용사가 와야 하므로 eastern이 적절하다. (B) 셰르파는 산의 높은 곳에서 호흡하는 데 어려움이 '거의 없다'고 해야 하므로 little이 적절하다. (C) 사람들이 산 정상에서 등산가들만 찍힌 사진을 자주 보기 때문에 셰르파는 종종 에베레스트산의 '보이지 않는' 사람들로 불린다고 해야 하므로 invisible이 적절하다. invisible 보이지 않는, 볼 수 없는

24 help+목적어+(to+)동사원형: ~가 …하는 것을 돕다

25 셰르파가 어떻게 산의 높은 곳에서 호흡하는 데 어려움이 거의 없는지는 알 수 없다. ① No, it is named after the Sherpa tribe. ② It lives in the eastern part of Nepal. ③ They have good climbing skills. ⑤ No, they often see a picture of only the climbers.

🦉 **서술형 시험대비**   p.154~155

01 as   02 (a) hidden   (b) attention
03 the same → different   04 which[that] show

05 pacers run but they don't run to win

06 (A) a particular time   (B) keeps track of

07 (A) during   (B) change   (C) short

08 after → during

09 (A) pit crew   (B) pit crew

10 breathing   11 and it

12 the sherpas → the climbers

13 (A) lead   (B) good climbing skills

01 동등한 두 대상을 비교할 때는 'as+형용사/부사+as'의 형태로 '~만큼 …한/하게'라는 뜻이다.

02 그들은 스포츠에서 선수들이 이기도록 돕지만, '주목'을 받지 못한 채 종종 '숨겨져' 있다.

03 각각의 페이서는 '다른' 속도로 달리고 다른 시간대에 경기를 마친다고 했으므로, the same을 different로 고치는 것이 적절하다.

04 현재분사 showing을 '주격 관계대명사 which[that] show'로 바꿔 쓰는 것이 적절하다.

05 to win: to부정사의 부사적 용법(목적)

06 페이서가 시간을 '계속해서 파악하기' 때문에, 선수들은 자신들의 목표 완주 시간에 따라 페이서를 선택함으로써 선수는 '특정 시간에' 마라톤을 완주하려는 자신의 목표를 더 쉽게 달성할 수 있다.

07 (A) during+기간을 나타내는 명사, while+주어+동사, (B) to check와 병렬을 이루도록 (to) change라고 하는 것이 적절하다. (C) be동사의 보어이므로 형용사 short가 적절하다. shortly: (시간상으로) 얼마 안 되어, 곧(부사)

08 레이서들은 경주 '도중에' 피트에서 여러 번 정지한다.

09 레이서들이 자동차를 점검하고 타이어를 교체하기 위해 피트에 정지할 때, '피트 크루'는 매우 짧은 시간 내에 완벽한 조화를 이루며 일해야 하므로, '피트 크루'의 완벽한 작업이 레이스의 승리에 매우 중요한 역할을 한다.

10 have difficulty -ing: ~하는 데 어려움이 있다

11 계속적 용법의 관계대명사는 '접속사+대명사'로 바꿔 쓸 수 있다. 관계대명사가 who가 아닌 which이므로 and he(she)가 아니라 'and it'으로 고치는 것이 적절하다.

12 사람들이 산 정상에서 '등산가들'만 찍힌 사진을 자주 보기 때문에 셰르파는 종종 에베레스트산의 보이지 않는 사람들로 불린다고 해야 하므로, the sherpas를 the climbers로 고치는 것이 적절하다.

13 셰르파족은 네팔의 동쪽 지역에 살고 있고, 셰르파는 '훌륭한 등반 기량'을 갖고 있으며 산 지리를 잘 알기 때문에 등산가들을 산 정상까지 '이끈다.'

01 ①

02 (c)rew / (p)articular / (d)irection
   (1) particular   (2) crew   (3) direction

03 wear out

04 (A) (h)armony   (B) (d)ifficulty   (C) (r)ole

05 (1) invisible   (2) inexperienced   (3) impatient

06 ④   07 ③   08 ②   09 limit

10 register   11 ④   12 ①   13 ①

14 ②   15 written by Susan is for   16 ⑤

17 ⑤   18 ②, ⑤, ⑦   19 ③

20 themselves → others **또는** other runners

21 ⑤   22 ②   23 ④   24 ③

25 ②

01 <보기>와 ①번은 '가입하다'라는 의미로 쓰였다. <보기> 그는 나름대로 이유가 있어서 그 클럽 가입을 거절했다. ① 새로 가입한 체육관은 어때요? ② 그는 파이프 한 쪽을 그 다음 것과 연결했다. ③ 목요일에 저희와 함께 저녁식사하실 시간 있으세요? ④ 1189년, 리차드는 프랑스의 필립 II세와 힘을 합쳐 그의 아버지와 맞서 싸웠다. ⑤ 단단히 붙어서 이음새를 찾을 수 없었다.

02 (1) particular: 특정한. 특별한, 또는 보통 이상의. 그가 즐기는 특정한 종류의 책이 있나요? (2) crew: 팀, 조. 함께 일하는 특정한 기술을 가진 한 무리의 사람들. 촬영 팀이 그 장면을 찍으려고 바다로 들어갔다. (3) direction: 방향. 무언가 또는 누군가가 움직이거나, 향하는 길. 나는 모든 방향 감각을 상실해 버렸다.

03 '어떤 것을 많이 사용하여 더 이상 작동하지 않거나 더 이상 사용될 수 없다'라는 의미로 'wear out((낡아서) 떨어지다, 헤지다)'이 적절하다.

04 (A) harmony: 조화, 화합. 그들은 서로 사이 좋게 살았다. (B) have difficulty –ing: ~하는 데 어려움을 겪다. 십대들은 흔히 의사[감정] 표현에 어려움을 겪는다. (C) play an important role: 중요한 역할을 하다. 관광 산업이 국가 경제 발전에 중요한 역할을 할 것으로 예상된다.

05 (1) 접두사 'in'을 붙여 반의어가 되는 어휘이다. invisible: 보이지 않는. 선의는 무형의 자산이다. (2) 동사 experience의 과거분사에 'in'을 붙여 반의어가 된 어휘이다. inexperienced: 경험이 없는. 그녀는 경험이 없어서 지도의 손길[지도해 줄 사람]이 필요했다. (3) 접두사 'im'을 붙여 반의어가 되는 어휘이다. impatient: 초조해 하는. 시간이 흐를수록 그는 더욱 더 조급해졌다.

06 (D)의 얼마나 자주 수영을 하는지 묻는 말에 이어, (B)에서 일주일에 네 번 수영을 한다고 답하고, (A)에서 '그렇게 자주?'라며 (B)의 내용을 확인하며 묻고, (C)에서 수영하기 전에 스트레

칭을 하는 것을 제안한 후, 좋은 생각이라는 주어진 문장으로 이어지는 것이 적절하다.

07 (a)와 ③: 지시부사. [수량·정도를 나타내는 말을 한정하여] 그만큼, 그렇게 ① 지시형용사 저(말하는 이 가까이에 있지 않은 사람이나 사물을 가리킬 때 씀) ② 접속사. so ~ that ...: 너무 ~해서 …하다 ④ 관계대명사 ⑤ 접속사. [동격절을 이끌어] ~이라는, ~하다는

08 'I eat fast food three times a week.'이라고 대답하고 있으므로 빈도를 묻는 'How often do you eat fast food?'가 적절하다.

09 규칙, 법 등 때문에 허용되는 시간이나 돈의 가장 크거나 작은 양은 'limit(한계)'이다.

10 sign up for = register for: ~에 등록하다

11 ① Bong에 의해 '연출된 영화'가 되어야 하므로 directed를 써야 한다. ② which 뒤에 be동사를 써주거나, which를 생략해서 뒤에서 명사를 꾸미는 형태로 쓰는 것이 적절하다. ③ Bow라고 '이름 불리는 개'이므로 named가 적절하다. ⑤ 회의에 '초대받은 정치인들'이므로 invited가 적절하다.

12 각각 '프랑스어로 쓰여진 편지(수동)', '기타를 연주하는 남자(진행)', '자전거를 고치는 소년(진행)'이다.

13 'as ~ as'에는 수식어의 원급을 쓴다. 비교급이나 최상급은 쓸 수 없으며, high(높은; 높게)와 highly(상당히)의 쓰임새 구분을 명확하게 해야 한다.

14 'with+A+형용사/분사' 형태는 A의 능동/수동 여부에 따라 현재분사 또는 과거분사를 활용한다. ② '다리를 꼰 채로'는 'with one's legs crossed'로 써야 한다. ① with the TV on: TV를 켠 채로 ③ with one's arms folded: 팔짱을 낀 채로 ④ with one's eyes closed: 눈을 감은 채로 ⑤ with one's clothes wet with sweat: 옷이 땀에 젖은 채로

15 Susan이 카드를 썼으므로, 한 문장으로 만들 때, 'The card that Susan wrote' 또는 'The card (that was) written by Susan'이 가능하다. 분사를 이용해야 하므로 후자를 쓴다.

16 be busy ~ing는 '~하느라 바쁘다'라는 뜻의 동명사의 관용적 표현이다. 다른 문장들에서는 밑줄 친 부분들 모두가 현재분사로 사용되었다.

17 'as ~ as'에는 수식어의 원급을 쓴다. 비교급이나 최상급은 쓸 수 없다. more valuable → valuable

18 명사를 꾸미는 분사가 다른 어구와 결합해서 뒤에서 꾸밀 때는 '관계대명사+be동사'가 생략된 것으로 볼 수 있다. 따라서, 명사를 앞에서 꾸미거나, 서술적 용법으로 사용된 분사를 찾으면, '관계대명사+be동사'가 생략된 것이 아닌 경우에 해당한다. ②는 분사가 앞에서 수식 ⑤, ⑦은 서술적 용법으로 사용되었다.

19 ⓐ와 ③: 동격 관계(~이라고 하는, ~인), ① [거리·위치·시간] ~의, ~부터, ② [재료·구성 요소] ~으로 (만든), ④ [목적격 관계] ~을, ~에 대한, ⑤ [성질·상태] ~의, ~을 지닌

20 그들은 '다른 선수들'을 위해 달린다고 하는 것이 적절하다.

21 앞의 내용의 결과가 나오고 있으므로 Therefore가 가장 적절하다. ② 그렇기는 하지만, 그렇더라도, ③ 즉[말하자면], ④ 그 대신에

22 ⓑ와 ②: ~하는 것처럼(접속사), ① ~함에 따라(접속사), ③ ~로서(전치사), ④ ~이므로(접속사), ⑤ [보통 as ~ as ...로 형용사·부사 앞에서] …와 같은 정도로, (as ~ as ...에서, 앞의 as는 지시부사, 뒤의 as는 접속사)

23 피트에서의 정지는 짧게는 '2초' 정도이다.

24 ③them은 등산가들을 가리키고, 나머지는 다 Sherpas를 가리킨다.

25 이 글은 '등산가들이 등반할 때 셰르파가 하는 역할'에 대한 글이므로, 주제로는 ②번 '등산에서의 셰르파의 역할'이 적절하다.

단원별 예상문제   p.162~165

01 ②   02 ④
03 (1) (h)ired   (2) (o)ver   (3) (a)ttention
04 of / of   05 ①
06 토요일과 일요일에 수업이 있는 초급 1반을 수강하는 것.
07 ④
08 It's because Suji's bowling ball looks heavy for her.
09 bowling ball   10 embarrassed, broken
11 ③   12 ④   13 ③
14 experiencing → experienced
15 ②, ⑤   16 ②   17 ④   18 ①
19 ③   20 tribe   21 ①
22 ⓐ a blind runner   ⓑ a shooting assistant
12 they should
24 (A) A tapper   (B) a guide runner
   (C) a shooting assistant

---

01 ②번은 동의어 관계이다. 나머지는 모두 반의어 관계이다. allow: 허용하다, permit: 허가하다 ① perfect: 완전한, imperfect: 불완전한 ③ complete: 완전한, incomplete: 불완전한 ④ hire: 고용하다, fire: 해고하다 ⑤ full: 가득 찬, empty: 비어 있는

02 ① 달리기에서, guide runner는 시각 장애인 선수와 함께 달리며 그들이 트랙에서 벗어나지 않도록 돕는다. ② 마일리지 프로그램은 어떻게 신청합니까? ③ 손님을 상대하는 일은 결코 쉬운 일이 아니다. ④ most of all: 무엇보다도. 그것은 그녀가 무엇보다도 원하던 것이었다. ⑤ 그녀는 연설을 하느니 차라리 죽는 게 나을 것 같았다.

03 (1) hire: 고용하다 (2) be over: 끝나다 (3) attention: 주의, 주목

04 • take care of: ~을 돌보다. 그는 스스로를 돌볼 수 있다. • keep track of: ~을 파악하다. 은행 입출금 내역서는 당신의 돈이 어디에 쓰이고 있는지를 계속 파악하는 데 도움이 된다.

05 ① 소년이 언제 방문했는지는 알 수 없다. ② Twice a week. ③ On weekends. ④ On Saturdays and Sundays. ⑤ The Beginner 1 class.

06 여자가 앞에서 한 말의 내용을 요약해서 쓰면 된다.

07 '볼링공이 무거워 보인다.'라고 한 후, 더 가벼운 공을 쓰는 것을 제안하는 것이 자연스러우므로 ④번이 적절하다.

08 Suji의 볼링공이 무거워 보인다며 더 가벼운 공을 쓸 것을 제안하고 있다.

09 one은 'bowling ball'을 대신하는 부정대명사이다.

10 Jeffrey는 자전거를 어떻게 수리할지 몰랐기 때문에 그의 고장 난 자전거에 당황했다.

11 'as ~ as'에는 수식어의 원급을 쓴다. ③ 내용상 '배우기 어렵지 않다'는 뜻이므로 hardly가 아닌 hard로 쓰는 것이 적절하다.

12 ④번은 help의 목적어로 쓰인 동명사(can't help ~ing: ~하지 않을 수 없다)이다. 나머지는 모두 명사의 뒤에서 꾸미는 분사로 사용되었다.

13 ③ Jim이 Mary, Steve와 함께 가장 나이가 많으므로, 'Jim이 Paul만큼 나이 들지 않았다'는 문장은 'Jim이 Paul보다 어리다'는 뜻과 같기 때문에 적절하지 않다.

14 페이서들은 '경험이 많은' 선수들이라고 해야 하므로, experiencing을 experienced로 고치는 것이 적절하다. experienced: (특정 분야에) 경험[경력]이 있는, experiencing: 경험하는

15 in short = in brief = to put it shortly[briefly] = in a word: 요약하면, 요컨대, ② in addition: 게다가 ⑤ in other words: 바꿔 말하면

16 처음에 페이서들이 어떻게 그들의 달리는 속도를 결정하는지는 알 수 없다. ① They help other runners manage their race better by running with them and leading them in a marathon. ③ They usually have flags or balloons showing their finish time. ④ Depending on their target finish time. ⑤ By choosing a pacer depending on their target finish time and following the pacer.

17 ⓐ on: '소속'을 나타냄, ⓑ in harmony: 조화를 이루며

18 우리는 대부분의 자동차 경주에서 자동차와 레이서만 보게 되고, 그 레이서 뒤에 있는 팀이 피트 크루이다.

19 이 글은 '자동차 경주에서 피트 크루가 하는 역할'에 대한 글이므로, 제목으로는 ③번 '피트 크루는 주로 무슨 일을 하는가?'가 적절하다.

20 tribe: 부족, 종족. 같은 인종의, 같은 언어와 풍습을 가진 사람들의 집단

21 ①번 다음 문장의 also에 주목한다. 주어진 문장의 내용에 이어

셰르파에 대한 설명을 계속하는 것이므로 ①번이 적절하다.

22 ⓐ '시각 장애인 선수', ⓑ '슈팅 보조원'을 가리킨다.

23 의문사+to부정사 = 의문사+주어+should+동사

24 'tapper', 'guide runner', 그리고 'shooting assistant'는 모두 패럴림픽의 조력자들이다.

01 Because he wants to take classes twice a week on weekdays.

02 He wants to take the lessons twice a week.

03 He will take the swimming classes on Tuesdays and Thursdays.

04 (1) India's population growth rate is as fast as that of China.
   (2) The Chinese government is as unashamed as the Japanese political leaders.

05 ⓐ boiling ⓑ written ⓒ leaving ⓓ covered
   ⓔ crying ⓕ sleeping ⓖ composed
   이유: ⓕ는 동명사이고, 나머지는 모두 분사이다.

06 (A) pacer runs (B) four hours (C) four-hour

07 the runner can achieve his or her goal of finishing the marathon in a particular time more easily

08 It is to help other runners manage their race better.

09 is called   10 are → is

11 (A) the side (B) a race

01 소년이 일주일에 두 번 주중에 수업을 듣길 원하기 때문이다.

02 소년은 일주일에 두 번 수업을 듣길 원한다.

03 초급 2반의 수업은 화요일과 목요일에 있다고 했다.

04 'as ~ as' 원급 비교 표현을 사용하여, 주어진 단어들을 알맞게 배열한다. *a population growth rate: 인구 성장률 *unashamed: 부끄러움을 모르는

05 ⓐ '끓는 물'(능동) ⓑ '윤동주에 의해 쓰여진 시'(수동) ⓒ '뉴욕행 열차'(능동) ⓓ '눈으로 덮인 산'(수동) ⓔ '울고 있는 아기'(능동) ⓕ '침낭'은 '잠을 자기 위한 용도의 가방'이므로 동명사 ⓖ '작곡된 음악'(수동)

06 (A) each는 단수 취급해야 하므로 pacer runs가 적절하다.
   (B) in four hours: 4시간 안에, (C) 명사 pacer를 수식하는 형용사로 쓰인 것이므로 four-hour가 적절하다.

07 동격을 나타내는 전치사 of를 보충하여, 'his or her goal'이 'finishing the marathon in a particular time'임을 나타내도록 하는 것이 적절하다.

08 페이서의 역할은 다른 선수들이 경기를 더 잘 운영하도록 돕는 것이다.

09 피트 크루라고 '불린다'고 해야 하므로 수동태로 쓰는 것이 적절하다..

10 주어가 동명사 Changing이므로, 동사를 is로 고치는 것이 적절하다.

11 '피트'는 레이서들이 경주 도중에 자동차를 점검하고 타이어를 교체하기 위해 여러 번 정지하는, 경주 트랙의 한쪽에 있는 공간이다.

|모범답안|

01 (1) often do you play computer games, play computer games three times a week
   (2) often do you eat late at night, eat late at night five times a week
   (3) often do you take swimming classes, take swimming classes twice a week

02 (1) Sein runs as fast as Bona.
   (2) Minju is not so fast as Sein.
   (3) Bona jumps as high as Minju.
   (4) Seohyun can throw the ball as far as Ahrin.

03 (A) cheering (B) team spirit
   (C) their team and fans (D) fit and strong
   (E) jumping and dancing

01 hire   02 breathe   03 tribe   04 ④

05 (1) My boots are beginning to wear out.
   (2) There is heavy traffic, therefore, we should take the subway.
   (3) Do you have a particular restaurant in mind?

06 I suggest you bring a swimming cap.

07 ②

08 I suggest that you should wear running shoes

09 She comes here every day to run.

10 how to swim   11 ①   12 ④

13 have flags or balloons showing their start time / since a pit stop can be as short as 2 minutes

14 ④

15 (1) My pencil case is as light as Mina's.
   (2) Isabelle is as tall as John, but she isn't so heavy as he.

16 ⑤

17 Mom makes as delicious dishes as a man called 'Housewife Baek.'

18 ④   19 ④   20 ③   21 ③

22 win → are won

23 (A) the attention   (B) pit crew   24 ①

25 because people often see a picture of only the
   climbers at the top of the mountain

26 ④

27 (A) Although   (B) at (C) hard

28 ②, ④, ⑤   29 ④

01 동의어 관계이다. suggest: 제안하다 – propose: 제안하다,
   employ: 고용하다 – hire: 고용하다

02 breathe: 숨을 쉬다. 공기를 체내로 빨아들이고 다시 내보내다

03 tribe: 부족, 종족. 자신들의 언어와 생활 방식을 가지고 있는 사
   람들의 집단. 이 수업에서 우리는 마사이 부족의 문화를 배울 수
   있다.

04 allow: 허용하다. 홀 안에서는 흡연을 허용하지 않습니다.
   suggest: 제안하다. 전 나가서 외식할 것을 제안해요.

05 (1) wear out: (낡아서) 떨어지다, 헤지다 (2) therefore: 그러
   므로 (3) particular: 특정한, have ~ in mind: ~을 생각하고
   있다

06 suggest 다음에 나오는 that절에서 '주어+(should)+동사원형
   ~'으로 쓰는 것에 주의한다.

07 ⓑ의 'to swim'을 swimming으로 고치는 것이 적절하다. go
   ~ing: ~하러 가다

08 suggest 다음에 나오는 that 절에서 '주어+(should)+동사원
   형 ~'으로 쓴다. that과 should는 생략할 수 있다.

09 '여기에 얼마나 자주 달리기를 하러 오니?'라는 질문에 '매일
   와.'라고 답하고 있다.

10 의문사+to부정사 = 의문사+주어+should+동사원형

11 '제한 인원이 열 명'이라는 의미이므로 limit이 알맞다.

12 소년은 주말이 아니라 주중에 수업을 듣고 싶다고 말하고 있다.

13 (A) 현재분사가 이끄는 형용사구 'showing their start time'
   이 앞의 명사들을 뒤에서 수식하는 것에 유의한다. (B) 'as ~ as
   구문'을 활용하되, 조동사 can 뒤에 be동사의 '원형'을 쓰는 것에
   유의한다.

14 included → including ④ '종이, 연필, 지우개 등을 포함한
   많은 문구류'(능동)

15 'as 원급 as'를 활용하여, 주어진 단어를 알맞게 배열한다.

16 주어진 문장과 ①, ②, ③, ④는 모두 수동의 의미로 명사를 뒤
   에서 꾸미는 과거분사를 써야 한다. ⑤번만 현재분사이다. 'the
   elderly living alone: 독거 노인들'(능동)

17 주어가 3인칭 단수 현재이므로 makes, '~라고 불리는 남자'이
   므로 'a man called'를 쓰는 것에 유의하여, 'as ~ as'를 활용
   하여 알맞게 배열한다.

18 명사를 뒤에서 꾸며주는 분사의 능동/수동을 적절하게 구분해야
   한다. ④ '옛날에 만들어진 오래된 동전들'이므로 '수동'의 의미
   를 가진 made가 적절하다.

19 페이서가 시간을 '계속해서 파악한다'고 하는 것이 적절하다.
   keep track of: (계속해서) ~을 파악하다, ~에 주의를 기울이
   다, ① (먼저 간 사람을) 따라 잡다[따라가다], (정도나 수준이
   앞선 것을) 따라잡다, ② ~을 참다, ③ ~을 생각해 내다, ⑤ (손
   실 따위를) 보상하다

20 ⓑ와 ②, ⑤: 부사적 용법, ①, ④: 명사적 용법, ③: 형용사적
   용법

21 ③번 다음 문장의 Changing the tires에 주목한다. 주어진 문
   장의 change the tires를 가리키는 것이므로 ③번이 적절하다.

22 '경주의 우승은 피트에서 이루어진다'고 해야 하므로, 수동태로
   고치는 것이 적절하다.

23 자동차 경주에서 레이서만 '주목'을 받을지 모르지만, '피트 크
   루'라고 불리는 팀이 레이서가 경주에서 이기도록 레이서 뒤에
   서 도와주는 중요한 역할을 한다.

24 ⓐ: 앞의 내용의 결과가 나오고 있으므로 Therefore가 가장 적
   절하다. ⓑ: 앞의 내용의 예가 나오고 있으므로 For example
   이 가장 적절하다. ② 다시 말해서 - 그에 반해서, ③ 게다가 -
   따라서, ④ ~임에 비하여[반하여] - 게다가, ⑤ 예를 들어 - 똑
   같이

25 a picture of only the climbers at the top of the
   mountain: 산 정상에서 등산가들만 찍힌 사진

26 셰르파는 산의 높은 곳에서 호흡하는 데 '어려움이 거의 없다.'

27 (A) 사람들이 보통 치어리더는 미식축구팀의 일원이라고 생각
   하지 '않을지라도' 그들은 축구 경기에서 중요한 역할을 한다고
   해야 하므로 Although가 적절하다. (B) be good at: ~을 잘
   하다, be good for: ~에 좋다, (C) 선수들만큼이나 '열심히' 일
   해야 한다고 해야 하므로 hard가 적절하다. hardly: 거의 ~ 아
   니다[없다]

28 most of all = first of all = above all = more than
   anything else: 무엇보다, ① 처음에는, ③ 결국에는

29 점프하는 것과 '춤추는 것'을 잘해야 한다.

교과서 파헤치기

Lesson **3**

단어 TEST Step 1　　　p.02

01 초래하다; 원인	02 현재의	03 결심하다
04 접촉	05 탐험가	06 공장
07 노예	08 홍수	09 화나게 하다
10 세기, 100년	11 문명	12 제안하다
13 진보한, 발전된	14 곧, 즉시	15 원래, 본래
16 의미	17 우주, 은하계	18 상인, 거래자
19 설계하다	20 경험하다	21 정의
22 표현	23 법	24 신화
25 포함하다	26 불안한	27 기원, 유래
28 폭풍	29 재판관, 판사; 재판하다	
30 유래하다	31 생산하다	32 도구
33 빌리다	34 얇게 썬 조각; 한 조각	
35 거쳐 지나가다	36 ~에서 오다, 유래하다	
37 ~로 만들어지다	38 ~을 익히게 되다	
39 비가 세차게 내리다		40 연락하다
41 우울한 얼굴을 하다		
42 …을 본떠 ~의 이름을 부르다		43 의견을 같이하다

단어 TEST Step 2　　　p.03

01 advanced	02 cause	03 experience
04 anger	05 Spanish	06 borrow
07 expression	08 factory	09 contact
10 flood	11 century	12 shortly
13 civilization	14 include	15 explorer
16 create	17 trader	18 storm
19 justice	20 law	21 produce
22 language	23 slice	24 suggest
25 judge	26 nervous	27 meaning
28 origin	29 present	30 slave
31 universe	32 originate	33 originally
34 myth	35 come from ~	36 pull one's leg
37 make a long face		38 pass through
39 break a leg	40 under the weather	
41 keep in touch	42 not ~ at all	43 be made into ~

단어 TEST Step 3　　　p.04

1 shortly, 곧, 즉시　2 anger, 화나게 하다

3 present, 현재의　4 century, 세기, 100년

5 civilization, 문명　6 flood, 홍수　7 originally, 원래

8 trader, 무역업자　9 universe, 우주, 은하계

대화문 TEST Step 1　　　p.05~07

Listen and Talk A 1

cats and dogs / cats and dogs, that mean / means, raining a lot / Don't worry, in my backpack

Listen and Talk A 2

on me / Excuse me, Can, say that / on me, means, pay for / a lot / You're welcome

Listen and Talk A 3

looks delicious / Would, like some / thanks, not, tea / Not, tea, does, mean / don't like something / see, don't like

Listen and Talk A 4

under the weather / Excuse me, can, say that again / under the weather, don't feel well, have a cold / Why don't you, get, get medicine, over there / should

Listen and Talk B 1

make a long face / Excuse me, can you please say that again / make a long face / What does that mean / means, feel sad

Listen and Talk B 2

Break a leg / Excuse me, can you please say that again / Break a leg / What does that mean / Good luck

Listen and Talk B 3

under the weather / Excuse me, can you please say that again / under the weather / What does that mean / don't feel

Listen and Talk C

had a great time / My pleasure, come visit / love to, like to invite, to visit / it, that, come / can't say longer, keep my fingers crossed / Excuse me, can you, say that again / keep my fingers crossed, wish you good luck / Have, trip / keep in touch

Review 1

keep my fingers crossed / can you please say that again / keep my fingers crossed, wish you good luck

Review 2

feel under the weather / can you please say that again / feel under the weather / What does that mean / don't feel well, have a cold / Why don't you buy, get medicine, over there / will

Review 3

cats and dogs / Can you say that again / cats and
dogs / What does that mean / means, raining a lot

Review 4

is on me / What does that mean / pay for

대화문 TEST Step 2   p.08~10

Listen and Talk A 1

G: Look. It's raining cats and dogs.

B: Raining cats and dogs? What does that mean?

G: It means "It's raining a lot."

B: Oh. Don't worry. I have an umbrella in my backpack.

Listen and Talk A 2

G: This juice is on me, Suho.

B: Excuse me? Can you say that again?

G: I said, "This juice is on me." It means "I'll pay for
the juice."

B: Oh. Thanks a lot.

G: You're welcome.

Listen and Talk A 3

B: Everything looks delicious.

G: Yes. Would you like some of my spaghetti?

B: No, thanks. Spaghetti is not my cup of tea.

G: Not your cup of tea? What does that mean?

B: It means "I don't like something."

G: Oh, I see. You don't like spaghetti.

Listen and Talk A 4

G: I feel under the weather.

B: Excuse me, but can you please say that again?

G: I said, "I feel under the weather." It means "I don't
feel well." I think I have a cold.

B: Oh. Why don't you buy some medicine before
you get on the plane? You can get medicine at
the store over there.

G: I guess I should.

Listen and Talk B 1

A: Don't make a long face.

B: Excuse me, but can you please say that again?

A: I said, "Don't make a long face."

B: What does that mean?

A: It means "Don't feel sad."

Listen and Talk B 2

M: Break a leg.

W: Excuse me, but can you please say that again?

M: I said, "Break a leg."

W: What does that mean?

M: It means "Good luck."

Listen and Talk B 3

M: It means "Good luck."

W: Excuse me, but can you please say that again?

M: I said, "I feel under the weather."

W: What does that mean?

M: It means "I don't feel well."

Listen and Talk C

G: Thank you for everything, Jiho. I had a great time
in Korea.

B: My pleasure. Please come visit me again, Lucy.

G: I'd love to, but before I do, I'd like to invite you to
visit me in London.

B: Thanks. Anyway, it's too bad that you can't come
to my soccer game tomorrow.

G: I'm sorry that I can't stay longer. I'll keep my
fingers crossed for you.

B: Excuse me, but can you please say that again?

G: I said, "I'll keep my fingers crossed for you." It
means "I wish you good luck."

B: Oh. Thanks. Have a nice trip.

G: Thanks. I'll keep in touch.

Review 1

G: I'll keep my fingers crossed for you.

B: I'm sorry, but can you please say that again?

G: I said, "I'll keep my fingers crossed for you." It
means "I wish you good luck."

Review 2

W: I feel under the weather.

M: Excuse me, but can you please say that again?

W: I said, "I feel under the weather."

M: What does that mean?

W: It means "I don't feel well." I think I have a cold.

M: Oh. Why don't you buy some medicine? You can
get medicine at the store over there.

W: OK, I will.

Review 3

M: Look. It's raining cats and dogs.

W: Can you say that again?

M: It's raining cats and dogs.

W: What does that mean?

M: It means "It's raining a lot."

Review 4

G: This pizza is on me, Suho.

B: What does that mean?

G: It means "I'll pay for the pizza."

01 Words, Foreign Origin
02 borrowed words, other, languages
03 Here, examples with
04 comes from, means, press
05 was used, head massage
06 traders, experienced, with, introduced
07 meaning, few, entered, around
08 century, present, washing, hair
09 Shortly, be also used
10 play, which, written, by   11 look like humans
12 are designed, work, produced
13 idea of using, himself
14 called, from, for work
15 However, salve, in Czech
16 idea, to use, word   17 play, made into, fiction
18 comes, originates from, name
19 creation myth, gods, created
20 However, angered, so, caused
21 Spanish contact with, civilization
22 passing through, picked up
23 In, early uses, by
24 word, originally, from, second-largest
25 means, things, in German
26 origin, not clear
27 believed that, between, and
28 placed, slices, such food

01 Words, Foreign Origin
02 has often borrowed words, other cultures
03 are, with interesting stories
04 comes from, which, to press
05 was used
06 with a head massage, introduced, to
07 a few times, entered, around
08 present, washing the hair
09 Shortly after that, to be also used for
10 was written, Czech writer
11 look like
12 are designed to work, are produced
13 It, the idea of using, come from, himself
14 originally called, from, for
15 However, suggested, which, in Czech
16 decided to use
17 was made into, on television

18 comes from, originates from
19 creation myth, one of the three gods, created humans
20 angered, so, caused, flood
21 Spanish contact with, civilization
22 explorers, were passing through, picked up, for it
23 In English, early uses, by
24 originally comes from, second-largest
25 from, in German   26 is not clear
27 it is believed that, between, and
28 placed, Hamburg-style, two slices of bread, call such food

1 외국어에서 유래된 영어 단어
2 영어는 종종 다른 문화나 언어에서 단어를 빌려왔다.
3 여기 재미있는 이야기가 있는 몇 개의 예가 있다.
4 shampoo라는 단어는 힌디어 chāmpo에서 왔고, '누르다'라는 의미이다.
5 인도에서 그 단어는 머리 마사지라는 의미로 쓰였다.
6 인도에 있는 영국 상인들은 머리 마사지를 함께하는 목욕을 경험했고 마사지를 18세기에 영국에 소개했다.
7 shampoo라는 단어의 의미는 그 단어가 1762년쯤 영어에 처음으로 들어온 이후 몇 번 바뀌었다.
8 19세기에, shampoo는 '머리 감기'라는 현재의 의미를 갖게 되었다.
9 그 후 얼마 지나지 않아, 그 단어는 머리에 사용하는 특별한 비누에도 쓰이기 시작했다.
10 robot이라는 단어는 "R.U.R."에서 왔는데, 그 연극은 1920년 체코의 작가 Karel Čapek에 의해 쓰였다.
11 그 연극에서 로봇은 인간처럼 생긴 기계이다.
12 그들은 인간을 위해 일하도록 설계되고, 공장에서 생산된다.
13 robot이라는 단어를 사용하려는 생각이 Karel Čapek 자신에게서 나온 게 아니었다는 것이 흥미롭다.
14 그는 원래 자신의 연극에서 그 기계들을 '일'을 의미하는 라틴어에서 온 labori라고 불렀다.
15 하지만, 그의 형이 roboti를 제안했는데, roboti는 체코어로 '노예 근로자들'을 의미한다.
16 Karel Čapek은 그 아이디어가 마음에 들어 roboti라는 단어를 사용하기로 결정했다.
17 1938년에 그 연극은 영국 TV에서 공상 과학물로 만들어졌다.
18 hurricane이라는 단어는 스페인어 단어 huracán에서 왔고, 그것은 마야 신의 이름에서 유래한다.
19 마야의 창조 신화에서, Huracán은 바람, 폭풍우, 그리고 불에 관한 날씨의 신이며, 그는 인간을 창조한 세 명의 신들 중 한 명이다.

20 하지만, 최초의 인간들이 신들을 화나게 해서 Huracán은 거대한 홍수를 일으켰다.

21 스페인이 마야 문명과 했던 첫 접촉은 1517년이었다.

22 카리브 제도를 지나던 스페인 탐험가들이 허리케인을 겪었고, 그 지역 사람들로부터 그것을 의미하는 단어를 듣게 되었다.

23 영어에서 일찍이 hurricane을 사용한 것 중 하나는 1608년 셰익스피어의 희곡에서였다.

24 hamburger라는 단어는 원래 독일에서 두 번째로 큰 도시인 함부르크에서 왔다.

25 hamburger는 독일어로 '함부르크 출신의 사람 또는 사물'을 의미한다.

26 최초의 햄버거의 기원은 분명하지 않다.

27 하지만 햄버거는 1885년에서 1904년 사이의 언젠가 미국 텍사스에 있는 작은 마을에서 발명되었다고 믿어진다.

28 한 요리사가 빵 두 조각 사이에 함부르크 스타일의 스테이크를 넣었고, 사람들은 그런 음식을 햄버거라고 부르기 시작했다.

---

1 English Words of Foreign Origin

2 English has often borrowed words from other cultures or languages.

3 Here are some examples with interesting stories.

4 The word *shampoo* comes from the Hindi word *chāmpo*, which means "to press."

5 In India, the word was used for a head massage.

6 British traders in India experienced a bath with a head massage and introduced it to Britain in the 18th century.

7 The meaning of the word *shampoo* changed a few times after it first entered English around 1762.

8 In the 19th century, *shampoo* got its present meaning of "washing the hair."

9 Shortly after that, the word began to be also used for a special soap for the hair.

10 The word *robot* comes from the play *R.U.R.*, which was written in 1920 by a Czech writer Karel Čapek.

11 In the play, robots are machines that look like humans.

12 They are designed to work for humans and are produced in a factory.

13 It is interesting that the idea of using the word *robot* didn't come from Karel Čapek himself.

14 He originally called the machines in his play *labori* from the Latin word for "work."

15 However, his brother suggested *roboti*, which

means "slave workers" in Czech.

16 Karel Čapek liked the idea and decided to use the word *roboti*.

17 In 1938, the play was made into a science fiction show on television in Britain.

18 The word *hurricane* comes from the Spanish word *huracán*, which originates from the name of a Mayan god.

19 In the Mayan creation myth, Huracán is the weather god of wind, storm, and fire, and he is one of the three gods who created humans.

20 However, the first humans angered the gods, so Huracán caused a great flood.

21 The first Spanish contact with the Mayan civilization was in 1517.

22 Spanish explorers who were passing through the Caribbean experienced a hurricane and picked up the word for it from the people in the area.

23 In English, one of the early uses of *hurricane* was in a play by Shakespeare in 1608.

24 The word *hamburger* originally comes from Hamburg, Germany's second-largest city.

25 *Hamburger* means "people or things from Hamburg" in German.

26 The origin of the first hamburger is not clear.

27 However, it is believed that the hamburger was invented in a small town in Texas, USA, sometime between 1885 and 1904.

28 A cook placed a Hamburg-style steak between two slices of bread, and people started to call such food a hamburger.

After You Read A

1. Dictionary
2. from other cultures, languages
3. comes from, which, to press
4. which, slave workers, in Czech
5. Spanish word, which originates from
6. Hamburg, the second-largest city in Germany

Around the World

1. English words, come from French
2. include, like judge, justice
3. There are many English words, that
4. For example, come from Italian
5. vegetables, Spanish

6. For example, comes from, in Spanish

Think and Write Step 2

1. Origin, Word *Sandwich*

2. comes from, who, the 4th Earl

3. enjoyed eating, two slices of bread, while he was eating

4. thought that, such food a sandwich after

구석구석지문 TEST Step 2   p.23

After You Read A

1. Online Dictionary

2. English words from other cultures or languages

3. shampoo: It comes from the Hindi word *chāmpo*, which means "to press."

4. robot: It comes from *roboti*, which means "slave workers" in Czech.

5. hurricane: It comes from Spanish word, *huracán*, which originates from the name of a Mayan god.

6. hamburger: It comes from Hamburg, the second-largest city in Germany.

Around the World

1. 1. Many English words about law come from French.

2. Examples include words like judge and justice.

3. 2. There are many English words about music that come from Italian.

4. For example, piano and violin come from Italian.

5. 3. Many English words for vegetables come from Spanish.

6. For example, tomato comes from *tomate* and potato comes from *patata* in Spani

Think and Write Step 2

1. The Origin of the Word *Sandwich*

2. The word sandwich comes from John Montagu, who was the 4th Earl of Sandwich.

3. He enjoyed eating meat between two slices of bread because he could play a card game while he was eating.

4. People thought that it was a great idea and began to call such food a sandwich after him.

단어 TEST Step 1   p.24

01 빠듯한, 꽉 조이는[딱 붙는]		02 환불; 환불받다
03 균형, 통장의 잔액	04 사례, 경우	05 자선 단체
06 편안한	07 영수증	08 용돈
09 남아 있는	10 바로 잡다	11 예산
12 소파	13 나누다	14 반품하다
15 교환; 교환하다	16 비록 ~이지만	17 저축하다, 구하다
18 기부하다	19 노력	20 마지막으로
21 용돈	22 대다수	23 의약품
24 그 대신에	25 가격, 가치	26 관리하다
27 작동하다	28 받다	29 헐렁한, 느슨한
30 결과	31 설문조사	32 최근에
33 ~하는 동안, ~하는 반면에		34 이미, 벌써
35 환불받다	36 ~하기를 원하다, 좋아하다	
37 ~을 돌보다, ~을 처리하다		38 즉시
39 다 쓰다, 완전히 소모하다		
40 ~하는 데 어려움을 겪다		41 가지고 다니다
42 할인 중인, 판매되는		43 돈을 돌려받다

단어 TEST Step 2   p.25

01 refund	02 although	03 price
04 comfortable	05 couch	06 return
07 effort	08 weekly	09 correct
10 instead	11 budget	12 exchange
13 charity	14 lastly	15 remaining
16 donate	17 result	18 loose
19 receipt	20 majority	21 paper money
22 balance	23 allowance, pocket money	
24 divide	25 receive	26 tight
27 rainy	28 already	29 medicine
30 recently	31 case	32 manage
33 save	34 survey	35 right away
36 get a refund	37 take effort	38 on the spot
39 carry around	40 would like to	
41 get an exchange		
42 change one's mind		43 take care of ~

단어 TEST Step 3   p.26

1 loose, 느슨한   2 medicine, 의약품   3 donate, 기부하다

4 majority, 대다수   5 refund, 환불   6 advice, 충고

7 correct, 바로 잡다   8 budget, 예산

37

9 remaining, 남아 있는　10 balance, 잔액

11 effort, 노력　12 exchange, 교환

13 allowance, 용돈　14 receipt, 영수증

15 couch, 소파　16 charity, 자선 단체

Listen and Talk A 1

help you / like to get, refund / wrong with / changed, mind, get, back / take care of, right away

Listen and Talk A 2

need some help / like to return / Let's see, receipt with / Here it is, it / it's possible

Listen and Talk A 3

looking for, special / like to exchange / would you like / Here you are

Listen and Talk A 4

What, do for you / exchange, for, different / What, would, like / I'd like, yellow one / Here you are

Listen and Talk B 1

May I help you / I'd like to exchange / What, it for / like to, it for

Listen and Talk B 2

May I / get a refund for / receipt / do, Here it is

Listen and Talk C

May I help you / get a refund for / receipt / don't, received, it as / it's, to get, refund / I see, exchange, for something else / can, would you like to get / want to get / Let me see, price, same, take it

Listen and Talk D

bought, last week, look good on, wonder if, exchange it for / up to you

Talk and Play

Excuse me, exchange, for / anything wrong with / don't like

Excuse me, get a refund for / anything wrong

Review 1

May I help you / I'd like to return / anything wrong with / changed, mind, have, back / Here's your money

Review 2

Can I help you / I'd like to exchange / too small for / would you like to exchange it for / Medium, have it in / Here you are

Review 3

May, help / get a refund for / afraid you can't / exchange, for, over / can

Review 4

May, help / get a refund for / receipt / do, Here it is

Listen and Talk A 1

W: Hello. May I help you?

B: Yes, please. I'd like to get a refund for this watch.

W: OK. Was there anything wrong with it?

B: No, I just changed my mind. Can I get my money back?

W: OK. I'll take care of it right away.

Listen and Talk A 2

W: Hello. Do you need some help?

B: Yes. I'd like to return this smartphone case.

W: Let's see. Do you have the receipt with you?

B: Here it is. I bought it three days ago.

W: Oh, then it's possible.

Listen and Talk A 3

W: Hello. Are you looking for anything special?

B: No, I'm not. I'd like to exchange this T-shirt. It's too small.

W: Sure. What size would you like?

B: Large, please.

W: Here you are.

B: Thank you.

Listen and Talk A 4

W: Hello. What can I do for you?

B: Can I exchange this black umbrella for a different color?

W: Sure. What color would you like?

B: I'd like a yellow one, please..

W: OK. Here you are.

Listen and Talk B 1

A: Hello. May I help you?

B: Yes, please. I'd like to exchange this bag.

A: Sure. What would you like to exchange it for?

B: I'd like to exchange it for a cap.

A: OK.

Listen and Talk B 2

A: Hello. May I help you?

B: Yes, please. I'd like to get a refund for this bag.

A: Sure. Do you have the receipt?

B: Yes, I do. Here it is.

Listen and Talk C

M: Hello. May I help you?

G: Yes, please. I'd like to get a refund for this cap.

M: Do you have the receipt?

G: No, I don't. I received it as a gift.

M: If you don't have the receipt, then, it's not possible to get a refund.

G: I see. Then, can I exchange it for something else?

M: Yes, you can. What would you like to get?

G: I want to get this blue bag.

M: Let me see .... The price is the same, so you can just take it.

G: Thank you.

Listen and Talk D

G: I bought this red skirt last week. I like the skirt, but my sister says that the color doesn't look good on me. I wonder if I should exchange it for a different color.

B: It's up to you but I think it's fine.

Talk and Play

A: Excuse me. I'd like to exchange this T-shirt for these pants.

B: OK. Is there anything wrong with it?

A: I don't like the color.

B: I see.

A: Excuse me. I'd like to get a refund for this cap.

B: OK. Is there anything wrong with it?

A: I don't like the color.

B: I see.

Review 1

W: Hello. May I help you?

B: Yes, please. I'd like to return this baseball glove.

W: OK. Was there anything wrong with it?

B: No, I just changed my mind. Can I have my money back?

W: OK. Here's your money.

Review 2

M: Hello. Can I help you?

W: Yes, please. I'd like to exchange this yellow T-shirt. It's too small for me.

M: Sure. What size would you like to exchange it for?

W: Medium size, please. Oh! Can I have it in red?

M: OK. Here you are.

Review 3

M: Hello. May I help you?

G: Yes, please. Can I get a refund for this hat?

M: I'm afraid you can't.

G: Then, can I exchange this hat for the gloves over there?

M: Yes, you can.

Review 4

A: Hello. May I help you?

B: I'd like to get a refund for this cap.

A: Sure. Do you have the receipt?

B: Yes, I do. Here it is.

본문 TEST Step 1   p.33~35

01 Ask Dr.

02 Green, Times

03 Teens', Habits

04 How smart, with

05 results, survey, students

06 asked, smart with

07 As, shows, while

08 what, biggest, worry is

09 enough allowance, difficulty saving

10 Lastly, spent, on, need

11 survey, majority, smart with

12 Managing, becoming, takes effort

13 have, money worries

14 Let's talk with

15 I'm Jason

16 weekly allowance, never, enough

17 By, all, is gone

18 how to solve

19 I'm Dr. Money

20 Let's, at, spending diary

21 used up, at, beginning

22 Here's, tip

23 carry around, weekly allowance

24 Divide, into days

25 carry, for each day

26 Dr. Money

27 I'm Steve

28 have difficulty saving

29 been saving, for, last

30 However, still, enough money

31 what to do

32 Let's see

33 last few, spent, saved

34 think, been spending

35 save, need, tighter budget

36 For example, follow, rule

37 save, donate, remaining, charity

38 By following, rule, manage

39 save, faster, buy, ticket

40 I'm Minji

41 buy, on sale

42 sale, buy, although, need

43 Last, bought, sale, already

44 Buying, good, buy, need

45 case, that, things, even

46 Here's, advice

47 Before, something, yourself

48 go shopping, make, list

49 items, on, if, sale

50 won't buy, on, spot

01 Ask, Money
02 Middle School Times
03 Spending Habits
04 How smart, with
05 results, a survey
06 smart with
07 As, shows, while
08 asked, answered, biggest money worry
09 As, shows, think, enough allowance while, have difficulty saving
10 Lastly, spent, on, didn't need
11 shows, the majority, smart with
12 Managing, becoming, takes
13 money worries
14 Let's talk with
15 I'm
16 weekly allowance, enough
17 By, is gone
18 how to solve
19 I'm
20 look at, spending diary
21 used up, at the beginning of the week
22 my tip
23 carry around, weekly allowance
24 Divide, into
25 carry, for each day
26 Hello
27 I'm
28 have difficulty saving
29 I've been saving, for the last two months
30 However, still don't, enough money
31 what to do
32 Let's see
33 In the last few, allowance, saved
34 you've been spending
35 To save, have a tighter budget
36 follow the 50%-40%-10% rule
37 Save, donate the remaining, charity
38 By following, manage, better
39 faster to buy
40 I'm
41 on sale
42 on sale, although
43 bought, already have
44 Buying, is, things you need
45 In your case, don't even need
46 Here's, advice
47 ask yourself
48 go shopping, make
49 Don't buy, on the list
50 won't buy, on the spot

1 Dr. Money에게 물어보세요.
2 그린 중학교 타임스
3 10대들의 소비 습관
4 당신은 돈에 관해 얼마나 현명한가?

5 이것은 Green 중학교 학생 100명의 설문 조사 결과이다.
6 우리는 먼저 학생들에게 "당신은 돈에 관하여 현명한가?"라고 물었다.
7 그래프 1이 보여 주듯이, 30%가 "예"라고 대답한 반면 70%가 "아니요"라고 답했다.
8 그 다음 우리는 "아니요"라고 대답한 학생들에게 그들의 돈에 대한 가장 큰 고민이 무엇인지 물었다.
9 그래프 2가 보여주듯이 28%가 자신들이 돈을 모으는 것에 어려움이 있다고 생각하는 반면, 60%는 충분한 용돈을 받지 못한다고 생각한다.
10 마지막으로, 12%는 필요하지 않은 것에 돈을 소비했다고 말했다.
11 우리의 설문 조사는 대다수의 학생들이 자신들이 돈에 관련하여 현명하지 못하다고 생각한다는 것을 보여준다.
12 돈을 관리하는 것은 쉽지 않고 현명한 소비자가 되는 것에는 노력이 필요하다.
13 여러분은 돈과 관련된 걱정거리가 있는가?
14 Dr. Money와 이야기해 보자.
15 저는 Jason이에요.
16 저는 매주 용돈을 받지만, 절대로 충분하지 않아요.
17 목요일쯤이면 용돈이 모두 사라져요.
18 이 문제를 해결할 방법을 모르겠어요.
19 안녕하세요, Dr. Money입니다.
20 용돈 기입장을 한번 봅시다.
21 주의 초반에 용돈의 대부분을 다 썼군요.
22 이게 내 조언이에요.
23 일주일 용돈 전부를 가지고 다니지 마세요.
24 용돈을 하루 단위로 나누세요..
25 그리고 하루에 필요한 돈만 들고 다니세요.
26 안녕하세요, Dr. Money.
27 저는 Steve예요.
28 저는 돈을 모으기가 어려워요.
29 예를 들면, 저는 좋아하는 가수의 콘서트에 가려고 지난 두 달 동안 돈을 저축해 오고 있어요.
30 하지만 저는 여전히 충분한 돈을 가지고 있지 않아요.
31 어떻게 해야 할지 모르겠어요.
32 어디 봅시다.
33 지난 몇 주에 용돈의 80%를 사용하고 20%만을 저축했군요.
34 나는 Steve가 돈을 너무 많이 써 왔다고 생각해요.
35 돈을 모으기 위해서, 더 빠듯한 예산을 세우는 것이 필요해요.
36 예를 들어, Steve는 50%-40%-10%의 규칙을 따를 수 있어요.
37 50%를 저축하고, 40%를 쓰고, 남아 있는 10%를 자선 단체에 기부하세요.
38 이 규칙을 따름으로써 돈을 더 잘 관리할 수 있어요.
39 그러면 그 티켓을 사기 위해 돈을 더 빨리 모을 수 있답니다.
40 저는 민지입니다.
41 저는 할인 판매하는 물건을 사는 것을 좋아해요.
42 어떤 물건이 할인 판매를 하면 저는 그것이 필요하지 않더라도 사요.

43 지난주에는 할인 판매하는 티셔츠 두 장을 샀지만 이미 많이 가지고 있었어요.

44 민지가 필요한 물건을 산다면 할인 판매하는 물건을 사는 것은 좋습니다.

45 민지의 경우에, 문제점은 필요하지 않은 물건도 산다는 거예요.

46 여기 몇 가지 조언이 있어요.

47 민지는 무언가를 사기 전에 "이것이 정말 필요한가?"라고 스스로에게 물어보세요.

48 또한 쇼핑하러 가기 전에 쇼핑 목록을 만드세요.

49 만약 물건들이 할인 판매 중이라고 해도 목록에 없는 물건들은 사지 마세요.

50 그러면 즉석에서 물건을 사지 않게 될 거예요.

본문 TEST Step 4 - Step 5
p.42~47

1 Ask Dr. Money

2 The Green Middle School Times

3 Teens' Spending Habits

4 How smart are you with your money?

5 These are the results of a survey of 100 students at Green Middle School.

6 We first asked students "Are you smart with your money?"

7 As Graph 1 shows, 70% answered "No" while 30% answered "Yes."

8 We then asked the students who answered "No" what their biggest money worry is.

9 As Graph 2 shows, 60% think they don't have enough allowance while 28% think they have difficulty saving money.

10 Lastly, 12% said they spent money on things they didn't need.

11 Our survey shows that the majority of students think they are not smart with their money.

12 Managing money is not easy, and becoming a smart spender takes effort.

13 Do you have any money worries?

14 Let's talk with Dr. Money.

15 I'm Jason.

16 I get a weekly allowance, but I never have enough.

17 By Thursday, all of my money is gone.

18 I don't know how to solve this problem.

19 Hi, I'm Dr. Money.

20 Let's look at your spending diary.

21 You used up most of your money at the beginning of the week.

22 Here's my tip.

23 Don't carry around all of your weekly allowance.

24 Divide the money into days.

25 Then carry only the money you need for each day.

26 Hello, Dr. Money.

27 I'm Steve.

28 I have difficulty saving money.

29 For example, I've been saving to go to my favorite singer's concert for the last two months.

30 However, I still don't have enough money.

31 I don't know what to do.

32 Let's see.

33 In the last few weeks, you spent 80% of your allowance and only saved 20%.

34 I think you've been spending too much.

35 To save money, you need to have a tighter budget.

36 For example, you can follow the 50%-40%-10% rule.

37 Save 50%, spend 40%, and donate the remaining 10% to charity.

38 By following the rule, you can manage your money better.

39 Then you can save money faster to buy the ticket.

40 I'm Minji.

41 I like to buy things on sale.

42 If something's on sale, I buy it although I don't need it.

43 Last week, I bought two T-shirts on sale, but I already have many.

44 Buying things on sale is good if you buy things you need.

45 In your case, the problem is that you buy things you don't even need.

46 Here's some advice.

47 Before you buy something, ask yourself, "Do I really need this?"

48 Also, before you go shopping, make a shopping list.

49 Don't buy items that aren't on the list even if they're on sale.

50 Then you won't buy things on the spot.

After You Read C

1. Teens', Worries, Advice

2. get an allowance, never have enough

3. By Thursday, all of, is gone

4. Don't carry around, weekly allowance

5. Divide, into, carry, need for each day

Language in Use A

1. bought on sale, cheap

2. It, to go camping, rainy reason

3. too light, so, exchange, for a bigger size

Think and Write

1. that, buy things on the spot

2. bought, because it looked nice

3. However, found out, already had three cases

4. how to stop buying things

After You Read C

1. Teens' Money Worries and Dr. Money's Advice

2. Jason's Worry: I get an allowance, but I never have enough.

3. By Thursday, all of my money is gone.

4. Dr. Money's Advice: Don't carry around all of weekly allowance.

5. Divide the money into days and carry only the money you need for each day.

Language in Use A

1. The computer I bought on sale was very cheap.

2. It is foolish to go camping during the rainy reason.

3. My jeans are too light, so I am going to exchange them for a bigger size.

Think and Write

1. My money problem is that I buy things on the spot.

2. One time, I bought a smartphone case because it looked nice.

3. However, I found out that I already had three cases at home.

4. I don't know how to stop buying things on the spot.

Lesson 5

01 주된	02 고용하다	
03 (눈에) 보이지 않는, 볼 수 없는		04 운반하다
05 홍보하다	06 이미	07 팀, 조
08 추천	09 값비싼	10 완벽한
11 관리하다	12 몇몇의	13 주의, 주목
14 한계	15 보조자	16 다치다
17 선택하다	18 그러므로	19 특히
20 부족, 종족	21 등록하다	22 활동
23 방향	24 경험 있는	25 돕다, 지원하다
26 두드리는 사람	27 제안하다	28 특정한
29 숨쉬다	30 달성하다, 성취하다	
31 조화, 화합	32 숨겨진	33 허용하다
34 바람이 심한	35 간단히 말해서	36 무엇보다도
37 (낡아서) 떨어지다, 헤지다		
38 ~에 어려움을 겪다		
39 등록하다, 신청하다		40 혼자서
41 ~을 파악하다	42 여러 가지 면에서	43 ~에 따라

01 achieve	02 carry	03 expensive
04 harmony	05 support	06 attention
07 breathe	08 therefore	09 assistant
10 hidden	11 cheer	12 suggest
13 experienced	14 choose	15 windy
16 main	17 invisible	18 promote
19 tribe	20 lead	21 shoot
22 already	23 limit	24 particular
25 crew	26 recommendation	
27 register	28 several	29 direction
30 especially	31 manage	32 perfect
33 allow	34 tapper	35 depending on
36 be over	37 in short	38 wear out
39 sign up for	40 get attention	41 take care of
42 have difficulty -ing		43 most of all

1 hire, 고용하다   2 invisible, (눈에) 보이지 않는, 볼 수 없는

3 promote, 홍보하다   4 achieve, 달성하다, 성취하다

5 breathe, 숨쉬다   6 crew, 팀, 조

7 register, 등록하다   8 assistant, 보조자

9 wear, 입다   10 support, 돕다, 지원하다
11 tribe, 부족, 종족   12 choose, 선택하다
13 trophy, 트로피   14 suit, 정장, 옷 한 벌
15 pit, (자동차 경주의) 피트
16 wear out, (낡아서) 떨어지다, 헤지다

Listen and Talk A 1

often, play basketball / once, more often / suggest,
three times / good, to play

Listen and Talk A 2

about, How often, swim / four times a week / That,
Anyway, it, swimming / suggest, do stretching

Listen and Talk A 3

how often, take, lessons / Twice, beginner / heavy,
suggest, use, lighter ball / for, one

Listen and Talk A 4

how often, to run / Every / with / suggest, wear,
good for running

Listen and Talk B

how often, exercise / once a week / suggest,
exercise / try

Listen and Talk C

Welcome to / to register for, class / taking
swimming lessons / how to swim at all / How often,
take / take, twice a week, take, on, on / that, take,
on / sounds good, sign up for / a limit of / perfect

Talk and Play

how often, exercise / three times a week

Review 1

how often, swim / every day / go swimming with /
suggest, bring, Without, aren't allowed

Review 2

practice over / How often, practice / twice a week

Review 3

register for, soccer class / How often, take classes /
take, twice a week, take, on / suggest, take, on /
good

Listen and Talk A 1

B: How often do you play basketball?

G: I play once a week, but I want to play more often.

B: I suggest you join my basketball club. We play
three times a week.

G: That sounds good! It'll be fun to play with you.

Listen and Talk A 2

B: I don't swim often. How about you, Kate? How
often do you swim?

G: I swim four times a week.

B: That often? Anyway, it'll be fun swimming together
today.

G: Yes, but before we swim, I suggest we do
stretching exercises.

B: That's a good idea.

Listen and Talk A 3

B: Suji, how often do you take bowling lessons?

G: Twice a week. I'm just a beginner. I heard you're
very good.

B: Well, I love bowling. Hmm. Your bowling ball
looks heavy for you. I suggest you use a lighter
ball.

G: OK. I'll look for a lighter one, then.

Listen and Talk A 4

B: Mina, how often do you come here to run?

G: Every day.

B: Can I run with you today?

G: Sure, but I suggest you wear running shoes. Your
shoes aren't good for running.

Listen and Talk B

A: Minsu, how often do you exercise?

B: I exercise once a week.

A: I suggest you exercise more often.

B: OK. I'll try.

Listen and Talk C

W: Hello. Welcome to Sports World. May I help you?

B: Yes, I came to register for a swimming class.

W: Is this your first time taking swimming lessons?

B: Yes, it is. I don't know how to swim at all.

W: I see. How often do you want to take classes?

B: I want to take classes twice a week. I'd like to
take classes on weekdays andnot on weekends.

W: Then, I suggest that you take the Beginner 2
class. This class meets on Tuesdays and
Thursdays.

B: That sounds good. I'd like to sign up for that
class. How big is the class?

W: The class has a limit of 10 people.

B: That's perfect.

Talk and Play

A: Jiho, how often do you exercise?

B: I exercise three times a week.

A: That's good.

Review 1

B: Mina, how often do you swim?

G: I swim every day.

B: Can I go swimming with you this afternoon?

G: Sure, but I suggest you bring a swimming cap. Without a swimming cap, you aren't allowed in the pool.

Review 2

B: Somi, is your piano practice over?

G: Yes, it is.

B: How often do you practice?

G: I practice twice a week.

Review 3

W: Hello. May I help you?

B: Yes, I came to register for a soccer class.

W: I see. How often do you want to take classes?

B: I want to take classes twice a week. I'd like to take classes on weekends.

W: Then, I suggest that you take the Beginner 1 class. This class meets on Saturdays and Sundays.

B: That sounds good.

본문 TEST Step 1 p.57~58

01 Hidden, in Sports
02 only, but, on, own
03 There, who, players
04 often hidden, get attention
05 However, as important
06 Here are, examples
07 Pacers in, Marathon
08 run with, runners, lead
09 experienced, other, manage, better
10 There can be
11 runs, speeds, finishes, times
12 Pacers, have, showing, finish
13 choose, depending on, target
14 finish, hours, follow, pacer
15 Since, track, finishing, particular
16 In short, to win
17 run for others
18 Pit Crews, Car Racing
19 during, there, behind, driver
20 is called, pit crew
21 on, of, track, several

---

22 main job, check, change
23 Changing, because, wear out
24 as short, seconds, crew
25 has, in perfect harmony
26 get, attention, won, pits
27 in Mountain Climbing
28 comes, tribe, which, eastern
29 climbing skills, way around
30 have little difficulty breathing
31 hire, to help, climb
32 lead, climbers to, top
33 support, in, ways
34 For, put up, carry
35 invisible, because, climbers, top

본문 TEST Step 2 p.59~60

01 Hidden
02 only, win on their own
03 people who help
04 hidden, get attention
05 However, as important as
06 Here are, examples
07 Pacers
08 run with other runners, lead
09 experienced, to help, manage their race better
10 There can be
11 at different speeds, finishes, in different times
12 showing
13 can choose, depending on
14 in four hours, follow, four
15 keeps track of, can achieve, easily
16 In short, to win
17 for others
18 Car Racing
19 during, behind the driver
20 is called
21 on the side of the race track, several times
22 main job, to check
23 Changing, is, wear out easily
24 as short as, seconds, as many as
25 Therefore, in perfect harmony
26 get all the attention, in the pits
27 Mountain Climbing
28 comes from, which, eastern part
29 good climbing skills
30 have little difficulty breathing
31 to hire, to help them climb
32 lead, to
33 in many ways
34 For, put up, carry
35 invisible, at the top of

p.61~62

1 스포츠 속 숨은 조력자들

3 스포츠에서 선수들만 트로피나 메달을 받지만, 그들은 혼자 힘으로 이긴 것이 아니다.

3 그 선수들을 돕는 사람들이 있다.

4 이 사람들은 종종 숨겨져 있고 주목을 받지 못한다.

5 하지만 그들은 선수들만큼 중요하다.

6 여기 몇 가지 예가 있다.

7 마라톤의 페이서들

8 페이서들은 마라톤에서 다른 선수들과 함께 달리며 그들을 이끈다.

9 페이서들은 경험이 많은 선수들이며 그들의 역할은 다른 선수들이 경기를 더 잘 운영하도록 돕는 것이다.

10 한 경기에는 여러 명의 페이서들이 있을 수 있다.

11 각각의 페이서는 다른 속도로 달리고 다른 시간대에 경기를 마친다.

12 페이서들은 주로 자신들의 완주 시간을 나타내는 깃발이나 풍선들을 가지고 있다.

13 선수들은 자신들의 목표 완주 시간에 따라 페이서를 선택할 수 있다.

14 예를 들어, 한 선수가 4시간 안에 경기를 마치고 싶다면, 그 선수는 4시간 페이서를 따라갈 것이다.

15 페이서가 시간을 계속해서 파악하기 때문에, 선수는 특정 시간에 마라톤을 완주하려는 자신의 목표를 더 쉽게 달성할 수 있다.

16 요컨대, 페이서들은 달리지만 우승을 하기 위해 달리는 것은 아니다.

17 그들은 다른 선수들을 위해 달린다.

18 자동차 경주의 피트 크루

19 여러분은 대부분의 자동차 경주에서 자동차와 레이서만 보겠지만 그 레이서 뒤에는 팀이 있다.

20 이 팀은 피트 크루라고 불린다.

21 피트는 경주 트랙의 한쪽에 있는 공간으로 레이서들은 경주 도중에 그곳에서 여러 번 정지한다.

22 피트 크루가 하는 주요 역할은 자동차를 점검하고 타이어를 교체하는 것이다.

23 빠른 속도의 경주에서는 타이어가 쉽게 마모되기 때문에 타이어를 교체하는 것이 특히 중요하다.

24 피트에서의 정지는 짧게는 2초 정도이고 한 팀에는 많게는 20명에 이르는 구성원이 있다.

25 그러므로 피트 크루는 완벽한 조화를 이루며 일해야 한다.

26 레이서만 주목을 받을지 모르지만 사람들이 말하는 것처럼, "경주의 우승은 피트에서 이루어진다."

27 등반에서의 셰르파

28 'Sherpa'라는 단어는 셰르파족에서 유래되었는데, 셰르파족은 네팔의 동쪽 지역에 산다.

29 셰르파는 훌륭한 등반 기량을 갖고 있으며 산 지리를 잘 안다.

30 그들은 또한 산의 높은 곳에서 호흡하는 데 어려움이 거의 없다.

31 그래서 등산가들은 자신들이 에베레스트산을 등반하는 것을 돕는 셰르파를 고용하기 시작했다.

32 셰르파는 등산가들을 산 정상까지 이끈다.

33 그들은 여러 방면에서 등산가들을 지원한다.

34 예를 들면, 그들은 텐트를 치고 등산가들의 가방을 운반한다.

35 셰르파는 종종 에베레스트산의 보이지 않는 사람들로 불리는데, 왜냐하면 사람들이 산 정상에서 등산가들만 찍힌 사진을 자주 보기 때문이다.

p.63~66

1 Hidden People in Sports

2 In sports, only the players get a trophy or medal, but they don't win on their own.

3 There are people who help the players.

4 These people are often hidden and don't get attention.

5 However, they are as important as the players.

6 Here are some examples.

7 Pacers in a Marathon

8 Pacers run with other runners and lead them in a marathon.

9 Pacers are experienced runners, and their job is to help other runners manage their race better.

10 There can be several pacers in a race.

11 Each pacer runs at different speeds and finishes the race in different times.

12 Pacers usually have flags or balloons showing their finish time.

13 Runners can choose a pacer depending on their target finish time.

14 For example, if a runner wants to finish the race in four hours, the runner will follow the four-hour pacer.

15 Since the pacer keeps track of the time, the runner can achieve his or her goal of finishing the marathon in a particular time more easily.

16 In short, pacers run but they don't run to win.

17 They run for others.

18 Pit Crews in Car Racing

19 You may only see the car and the driver during most car races, but there is a team behind the driver.

20 This team is called a pit crew.

21 A pit is a place on the side of the race track, and drivers stop there several times during a race.

22 The main job of the pit crew is to check the car and change the tires.

23 Changing the tires is especially important because the tires wear out easily in a high speed race.

24 A pit stop can be as short as 2 seconds, and there are as many as 20 members on a crew.

25 Therefore, the pit crew has to work in perfect harmony.

26 The driver may get all the attention, but as people say, "Races are won in the pits."

27 Sherpas in Mountain Climbing

28 The word *Sherpa* comes from the Sherpa tribe, which lives in the eastern part of Nepal.

29 Sherpas have good climbing skills and know their way around the mountains well.

30 They also have little difficulty breathing high up in the mountains.

31 Therefore, mountain climbers started to hire Sherpas to help them climb Mount Everest.

32 Sherpas lead mountain climbers to the top of the mountain.

33 They support climbers in many ways.

34 For example, they put up tents and carry climbers' bags.

35 Sherpas are often called the invisible people of Mount Everest because people often see a picture of only the climbers at the top of the mountain.

After You Read B

1. Is there anything interesting

2. showing their finish time

3. can be as short as 2 seconds

4. has to work in perfect harmony

5. have little difficulty breathing high up

Around the World

1. to help a blind swimmer swim

2. runs with a blind runner, helps, stay on the track

3. In blind football, a shooting assistant, direction to shoot

Think and Write

1. Cheerleaders, Football Games

2. Although, usually don't think, a part of, play an important role in

3. By cheering, create team spirit

4. also encourage

5. To do their job well, need to be fit, strong

6. need to be good at jumping, dancing

7. Most of all, work as hard as players

After You Read B

1. Host: Is there anything interesting about your job?

2. Pacer: Pacers have flags or balloons showing their finish time.

3. Pit Crew: A pit stop can be as short as 2 seconds.

4. So the pit crew has to work in perfect harmony.

5. Sherpa: Sherpas like me have little difficulty breathing high up in the mountains.

Around the World

1. In swimming, a tapper uses a long pole to help a blind swimmer swim.

2. In a race, a guide runner runs with a blind runner and helps him or her stay on the track.

3. In blind football, a shooting assistant tells his or her team players which direction to shoot.

Think and Write

1. Cheerleaders in Football Games

2. Although people usually don't think that cheerleaders are a part of a football team, they play an important role in a football game.

3. By cheering at a game, they create team spirit.

4. They also encourage their team and fans.

5. To do their job well, cheerleaders need to be fit and strong.

6. They also need to be good at jumping and dancing.

7. Most of all, they need to work as hard as players.

MEMO

MEMO

적중 100

영어 기출 문제집

정답 및 해설

동아 | 윤정미